COMING HOME FROM SEA

Coming Home
from Sea

Selected Poems

PRISCILLA NAPIER

Foreword by
THE DUKE OF GRAFTON
Introduction by
ALETHEA HAYTER

THE ERSKINE PRESS
1999

Coming Home From Sea

First published in 1999 by
The Erskine Press, The Old Bakery, Banham, Norwich, Norfolk NR16 2HW

ISBN 1 85297 060 X

British Library Cataloguing-in-Publication Data
A catalogue record of this book is available
from the British Library

Printed in England

To Miles
Or Lavinia
Or Anne

If, in the after years, you find this book
And with a hasty and embarrassed look
Exclaim, Good gracious, this is very rum,
Why, what a lot of poems,
                                 Oh *poor* Mum!

If, in a limping Tennysonian measure
I took what seems exaggerated pleasure,
This was a way to scatter my sad thinking,
This was a better plan than secret drinking.

Other Books by Priscilla Napier

POETRY
Sheet Anchor
Plymouth in War
The Kingdom of Edmund
A Ballad of Henry VIII and Sir Thomas Wyatt

HISTORY AND BIOGRAPHY
published by Michael Joseph
A Difficult Country
The Sword Dance
Revolution and The Napier Brothers

published by Michael Russell
I Have Sind
Raven Castle
Black Charlie
Henry At Sea
Henry Ashore

published by Brassey's
Barbarian Eye

Lady Delia Peel – A Memoir

AUTOBIOGRAPHY
published by Michael Joseph
A Late Beginner
Reprinted in 1998 by Michael Russell (Publishing) Ltd
Wilby Hall, Wilby, Norfolk NR16 2JP (£9.99)

FICTION
published by Coward, McCann & Geoghegan
Imperial Winds

TRANSLATION
Bishop Theophan's The Art Of Prayer

CONTENTS

Foreword   xi
Introduction   xii

PART I – The Poet Introduces Herself

Verbal Intoxication	3	Writers	8
Know Thyself	5	Freedom from Biography	9
Inspiration	6	Making	10
The Punch-Drunk Versifier	7		

PART II – Ancestors

Adam and Eve	15	The Killing	26
The Hunter	17	Renaissance Artist	30
Nauplion	18	Hell	32
Rose Tree	22	For Worthless Absalom	35
Faith	24	Sale of the Drawing Room	37
Norman Church	25	The Islanders	39

PART III – Contemporaries

Great House	43	Left Wing	60
Upper Crust	45	On the Towpath	61
Terra Incognita	47	Sketch for A Portrait	63
Lady in Harrods	50	Monarchist	68
No Circular, No Succour	51	Tea-Room	70
Political Meeting	52	Aunt	72
Minister of Agriculture	54	Down With Decimals – Twenty	
Epitaph for Democracy	55	Years On	74
February	56	Trespassers Unwelcome	76
Inventions	57	The Pet	77
Me And Aunt Edna Calling		Short Story	78
The Box Office	58	Colonel and Wife	79

CONTENTS

An Old Frenchman in the Park
   with his Grandson   80
Bowler Hat   81
Nile Island   82
Being Eighteen   84
Five-Year-Old   86

Grandchildren   88
Young Man in the Limewalk   89
Alice in London   91
Daughter – on Her
   Engagement   92
Parenthood   93

PART IV – Places & Seasons

The Orangery, Mount
   Edgcumbe   97
From a Train Window: West
   Country   98
Query   99
Generosity   100
May at Fonthill   101
Ely: a Water Colour   102
Portrait – Fonthill in
   Summer   103

July: Collingbourne Ducis   104
Beckford Lodge – One Dark
   July Evening   105
The Exile   106
Suffolk   107
Starlings at Nightfall   109
November   110
So Would Not I   111
Forest Under Thaw   112
The Dartmoor Stream   113

PART V – Mortal & Immortal

Subconscious   117
Dog   118
Travellers   119
Pass, Friend   120
Wolf-Being   121
Watch It   123
Persian Pattern   125
The Pagan Burial   126
Exiles   127
Collective Unconscious   129
Early Morning   131
The Ship Discovered   134
Double Life   136
Redundant Place   138

St James's Park   139
Back to the Beginning   141
The Churchgoer   142
Religion   143
Significance   144
The Prodigal   146
As a Child   150
Ultimate   152
The Burial   153
In the Dry Places   154
Prayer at Morning   155
Ascension Day   156
In My Father's House   157

PART VI – Love, War, Loss & Reconciliation
PN to TMN

The Recognition	161	Derby Station	203
Mediterranean	162	The Sailor's Widow	208
Malta	163	Autumn	210
The Skirmishers	165	As I Came Down from	
Ignorance	167	Faringdon	211
December on Dartmoor	168	The Prisoner	213
The Spirit of the Age	169	Hamoaze	214
September 1938	170	30 August 1961	215
Easter 1939	172	Ice in the River Breaking	216
Coming Home from Sea	174	First Years	217
Returning to Sea	175	Reconciliation – Welland Valley,	
Destroyer War: 1939–40	177	30 August 1970	219
Seen from a Train	179	Terminus	221
June 1940: Going West	180	Departed	223
Threshold	183	What Goes On?	225
To Trevie, Dying	185	August The Thirtieth	226
Deathbed	190	Forest	228
Leaving in August	192	Winter	229
The Only Consolation	193	The Voyage	231
Another Country	194	8 August 1991	232
Days after Death	195	End Of Year	233
Not That We Loved	197	Addict	234
Blitz	198	An Afternoon at Biddesden	235
Darkness in May	199	Ninety Year Old	236
After the Storm	200	Tavistock – a Fantasy	237
Indian Summer	201		

'The Hunter', 'The Orangery, Mount Edgcumbe' and 'Starlings at Nightfall' are reproduced by kind permission of *Country Life*.

FOREWORD
by the Duke of Grafton, K.G.

Priscilla Napier's family have asked me to write a short Foreword explaining how Priscilla made friends with Ted Hughes and how he came to write the really splendid Foreword to one of her major works, 'Ballad of King Henry VIII and Sir Thomas Wyatt'.

I had known her for some time when she came to live in one of my houses here at Euston in Suffolk. She stayed for nine years which was a particular pleasure to us. Not only did she write the epic 'Kingdom of Edmund' while she was here but I also got to know some of her amazing poetry.

Some years ago we were invited by the Queen Mother to the Royal Lodge at Windsor where in the spring she used to have small parties consisting of poetry readings and music. I remember we had John Betjeman and Peggy Ashcroft, and some beautiful music. Ted Hughes and his wife were asked to one of these gatherings and immediately made friends with Queen Elizabeth. I think they came several times and on one occasion I found myself talking to Ted about Priscilla's poetry. I put them in touch with each other and he was tremendously enthusiastic on hearing about 'Plymouth in War' particularly because he lived in Devonshire himself. I remember them going together to talk to the Librarian at Plymouth with a view to publishing the poem as a major book, with photographs of Plymouth in the terrible bombing, but this project, alas, had to be cancelled due to lack of money, though 'Plymouth in War' was eventually broadcast by the BBC.

It was really a wonderful piece of luck that brought the two of them together. Ted was immensely encouraging about all of Priscilla's writing and they continued to correspond until her death last year. He repeatedly urged her to get all of her shorter poems into print, and now her family have made a small and varied selection for this book.

INTRODUCTION

Priscilla Napier's earliest surviving poem was written when she was sixteen; the latest one seventy-four years later, six weeks before she died aged ninety. Writing poetry was for her an irresistible urge, a total delight, an intoxication, as she reveals in the poems in Part I of this selection 'The Poet Introduces Herself'. It was also a life-saving therapy to purge her emotions and her grief. She would have echoed Rose Macaulay's confession: 'One has to write poetry (at least I always have) to express things that don't go into prose so easily; also, I like playing with metres and rhythms; it was, in childhood and youth, one of my forms of insobriety ... I remember, as a child and girl, being poetry-drunk'.

Priscilla Napier's poetry is personal, an individual voice telling of one person's experiences and opinions. To provide the background for this selection from her poetry, a brief biographical record is needed. Her home for the first twelve years of life was in Egypt, where she spent a childhood both rapturous and turbulent, as she reveals in the poem *Nile Island*, and at length in her memoir *A Late Beginner*, her best-known and much-loved book about those early days in Egypt. Her father, Sir William Hayter, was Legal Advisor to the Egyptian Government in what was then a British Protectorate, and she was the middle child of three (her brother, another William Hayter, later became British Ambassador to Moscow and then Warden of New College, Oxford). At twelve she was sent to a boarding-school in England, Downe House, and when her father died, only three years later, the family settled in Berkshire. She won a scholarship to Lady Margaret Hall, Oxford, in 1926 to read History, a subject which remained a lifelong interest of hers, shaping her literary output, imbuing her with a love of tradition and country which aligned her political stance, and reinforcing the firm though unobtrusive religious faith which supported her in misery and joy, and to which she confessed in the poems in 'Mortal & Immortal', Part V of this selection.

Soon after leaving Oxford she married Trevylyan Napier, brother of a school friend. He was then a Lieutenant Commander in the Royal Navy; they spent the next nine years at his postings in Greenwich, Malta, Portland and Plymouth. Many of the poems in Parts II and VI celebrate the impact of Mediterranean beauty and history on her imagination, as well as the bliss of a totally compatible marriage. Their son was born in 1934 and a daughter followed in 1938.

When the Second World War broke out in 1939, Trevie Napier was Captain of the destroyer HMS *Jackal*, in which he took part in the naval campaign against the German occupation of Norway, and ranged the North Sea, among winter storms and German air and submarine attacks, to protect Britain's ill-defended east coast from the expected German invasion. Constantly on the bridge of his ship, once for eleven successive nights in which he only had a total of four hours' sleep, he wore out his strength, but refused to leave his ship in that hour of crisis. The novelist, Eric Linklater, who saw him often at this time, has left an account of him which, as a description drawn by an acute and objective witness of an exceptional man, illuminates the 'PN to TMN' sequence of poems which ends this selection, by justifying the lifelong devotion and admiration felt and expressed by that man's wife. Trevie Napier was, Eric Linklater writes, 'very tall and lean, with fair hair growing thick and straight, a good face with strong but lightly moulded features ... With his conservative instincts went a radical mind, and the thought of injustice worried him like an old sore. "I am the Red in my family" he once wrote ... He was a humane man and troubled by it, but in the fashion of his kind he had acquired the constant habit of dissembling his feelings. When he felt deeply, he would speak lightly; he would deny or deprecate his own knowledge and ability; he would shun heroics as nimbly as he had evaded falling bombs, and seek immediate refuge from emotion in the shelter of a joke'. In action he showed 'a combination of tranquillity and unhesitating decision' which repeatedly saved his ship. 'He was destined, as it falsely seemed, for ultimate service in the highest rank ... He might indeed have become an outstanding figure in Naval affairs, for he had a restless mind, a reformer's mind, and the practical ability as a seaman that would have made his opinion in other matters than seamanship respected ... He also had the unstudied charm ... which gathers adherents and makes devoted friends'.

This was the man who, in July 1940, had at last to be carried ashore dying of septic endocarditis (in those pre-penicillin days a deadly occupational disease among overworked naval officers in War-time). Sent back to his home, his wife and children in Devonshire, he died on 30 August; his third child, another daughter, was born a week later.

Priscilla Napier was left to contend with the grief which she so poignantly expressed in the 'PN to TMN' poems and in a longer poetic sequence, *Sheet Anchor*, which was published in 1944 under the pseudonym of Eve Stuart, for which Eric Linklater wrote the Foreword quoted above. She also began the verse documentary, *Plymouth in War*, whose theme was the perils of War-time sailors and the sorrows of their bereaved families, which was published after the War and was broadcast by the BBC in 1994, the fiftieth anniversary of the bombing raids in Plymouth.

She was left to bring up three small children on a tiny Naval pension, which she achieved so well that one of those children, Lavinia Robinson, in an address at her mother's funeral, could testify to their 'wonderfully happy and secure childhood'. In spite of shortage of money, she managed resourcefully to contrive a succession of homes in Devonshire, Northamptonshire, Wiltshire and Suffolk, where she created a series of beautiful gardens and entertained a wide circle of friends and family – eventually including grandchildren and great-grandchildren. She was always an expert raconteur and a centre of lively talk and laughter and forceful opinions. The poems in Parts Ill and IV express her vivid reactions to the countryside and her acute observation of the attitudes of family, neighbours, passing strangers. Her last years were spent in a cottage beside her younger daughter's house in Surrey. She died in hospital, after seeming to be recovering from a major operation, four days after her ninetieth birthday.

So much for the bare facts of her life, but there is a history of literary activity which ran alongside it and which provided an element of hard work and tough research in what might have sounded like a life of leisure. Already in the 1930s, before and after her marriage, she was writing a quantity of poetry, some of which was published in *Country Life*. In the 1950s and 1960s she wrote some hundreds of poems, mainly pen-portraits or on landscape and politics, and some of these, and also some prose articles, were published in *Punch* and *The Field* under the pseudonym of Penelope Hunt. In the 1960s and 1970s she concentrated more on prose, publishing in 1966 *A Late Beginner* in which, with an extraordinary total recall of the feelings and sayings of small children she described vividly and often hilariously the incidents of her own childhood. This witty and touching account of childhood raptures, fears and exploits showed the unusual insight into child psychology which also made her an understanding and much-loved matriarch. She then turned to biographies of the past military and naval celebrities of her husband's family, the Napiers. Ten volumes of these were produced in the next twenty-six years; the most effective of these were perhaps *The Sword Dance*, about the Napier brothers in the Peninsular War and their mother, Lady Sarah Lennox (one of the heroines of the recent TV sequence 'Aristocrats'), and *I Have Sind* about Charles Napier in India; but all of them showed thorough scholarly research combined with refreshing and astringent informality. She also wrote lives of the third Duke of Richmond and of Lady Delia Peel, and a novel *Imperial Winds*, about the Russian Revolution. Her considerable output also included two book-length poetic sequences, *The Kingdom of Edmund* and *A Ballad of King Henry VIII and Sir Thomas Wyatt*.

In 1954 she began to collect together her many poems in draft, in a notebook entitled *Verses Waiting To be Re-written*, and prefixed to it the address to her children which has been used as the dedication to this volume. A second series assembled in March 1960 had this deprecating foreword: 'These are just photographs of moods, observed in others, felt in myself, imperfectly developed and printed. There's altogether too much boo-hoo about them, but better to get it out of the system in verse'. The success of *A Late Beginner*, and *Punch*'s willingness to publish both poetry and prose of hers, made her in the 1960s at her most confident of her literary standing, and she made two more compilations of revised or to-be-revised poems, the fourth in 1963, probably with a view to a Collected Poems publication.

But in the 1970s and 1980s, a time of literary disappointment, and what she regarded as failure, set in. She continued to produce prose biographies on historic subjects, but her shorter poetic lyrics failed to find any outlet. Already in the 1957 poem *Know Thyself* she measured literary failure against the sheer delight, the 'verbal intoxication' which she celebrated in another poem, of writing poetry, which made her go on in spite of not getting her work published. Two poems of these years tell of 'Failure and failure and continued failure … the heavy thud of returning typescript, pushed through the letter-box' and of 'Rejection slips enough to paper walls, and cover up the mighty dome of St Paul's'.

Her confidence in her own talent was never unassailable; set-backs from what was a temporary change of fashion among poetry editors sometimes seemed to her a sign of enduring failure, though at other times it inspirited her to fight back.

In the early 1990s she was given a new impulse by a correspondence with the Poet Laureate, Ted Hughes, who not only wrote a laudatory foreword (partly quoted below) to her *Ballad of King Henry VIII and Sir Thomas Wyatt*, but also urged her in several long letters to get 'all your works – perhaps in 3 or 4 volumes' into print. On a poem of 1993 she noted 'Requested by Ted Hughes to type out all my poems', and she began arranging them in categories – mainly followed in this selection – and making renewed efforts to get them published. A poem of October 1993, *Defiance*, expressed her determination to 'keep on fighting', and in *Defiance II* of August 1996 she wrote:

> 'I'm having one enormous fling
> And sending almost any thing
> To almost any magazine,
> Entering for almost any prizes.
> Oh how I hope it may be seen
> That something comes of these devizes.'

But a sad footnote of September 1997 adds 'It didn't'.

This selection does not aspire to the '3 or 4 volumes' suggested by Ted Hughes, but it contains enough of her poetry to show that her defiance of failure, her hope that her poetry could be seen and read in some collected form, was justified by the value and originality of her talent.

The individual voice in her poetry is instantly recognisable but not so easy to characterize. She herself described her poetry as 'a limping Tennysonian measure', and there are certainly echoes of *In Memorian* in her sequence of poems about her husband's death and her grief. Sometimes, too, she sounds like Housman, and in her lighter verse she often resembled Betjeman; her loyalty and patriotism would have qualified her too as Poet Laureate material, as Ted Hughes suggested by his description of the historical sense of 'Englishness' which he and she shared. Her poetry could never be described as reticent or spare, it was always a vehement voice, whether in mourning or mockery, in rapture or distaste. But she was quite aware of her own vehemence, and mocked that too – 'altogether too much boo-hoo'. In a witty poem like *Me and Aunt Edna at the Box Office* she could combine strong opinions with comic inflections. At the other extreme, her most tragic poems are not weakened by self-pity; the classic maxim, '*Know Thyself*', to which she often referred, is honoured in such bleakly self-revealing poems as *Wolf-Being* and *Exiles*. She could also achieve a remarkable empathy, in such poems as *The Killing* and *Derby Station*, *Terra Incognita* and *Sketch for a Portrait*, with the hunted, the desiccated, the despairing, even the murderous.

Far the most important critical estimate of her poetry that has been given is that of Ted Hughes in his Foreword to *The Ballad of King Henry VIII and Sir Thomas Wyatt*. He begins by analysing her 'peculiar gift for writing dramatic verse that is both freely vernacular and loftily hieratic – the combination invented by Shakespeare. This combination has rarely appeared in our literature, because few writers have possessed both of the two main requirements. The first of these requirements is a facility, a knack, for writing pentameter lines that sound simultaneously direct, simple, spontaneous, and yet have a ring of inevitability, a moulded finality. The second requirement is a steady, vividly imagined, wide-open long-range historical perspective, in which all the big issues are assembled and pressing to be heard.

There is a third requirement, obviously which is: the ability to express, and dramatise, the latter through each phrase, each word, of the former. Priscilla Napier brings this off, in a fascinating manner, not just here and there but constantly, throughout; it is simply her natural style of writing, the way her mind works. The whole thing unfolds without any sense of labour of striving for special effects'. Of her more personal lyrical poems he says 'those short yet massively structured private poems of hers are moving, almost painful evidence that Priscilla Napier is a deeply subjective writer, and that her poetry, in general, expresses a profound and deeply seasoned emotional private life'. He concludes that 'In some real sense, this author has internalised England's history as her own history. Writing about the events and personalities of the one she is inevitably expressing the passions of the other. Each is suffused with the glamour, sorrow, grandeur and drama of the other. This being so, the actual form of her writing becomes understandable. The pageant-like medley of drama, epic and meditation is not what one would call "modern" in the sense that book-reviewers understand the term. At the same time, it is not archaic or dated. It exists, in its own unique fashion, within a certain sense of "Englishness". This Englishness constitutes a living tradition, and a real place, within which Shakespeare's verse, Milton's, Dryden's Pope's, Wordsworth's and perhaps Owen's, are all contemporary with each other, where all are simply dialects of that state of mind. It is a continuum in which time does not pass but history does accumulate and grow. For all who share this state of mind, the account of the Battle of Agincourt and the account of the Battle of Britain stir us as if they were happening right now, or might happen again tomorrow, with the sure knowledge that we are involved in those actions and cannot be separated from them. This is not everybody's state of mind, of course. One can easily find gifted young writers for whom Shakespeare is as alien, as obsolete, as Henry VIII's suits of armour. For Priscilla Napier, as for me, his language is closer, more deeply natural in its essential life, than that of any living writer'. He concluded that 'for those who feel, who solidly know, that England's history, in all its details, is somehow their own personal, secret history', Priscilla Napier's poetry is 'true work, deeply moving and satisfying'.

Alethea Hayter
(Priscilla Napier's sister)

The extract from Ted Hughes' foreword to *Ballad of King Henry VIII and Sir Thomas Wyatt* is reprinted by the kind permission of the Ted Hughes Estate.

The quotation from Eric Linklater's preface to 'Sheet Anchor' is reprinted by kind permission of Andro Linklater.

Part I

The Poet Introduces Herself

VERBAL INTOXICATION

I am drunk, but not with wine
In my head wild words entwine,
Callisthenics, dragon-fly,
Lanthorne, lapis lazuli,
Threnody of three times three
And sycamore, sycamore, sycamore tree.

Come for me, the Black Maria,
In some drunk-house I'll expire –
Sophocles, and Northern Fire,
Timbrel, tumbrill, lute and lyre,
I am mad, though not in wits,
Horoscope and Horowitz,
Dungeons, danger, Dungeness,
Fortunatus and largesse,
Hail, horizons, honey-bee,
And sycamore, sycamore, sycamore tree.

My mouth's full, but not with brandy,
Riotous and rope and randy
And the lane to Tonypandy,

Lullabies and macaroons,
Nincompoops and nightmare noons,
Neptune, Noah, and old Tom Noddy
Rive the heart from out the body
Swim the sense in hyssop Tea,
And blackamoor, sycamore, syllabub Sea.

1948

KNOW THYSELF

Times, with the happy mind in spate,
Ideas and form seem man and wife;
With words and rhythm intoxicate
I dream that what I write has life.

At other times, a calmer lover,
Sanely aware of total loss,
I read my verses dourly over
And know that most I write is dross.

And you, who once encouraged me
Not easily, but quite enough,
Lean over me, and silently
Beg me to shorten half the stuff.

Some lines are possible, some not;
Only, I don't know which is which,
Whether I soar above the plot?
Or fall ignobly in the ditch.

So what? Why is success the measure?
Why, when I fail, forbear to write?
It's long since I knew purer pleasure,
Or felt so total a delight.

1957

INSPIRATION

When first the words come singing into the mind
They have the grace and substance of finality.
Reading them over, later on, we find
Alas, that now
They seem in all their comfortless banality
Rather too like the thoughts of Chairman Mao.

August 1993

THE PUNCH-DRUNK VERSIFIER

I haven't a lot in any of my top stories,
And whatever is there is blurred;
But I am Caesar and all the Conquistadores
When it comes to the singing word,

When it comes to the gold raw dandelion dropping
Its yellow coins on the ear
It's a millionaire I am, on a horse past stopping
By the precipice of fear.

WRITERS

And do our songs of woe engender pity
Among the murmurous millions of Cathay?
Bland article, how much has it to say?
Illuminating tale, or tuneful ditty
How much of comfort can they now convey
To men who die of rage in Kansas City
To girls who die of grief in Colwyn Bay?

1979

FREEDOM FROM BIOGRAPHY

How wonderful it is to have no fame
To be anonymous, and certain sure
No-one can play Old Harry with your name –
Record some foul disease without a cure,
Think for you thoughts you never thought of thinking,
Invent unknown desires that they can blame,
Somehow suggest orgies of secret drinking,
Vices professors cannot leave alone
But still pursue with un-fatigued allure
As panders to the appetite for dirt,
Inflicting thus the maximum of hurt.

My faults are many but they'll be my own.
How excellent it is to be unknown
And only have God's judgement to endure –
Hard, loving, sure.

1993

MAKING

Everyone needs
Their kind of creation,
And all that this feeds
In warmth and elation;
Whether their artefact wildly succeeds
Or becomes ruination.
Building all day
And far into night
In work that is play,
Is absorption, delight.

Turning to nothing,
Or turning askew,
This touch of eternity's power to renew.
Even in this
Plain act of creation;
The heart's sure foundation
Measures its bliss.

Making a factory
Garage, or shop,
Loving it so
That they don't want to stop
Building a lamp post, a poem, a cake,

– No matter what, but something to make –
An oven, a tooth-brush, a finely carved font;
Giving full reign
To imagined creation,
Moulding a chimney-piece no-one could want
Making the tea, or a handsome bus station.
Painting a shed
With a muddy surround,
Or the diptych of Wilton
With angels rose-crowned.

Best of creation
(A dear home apart)
Is sowing a seed
Planting a plant
Hoping so much it will grow (when it can't);
Or giving a start
To what must outlive us –
Digging a hole
And inserting a tree
When there's no need
For anyone else to admire the result
Or gain by the deed;
When it's enough that it simply will be
Its excellent self
A flourishing tree –
Exuberant, leafy, and living and free.

Feeding and firming, labelling, staking,
Selfishly blind with the pleasures of making.
Of giving a start
To their own kind of shrub,
Or narcissus, or tree
Nearest the heart;
Feeling the full
Joy of creation
In this their very own manifestation.

December 1996

PART II

Ancestors

ADAM AND EVE

When we were innocent and animal
And in our animality were free,
When good and evil floated out of reach
Where knowledge hung, an orange in a tree,

Sometimes a sharp foreshadowing of fate
Gritted the honey seasons of delight,
And presences more lethal than the lion
Troubled the fear-filled darkness of the night;

In that far forest, dappled as we lay
Under the spread of some great ferny span,
Beast that was I, loving a beastly you,
Trembled to think that we must soon be Man.

No sound in all that silence of spent leaves;
Till the soft rustle of a passing snake
Found echo in the stirring of a branch
Heavy with fruit – and we were full awake.

That moment when our happy teeth engaged
And the sweet juices trickled down our chins
We knew no disobedience, nor that here
The forest ends, the dusty march begins;

But shudders of excitement and surmise
As the twigs cracked beneath our stretching feet,
When the first shame brought forth the first excuse –
The woman tempted me and I did eat.

There, like an orange sun, Consciousness glowed
So gaudily, and winked his golden lid,
That gates of Paradise began to close
And innocence lay gravelled; and we hid.

Crying in ringing anguish through the glades
Until the very birds grew still to hear,
Naked within our knowingness and shock
We fled before the fiery sword of fear;

Running as if uncounted dogs of time
Could hound us through the centuries, to see
Noon darkening on the silent olive grove,
Blood darkening on the stones of Calvary.

THE HUNTER

What did you do, Orion
In mortal life, that yours should be
Such happy immortality,
What dragon slew, what lion?
That you should walk the windy sky
Night long, and see the bird stars fly
And wheel and dip as they go by,
With a belt for your sword and your sword for the Bear
And the wind of Heaven in your hair,
And, cool and pressing, ever feel
The nose of the Dog Star at your heel.

Thatcham , 1929

NAUPLION

They have forgotten in the Argolid
Tranquil between the mountains and the bay
And ripening in the blaze of afternoon,
How by the light of such another day
Across this sparkling tide
Paris with stolen bride
Sailed eastward to the agony of Troy;
And men of Argos left their sheltered fields,
The wine, the bullocks and the olive yields,
Their homes and all their joy,
Beating for Sunion and the Aegean door,
Till Argos valley blurred before their sight
And the gulf whitened in the evening light
And widened to the sacrificial shore,
Till they could see no more
The slanting valley light;
And the long mountains faded into night.

Dusk hovers now on the hills in mourning grey,
And smoothes the gulf, and quiets the olive trees
And pales the placid waters of the bay.
The gentle evening smoulders, and the lights
Quicken on Argos hill as once they quickened
To hear of Helen stolen beyond the seas,

And trumpets cried, and Nauplion harbour thickened
With angry ships, and Argos shone with arms
And shook with marching men, and Nauplion rock
Echoed and trembled to the horn's alarms.

How light, in turning Time, are other feet
That walked the rich fields of the Argolid,
Since doomed Mycenae on her windy steep
Over those royal bones
Raised up her mighty stones
Large as the crimes and beauties that they hid;
And Golden Tiryns fell to rise no more.
Where are the other men, and where their lore?
Who came from Persia or from Macedon
To bleach their bones beneath this thunder sky,
What Roman, Norman, or Venetian prow
Sailed conquering by?

And what is it to know whose crescent moon
Blew on the banners of the Citadel,
Whose bugle tune
Sounded the evening knell?
If Turks in lazy, long, brutality
Their pattern set
Of handsome dome and graceful minaret?
If Englishmen, or French, or Germans came
Parting the lucent seas in other ships,
If Greek met Greek in recent bitter flame,
And other anchors stammered through the slips?

Only the fleet a women's beauty manned
Rides on this strand
Beneath the fierce feet of heroic men.
Whoever came since then
Left never a footprint on these lulling shores,
For history is dust, and only song endures.

Over the Argolid the evening flows,
Drowning the darkness of the cypress trees,
Folding the summer valley like a rose.
The lights are lit in happy Nauplion now,
Hibiscus lets her gaudy trumpet close,
And jasmine from Venetian balconies
Falls mild and sweet
Over the narrow street,
And by the sea the gay taverna glows;

The glasses clink beneath the trellised vine,
This is the hour of laughter and of wine
Of cloudy ouzo in the fig tree's arbour,
Of talk in lucid and exuberant Greek;
The music strums, and from the glassy harbour
Splash the slow anchors of a late caique.

Never remember in the Argolid
That love is grief, that towns forever burn,
Children are sacrificed, and women weep,
And heroes walk the road of no return.
Helen is dust: life is the great concern,

And Paris comes no more; so let your daughters,
Brown-satin-skinned, sweet-voiced,
Mocking and kind and chaste,
Flash their white laughter to the smiling boys;
Let them forget the torment that was Troy's,
The sadness of that long-disputed shore,
And love each other dearly all the more,
True love, beside the trembling summer waters.

ROSE TREE

Rhodanthe, Queen of Corinth
Dwelled in a haze of lust;
Desiring sweet Rhodanthe
Was a Corinthian must.

Scorched by the rays of longing
From hard and eager eyes,
Rhodanthe, with celestial aid
Arranged a great surprise.

Still beautiful, still fragrant,
Soft-petalled and serene,
With stem as long and graceful
But leaves of glossy green,

She turned into a rose tree
Set in the palace lawns,
And all her luckless lovers
Were met by piercing thorns.

Had she, with quips and jesting
Held the whole bunch at bay
And lived aloof and lonely
To fight another day?

Rhodanthe, Queen of Corinth,
She whom the gods transformed
To bloom in thorny solitude
Where once her lovers swarmed,

Sweet summer rose of Corinth
Aglow in a green sward,
Rhodanthe, did you presently
Become the least bit bored?

To feel the dews of morning
Cold on your petals fall,
And through chill winds of autumn
Prepare for winter's gall?

Is beauty self-sufficient
Can lonely splendour pall?
Too much of love is better
Perhaps than none at all.

The wisdom of Corinthian gods
In this most clearly shows –
We might have kept Rhodanthe
And never had the rose.

1977

FAITH

What knowledge did you bear with you, Columbus,
How much of science did you comprehend
When you spread sail from Palos
And steered for the world's end?
With how much certainty did you suppose
The world was really round
And not a carpet or flat strip of ground?
What though your spirit's eyes
Saw India, and sunrise,
And a green country through which rivers rolled
Whose sands were all of gold,
Did not your spirit's ear,
In the chill midnights, hear
The silence of Eternity come near,
Did not your blood run cold
To feel your vessel hurled
And with the sea, fall endlessly
Off the sheer edge of the world?

1929

NORMAN CHURCH

Out of the daub and wattle, and peril of fire
Here to find grace
We came, with all the anger, terror, hate
Wrought in us by our brutish brief estate.
Into this strength of new-cut stone, this space
Glass-cool in summer, warm in winter's wind –
Norman, Dane, Saxon, still in bitter stress,
Half-understanding, rough in speech and dress,
We came to cry Peccavi, I have sinned!
And knelt, astonished at our blessedness,

To find forgiveness, and love's carapace
To shield us from the danger and the cold,
The pain of conquest, slavery's dark face,
The sickness and the want, the growing old.
We came, a hungry wolf-pack, to devour
The light and splendour of this holy place,
And the unwonted safety of the hour;
Here to forget our serfdom, our disgrace,
And bathe our weakness in mysterious power.

THE KILLING

I heard the clamour of pursuit, and groaned.
Hollow and sombrely the sound came forth
As from a dried out well.

Courage died in me; all my force was spent,
Hope of escape incontinently fell.

That tiny hope, a scarce-delivered baby
Cried once, fluttered and went –
Faint as the ocean in a shell.

On the cliff wall I leant;
There was a grim relief in no more trying
In having no will left,
Nothing to do but to accept my dying,
No further haunt of hope.

Yet from the tawny cleft
Within the mountain's stone
A wild life-loving cry went echoing
– Mine and yet not my own –
Like a dog's rabies yelp,
From cliff to ledge, from height to shaly slope,
As if these harboured help.

And as its echo died
A stunning silence clutched from every side.

The steep descending curtain of the mountain
Had closed, for a sweet moment, the hot sounds –
The exultation of the men and hounds.

Water fell thinly somewhere overhead;
The faintest, sharpest sound of rustling leaves
Came from a cliff-grown tree.

The careless goats grazed on, their silly bleating
From crag to crag repeating.
A lonely bird sang free.

And still I leant there, supine, self-defeating,
Too dry for any phrases of entreating,
No more concealed, nor running, but enslaved
To the sword's final greeting.

On that high pathway, in that echoing cleft
I halted then, of potency bereft;
With too much fear to move, cry out, protest –
With too much fear to tell.

No voices for the while; but my heart's beating
Was all the sound in the world.
This cool and ferny place would see my end.
All my thought was incredulous surprise

At death, and at life's cheating,
At hate, drawing to finish
What once had been, so long ago, begun;
At the hard agony of such defeating.

Sudden, the roar of enmity was close –
The human voices, laughter, cry of dogs.
For a deceptive moment, I believed
In the essential friendliness of men
Merry and sane. And was the more deceived.
For this belief was fleeting.
Mercy was none. Hard eyes would shine triumphant
At this mad meeting.

They rounded soon the corner of the mountain,
These ordinary, reasonable men
Fuelled by their anger's fountain
Turned into beasts by being joined together
Packed closely in a merciless unity
To find me in my den,

And when they saw me, at the end of tether,
All their wide mouths howled an enormous gain
Tuned to one voice;
An echoing savage cry
Mouthing the mountain like a pack of wolves
Or some lone leopard rover;
As if humanity could have no choice
And sounds of pity never murmured by
The hunter's path.

And soon, in a wild hurricane of pain
It was all over;
Final extreme of hating.
The dying not more terrible than the waiting.

* * * * *

Who was I? Nobody and everyone,
All the pursued, all the out-numbered, all
The desperate fugitives, the sorry weavers
Of their own funeral pall;
Trembling, surrendering ere the fight's begun,
All the unwilling quitters, fearful leavers.

No-one and everyone, consumed by fears
And finding fear's reality at last –
Pursuit, and lonely death, from the enemy
Lodged in mankind over the countless years,
The rich, resounding, senseless cruelty
Our sad flesh wears.

RENAISSANCE ARTIST

We paint – to our paymaster's creed –
The face of pain, the hands that bleed.

We paint, because we have to paint,
The tortured head, the limbs that faint.

The harsh, the cruel, the placid stares
That lock upon the last despairs.

Christ's death, for sure, the world embraces –
Did painters scorn those other faces?

* * * * *

Joyful we paint, when free of check
The melting grace of some long neck,

Fold of a dress, or tiny flower
Pencilled in some unguarded hour,

Or let the loving paintbrush linger
With bright jewels on the crooked finger

And introduce in unseen whiles
Enchanted distant towns and isles

Where greed and malice never travel
And where the strands of pain unravel,

Bright mountains over peaceful seas,
The evening light amongst the trees.

Intoxicate with His creation
We tread with care in celebration

Of all that lavish loveliness
That we're forbidden to caress

And rebel brush-strokes thus indict
The creed that God abhors delight.

HELL

Dreadful is man in his complacency
Terrible in his rages.
And he needs fear as he needs daily bread.
And he needs frightening, frightening very badly
Till sober apprehension clears his head
And he can feel less madly;
Till fear his wrath assuages,
Or his light mind engages.

Frightened he surely was
In other, fiercer ages.
Fire, famine, conquest, treachery, were threats
Worse than the warnings of the priestly sages.

Just how effective was it – all this fear?
Did the enraged arm stay
Raised over cowering wife, or fallen foe,
Raised over crying child at dawn of day?

Idle to think that serf or baron paused
Or held their hand, discerning
In ruthless heart, or head obtusely thick,
A movement of compassion for their prey,
Some pang of fellow feeling

Over the luckless victim, vainly kneeling,
Over noosed innocent, or heretic
Tied there for burning.

Did anyone fear Hell?
Or pause, thinking it far enough away?
Did they fear God, or dread discovery
By priest or chieftain, on the final day
When in some coin of suffering they must pay?

And are we more concerned, more virtuous,
More civilised than they?
Seemingly fear alone
Was not enough for them
And love alone is not enough for us,
Since both are needful for the proper role
Saving the vagrant soul.

Love the most urgent seems still powerless
To change the stubborn heart and the set mind,
The excited will to turn.
Love's not enough, impotent to discern
The way we struggle desperately to find.

Must constant and imperious fear return
Would an insistent dread leave us less blind?

Possibly not.
But still we travel heavily
With fear of God forgot.

While loneliness, the leopard, waits to claim
The traveller at dusk
With fears that have no name.

Although we know there's no blank nothingness
No fiery death at God's compelling hand,
No sinful bodies will forever burn,
We shall have far and wearily to go –
A boring struggle with a hell self-made;
Stubborn apprenticeship
Striving to understand
Intricacies of some unyielding trade;
Waiting our turn,
We who rejected love and chose ourselves
As object of our worship and desire
Have longer and more painful journeyings
And harder truths to learn.

FOR WORTHLESS ABSALOM

For worthless Absalom, still waits
And weeps King David, loving-hearted;
Young Alexander's stol'n in death,
Dido and brave Aeneas parted.

For all our prayers, for all our passion
Experience no wisdom yields;
Brave bodies sprawled in the old fashion
Parch on a hundred battlefields.

The crucifix still crowns the hill;
Though war's forbidden, plague diminished
Nothing assuages man's ill-will
The tale of grief is never finished.

Slaves in the west maybe are freed
But Africans to Asia forced
Move still in chains, and still the Jews
Smoke in a timeless holocaust.

Streets redden yet with human blood
Mankind, uncaring, keeps few tallies,
And blind to the alternatives
They stab each other in dark alleys.

Nothing unwrites the ancient sorrows
There is no balm to heal death's sting,
But few of us can pause to listen
And fewer still can learn a thing.

SALE OF THE DRAWING-ROOM

The slender muslin girls holding a rose
Set on small tables in their silver frames,
And, splendid in their scarlet uniforms,
Great uncles with their scarce-remembered names,

Those graceful aunts, erect in flowing dresses
Who stumbled, all too soon, on World War One;
Piano-playing, violin-enjoying,
Their music drowned in noise of bomb and gun.

The Chelsea china in its cabinet,
The rosy-patterned chintz, the silver dog,
The gilded overmantel, Persian carpets,
Are now but numbers in a catalogue;

Victims of all the mercenary shouting,
Sold to the slavery of the highest bid;
And may they kindle in new habitats
Some of the gentleness those curtains hid.

Voice of the auctioneer, condign and crisp,
Aware of every nuance in their cost
Now drowns the echo of those quiet voices
Once dear, and now irrevocably lost;

Old loves, old heroes, old self-sacrifice
Never in vain to the large eye of time;
Gentle advice, and firmly voiced opinion,
Something ridiculous, but much sublime,

The lamps behind their silken pleated shades
Giving indifferent light, and those dear brittle
Ornaments ranged along the chimney piece
Now nothing worth, will go for very little;

The classic authors in the rosewood shelves
Whom everybody dusted, no-one read,
Gold-lettered backs, tied in uneasy bundles
Are lying flat, as if already dead.

A certainty, a confidence of good,
A way of life, on time's grim anvil shattered
Lies here, the debris of a thousand lives
As broken as though none of it had mattered.

Long may the kindliness, the self-restraint
That stilled life's storm, left bitter words unspoken –
Old voices reading stories, young ones singing,
Leave on a harsh new world some gentle token.

THE ISLANDERS

Well, it's been tiring, and at times, good fun –
Four hundred years spent as a major power.
The match, as far as we're concerned, is won;
Or lost, maybe? We've *had* our finest hour.

The blue-eyed dedicated empire builders
Bringing torn nations justice and new hope
Have done their stint and gone. (Although the nations
Might have preferred less justice and more scope.)

The golden lads who fought for social justice
Are fat and fifty-nine and super-taxed.
The lads today are barking up a tree
Long since cut down, a thicket all but axed.

So what's to bite on? Only rapid riches,
Tellies and cars and holidays and cricket,
And watching with derisive sympathy
While chaps less expert try to keep the wicket.

Theirs now to hold the fort, the palm, the baby,
The headaches over Serbs and over Thailanders.
Over to you, cousins; you'll find there are
No isolationists to match with Islanders.

You grew to strength behind us, friends, remember?
The century in which we kept away
Every potential danger from your shores
Leaving you to your politics and play.

Why grumble? We took Louis, and Napoleon,
The brunt of Kaiser Wilhelm and of Hitler,
And, some way back, the mighty swords of Spain,
All just as tough, although the scale was littler.

Our best good wishes, brothers, go to it:
Good luck to you with Pax Americana.
No headlines mucking up the football scores,
Tread softly round us, in our new Nirvana.

And don't forget – though sleepy, we're the same;
And when we've had a really cosy snooze
And charged our batteries, we shall be back
Right in the thick again, and making news.

1960

PART III

Contemporaries

GREAT HOUSE

We have been here before;
We know that grey-haired lady by the door
Her kindly manner, her assured technique
When selling picture postcards to the meek
And a nice oven-glove that never washes.
We know those smart asides
From experts in their belted mackintoshes
Who know it all much better than the guides.

Can you identify the second Duke?
The *label* says its Kneller, but the *book*
Settles for Willem Wissing.
And those two children kissing?
Here's parson uncle on his way to matins
By Reynolds, and the baby swathed in satins
Grown to an admiral; a sunset burns,
Lighting his flock of sails and high-built sterns
In smoky confrontation with the Dutch …
It's all too much …

The tapestry, the framed ancestral tree …
The long long passage where the learned loiter
In ecstasies before the Hondecoeter,
Almost contented to forego their tea;

Another floor? Well, what did you expect?
And, to be honest, most of us neglect
The loveliest Bellini upon earth
To see the snapshots of the family –
The Labradors, the twins soon after birth,
Duchess in wedding bliss,
The three grown children at a picnic lunch –
The lucky, moneyless, determined bunch
Whose habitat is this.

Too quickly one forgets
The gorgeous china in the cabinets,
The clocks, the swords, the chairs by William Kent,
The little lectures that are so well meant
– Do they do teas? –
The marble busts, the fragments brought from Greece,
Elegance of the Georgian chimney-piece ...
We mustn't miss the dungeon, or the fetter,
The seventh earl with gun and Irish setter,
Cavalier locks, or Queen Victoria's letter.
Do they do *teas*?
We thought the macaroons at Chatsworth better.

Here is the room with weapons on the wall
Which, thankfully, leads back into the hall
Where Lely ladies hold that sugared pout,
And German students hear their leader gassing.
From his wide ruff, the Founder of the House
Looks back at us, pink-lidded, land-amassing,
Canny as all get out

UPPER CRUST

The rent became impossible. She moved
Into a cheaper district far from friends.
The rooms are shabby; so's the clientele
That haunts the bus-stop where the terrace ends.

The paper bags abound, the shouting swells,
And the uncaring faces swim and pass
In rivers of indifference, and smells
Of un-disposed-of nappies haunt the grass.

Even the hymn in Church is not a hymn
But a request that Zambia is made strong;
The parson is progressive, and invents
Holy Communion as he goes along.

Sad and estranged, she takes her homeward way
On pavements still unswept, that turn her belly,
Treading across the black banana skins
And through the crumpled copies of Reveille.

This is the trial, and she must now be strong,
Adapt fastidious habits to new day.
Did not the Gospel tell her all along
To love her neighbour, be he whom he may?

But she's too old now to become a saint;
Scorn would receive her, kind words not disguise her.
Mockery follows, titters echo back;
How can she help a people who despise her?

Loneliness gathers round her, friends fall off,
Not of design, but through forgetfulness.
Only the bathroom floor receives her tears,
The early morning pillow her distress.

The sunlit lawns, the aproned parlour-maid,
The scented mother, and the carefree dad
Fade into distance; hope becomes mislaid,
And slowly she is turned a little mad.

Sins of the fathers, pride of other days
Gather against her bent and greying head.
When someone treats her kindly, her old face
Smiles like a resurrection from the dead.

The sound of cockcrow, rustle of old trees,
Happiness that was lent and never given
Float and dissolve about her as she treads
The rugged pathway to her hope of Heaven.

TERRA INCOGNITA

The faces in the city street assault
With their unguarded piteous nakedness –
A cry for help so sheer
So troubled by disquietude and fear
That stricken pulses halt
Dead in their tracks, so sharp a cry to hear
Loud through the underground, the Ticket Hall,
So desperate a call,

Grief we are deaf to hear
Or hearing, are still powerless to allay.

Knowing not how to answer, what to say
Or how to say it, we then hold our peace,
Facing each other in the railway carriage
With mutual visages contained and glum.
Here is the stop. The station buses come,
Lights swinging round the curve. Rain starts to fall.

Here is an evening drear
Ending a sullen day

Down parking lines, doors of the motors slam
Banging and crashing, a repeated drum
That sounds defiant to the folk outside

For whom no motors come,
Who have to find their route another way
Down asphalt walk or ride,

To certain houses and uncertain cheer,
While all await
The sometimes dreaded clicking of their gate,
The routine kiss, complaints about the day,
'You're late again, wherever have you been?'
Why can't he hurry home?
All the faint comfort gleaned from saccharine
By those who long for honey in the comb.

The door shuts, and aloneness rules again,
Like a dark beast on prowl
Padding from tree to tree through silent forest
Or stalking him across a desert plain,
Grinding blunt teeth within vindictive jowl.
He is forever islanded, apart,
Imprisoned in the silence of his heart
A speechless stranger, with a tongue unknown.

Where did the song of marriage drift away
Leaving them both alone?

Their love is in a log jam of stagnation –
Yet not past reparation.
At times a gentleness in ways and looks
Warms the returning heart; and not long after

The impulse of a deft surprising kindness,
And welcome voices of the very dear –
An eight-year-old transported by his laughter;
Young children, in a moment's gravity,
Within their crystal clarity of gaze
Suggest that a sublimity is near.
Even towards the ending of drab days
The smell of supper is a kind of praise,
Even in this red suburb, there is still
The sound of birds at morning from the hill
Though we are deaf to hear.

Even the shadows sanctify the light
With sense of some fond glory out of sight.
The hundred pains and perils of our life
Pierce us with waking sounds, as violins
Poignant, direct, and clear
Carry the tune above the music's strife.
Though we are strangers in an unknown land
With nothing as we dreamed, desired, or planned,
Trace of immortal music haunts the ear;
Though the dull ache of loss sounds and resounds
Its deep bassoon, though the shrill flutes of fear
And long anxiety, dwell ever near –
A fountain river this dry place surrounds
And a great orchestra enchants the ear,
Music of healing wraps the stubborn wounds
And the sure news that we ourselves are dear –
The news that mostly we are deaf to hear.

LADY IN HARRODS

My importance is to me
The fairy on the Christmas tree
The dearest thing on land or sea.

Facing fortune's onslaughts gaily
Cherishing my neighbour daily,
Never lost, or loitering palely.

Trifling stranger, do not shake
The tinselled branches, lest you break
The doll my darling virtues make,

The doll that I suppose is me
Full of charm and sympathy
And from vulgar passions free.

Hell is not the burning sea
Hell's the tumbling of the tree
Hell's myself alone with me.

1938

NO CIRCULAR, NO SUCCOUR

My face is inexplicably benign,
And all too often taken as a sign
Of willingness to tender information
To stranded characters of every nation.

Oh for a mug less vicarage, less kind
The mirror of a harsh derisive mind,
The look of someone certain not to care
Whether a 46 will get you there.

How much of *ennui* might be spared, or *honte*
If Frenchmen, seeking the Jardin des Plantes
Did not assume, on glancing at my phiz,
A readiness to tell them where it is.

Something is gained – a face whose cheques go home
In any bank from Yucatan to Suez
Is much. But not enough. Even in Rome
Frantic Italians ask me where the loo is.

POLITICAL MEETING

Listen, for you're the sovereign people
Supposed to anchor, not to float.
You'll rock no bells in any steeple
However you decide to vote,
And this is the unmentioned fact
That clamps you in a vast malaise
And makes a nonsense of my act
In praise of governmental ways.

Sit still, while I pontificate.
I have a matter to announce;
No matter if I irritate
No matter if my statements bounce
Like balls along an asphalt paving,
Insult the reason, dull the ears –
Simply by coming here you're waiving
Your right not to be bored to tears.

The chairs are hard; that's your misfortune,
Your feet grow colder as I talk,
The tales that now your minds importune
You knew as soon as you could walk.
No matter – it's democracy.

'And are there questions?' cries the Chair.
No fear. Not now he's stopped. We're free!
And in a trice the hall is bare.

Duty is done. So back to telly,
Or pull the blanket over head
And shut the ears against reveille
And snooze in comfort, fully fed.
We whom no speaker can arouse
And each advertisement can vamp,
Which cheese? Which caravan? Which blouse?
Which car? *Which concentration camp?*

1960

MINISTER OF AGRICULTURE

I do not care about the land, the trees,
Or the slow tractor crawling on the plough,
I scarcely know about the birds and bees –
I just want office, and I want it now.

I do not care if the long acres starve
Or when the hay is saved, harvest begins
It irks me not when cows omit to calve,
Since milk is something that I buy in tins.

I do not care that ham derives from pigs,
Hazily know that bread is made from flour.
I want, while shops supply bacon and eggs,
To stay in office and to stay in power.

Country is something that I see from trains,
A space that slows my way from town to town.
I do not share its pleasures or its pains.
Frankly, the whole arrangement wears me down.

EPITAPH FOR DEMOCRACY

It came, because of deep distress
At thought of folk with so much less.
It went, because nobody bore
The thought that anyone had more.

1960

FEBRUARY

Celestial month of income tax behind,
Of soppy Valentines with silver chimes,
Spring fashions on their battle fields aligned
And letters about migrants in the Times,

Of travel guides to beaches in Malay,
When aconites arrive, and plumbers lurk.
Blest month of getting thirty-one days' pay
For doing only twenty-eight days' work.

1962

INVENTIONS

Curses, not for nuclear fission
Which could be a useful Thing,
But on men who felt a Mission
To devise a Better String.

Flames no more are hell for me
Nor the smoking hills agape,
Hell for me's eternity
Tightly wound in Sellotape.

1958

ME AND AUNT EDNA
CALLING THE BOX OFFICE

I have been purged for long enough by terror and by pity,
Emotionally I'm bankrupt, there's nothing left in the kitty;
All I ask are the camel lines, and the lights of the desert city
And lashings more of the blissful secret life of Walter Mitty.

Oh for the cleft-chinned hero winning a golden fleece,
Two persons putting together a dinosaur, piece by piece,
And one of them tumbling the whole thing down by a slip in a
   pool of grease,
And an endless stream of dear Mack Sennett's belly-laugh police.

I crave for a level-crossing and a truck and an engine's scream,
And the purr of mink and the clink of ice and the sequin's wicked
   gleam,
Ruritania and Rose Marie, Anouilh and a-dash-of-cream,
Oklahoma and Pinafore and a Midsummer Night's long Dream.

I'll lay no more good money out to be harrowed about perversion,
A dowse to cats on hot tin roofs, and a lull in the Browning version,
What I require is three good hours of sumptuous total immersion
In the swish of Daimler tyres on the drive and a Golden Arrow
   Excursion.

I did not save for a taxi-ride to see a sick soul beaten,
I long for the innocent ageless dead-pan face of Buster Keaton,
A clash of the sunny temperaments of characters raised at Eton,
And the brittle charm of early Edwardians dressed by Cecil
    Beaton.

Guards officers planning adultery in a chi-chi Georgian setting,
And a bee-hive girl with a salty wit and a Dior dress abetting,
A blonde and a carefree sailor in some un-neurotic petting,
And a twelve stone dame in a feather boa receiving a sudden
    wetting.

Brother, oh brother, we *like* it Ham. We do not want Real Life.
Plenty of that outside in the rain, and sinks are all too rife.
Give us a romp in lollipop land and a pause from mental strife
And no more high-toned belly ache from a sex-starved teenage
    wife.

LEFT WING

Hate, they suggest, the rich, the grand, the clever,
Who, single-handed, never
Could have achieved this mess;
Loathe, above all, success,
Which is arrived at, they insist, by keeping
The poor in unendurable duress,
Stripping them bare, exploiting honest men,
All their good fortune built upon distress.

Some truth; but they are barking up a tree
That was cut down of yore
And is there not enough to hate already –
Envy and avarice and greed galore
The dreadful cruelty of civil war
Seditions, emulations, hate enough
Without inventing more?

ON THE TOWPATH

Her beauty is tarnished
Her lovers all dead
Her dwelling forsaken
Her children are fled,
She walks by the river
With clouds in her head,
The prodigal giver
Whose lovers are dead.

She's stolen, but nobody
Gains by the theft,
And when she departs
There'll be no-one bereft,
For with a precision
Uncannily deft,
The givers are taken,
The takers are left.

The breezes blow sweetly
The green rushes quiver
Escape for the taker
And woe to the giver.

Whose sad thoughts will make her
Incline to the brink,
And with a brief shiver
Too soon, too completely
She'll yield to the river.

SKETCH FOR A PORTRAIT

The true story behind this murder was that the young man had been sent by his mother to leave a Christmas card on old Miss Jones, who gave piano lessons and had a card in her window to say so. She lived in the last house in a blind alley, and was frightened out of her wits when she opened her door in the near darkness, to see a strange young man looming there. Afterwards, he spent a wretched Christmas and on Boxing Day told his brother-in-law what he had done, and was persuaded to go to the police. The death sentence was commuted to nine years.

When I became a murderer they treated me with love
The hand that clipped the irons on was in a velvet glove,
My unimportant mackintosh became Exhibit A
And clever men gave ear to me and let me say my say.

And poor Miss Ethel Jones the same, they seemed to find we
    mattered,
They photographed her body twice, and all her garments
    scattered.
And all the brains and brass and power, the prophets, priests and
    thrones
Were focussed in affection upon me and Ethel Jones.

They passed along the surface in a stately arabesque
The judge's cuffs were snowy white that lent upon his desk,
The trial was set to music with a tumty-tum-tara,
As distant as Arcturus from the way things really are.

They had such gentle faces and their questions were so kind,
Regretfully implacable, securely sound of mind,
With golden bright integrity that breathed in every breath
They did their duty as they should and sentenced me to death.

It was the dusk that did it,
And my soul's drouth,
East wind along the winter street,
Her open mouth,

Her mouth so terror-wide;
My frightened rage
Leapt out to meet her fear, my youth
Hated her age.

Women must never scream,
Rousing in men
Dragon that lies asleep
Deep in its den.

In that wild jungle roar
No voice was found
Far, in the thundering seas
Reason lay drowned.

Searing, unquiet in me
Life cried her doom;
Dread manhood in my guts
Hated her womb.

Locked in the same panic,
Held in one dream,
I held her throat, shouted
Don't scream, don't scream!

Locked in one hatred's power,
Bound in one fear,
We stilled each other's life.
I am still here.

The everlastings in a vase,
The pampas in the grate …
This poor old faggot – who?
What brought her fate?

Naked she lay and sprawled.
Who laid her there?
Who clawed her life out
On that dusk air?

The silence choked my ears –
One soundless cry.
Not I, my veins shouted
Did this, not I!

Some other, someone else
Led me along!
Judge, you who never hate
Never do wrong!

Cunning woke in me.
I scattered her stuff.
Made it look gang work –
Not cunning enough.

My new won happiness,
My wife new found,
All threatened by her cry,
That thin old sound.

Hide, and forget it all.
They'll never find me,
Only in childhood dreams
Men come to bind me.

* * * * *

Life without law is chaos, profanation,
Law is to succour, strengthen, and befriend.
Law has to be. But, for Christ's sake, remember
That law is means, and never can be end.

I am a human being and must bear
The weight of it. The weight is life, not death.
The weight is living with it, being man
And living through it, to my final breath.

* * * * *

66

When once I was a murderer how totally they cared,
Nobody came to lecture me, and no-one's teeth were bared,
Their eyes were clear of vengeance and their hearts were clear of
    hate
They looked on me and loved me but their loving came too late.

MONARCHIST

Since it's not broken, where's the need to break?
What's the alternative, for Heaven's sake?
Who is to reign – some deedy journalist?
An academic? Or some learned judge?
A newspaper proprietor, plus grudge?
A weary doctor, as our Head of State;
Some general with a passion to dictate?
A scientist, preferring chemistry,
Pushed into being great?
An admiral home from sea
Or a Pretender, flushed with pedigree?

A wise man from the east?
A holy but impracticable priest?
A failed ambassador? (The one that thrives
Has mostly had enough of public lives.)
What is the point of changing, may one ask
When we have well-trained experts at the task?

Where's the alternative, for goodness sake,
What option would *you* take?
Who is to save
Us moody millions from the fool or knave?
Some hermit plucked unwilling from his cave?

Alas – our likely fate –
A clapped-out politician on the make
Of personal importance, who will be
A substitute whom half of us will hate
And none of us will cross the road to see.

TEA-ROOM

Blind with the anguish of the negative answer,
Its slow devouring pain, she sits and stares
And nothing else. That purposeful machine,
Intricate plan of retina and nerve,
Ceases its task;
People and table and teapots are unseen.
The grief behind that still and stricken mask
Undoes the beauty and the youth she wears.

Her mother's friends are at a distant table
And put such gloss on it as they are able.
Clever, they said, she is, and went to Cambridge,
I was against the notion from the start.
Cassandra's youngest girl – perhaps too clever,
They're to be pitied, girls with too much brain,
Worse still when it's combined with too much heart;
Intellect's not an easy habitat.
Think of the strain
And toil of all that learning and endeavour!
What with their fancies, and their monthly pain,
They have enough to manage without that.

Somehow the friends have not the nerve to wend
A kindly way past intervening tables
And tell Cassandra's girl
That this is not the end,
That hearts were made to suffer and to mend;
Nor would she listen to them if they did.

But someone should have spoken, someone listened
Before those bright and broken teardrops glistened
With pain and grief. How their poor hearts will quiver
When three days on she's lifted from the river.

1982

AUNT

All her approaches
Were steep shingle beaches
Where no boat could land;
And unharboured vessels
Rolled sad in the offing
Or stayed in the reaches
Scarce daring at most
To careen on the strand.

And as you came nigh her
You felt the heart harden,
The warmness of greeting
Chilled in your hand,
Till friendliness curdled
And speech was a burden
And, fixed on your visage,
The smile became bland.
In arrogant youth
You held out no pardon
And stayed not to ask
By what broken promise
From what ruined garden
She came to this stand.

And never considered
– Chilled and repelled –
What sun of hope setting
What total eclipse
What ice of containment
Daily self-built
Within those cold walls
Was in bitterness held,
What sorrow begetting
What blankness of years
Furrowed that forehead,
Tautened those lips.

DOWN WITH DECIMALS
TWENTY YEARS ON

Impervious to decision-makers
We parcel out our land in acres;
Deaf to Napoleonic notions
Continue still to fathom oceans.

Though daily more instruction comes
Feet are still feet, and inches, thumbs.
Most stubborn of the race of men
We will not multiply by ten.

Our petrol is not bought in litres,
Our distance paced in yards, not metres.
No sacrifice of insularity
Is made towards imported clarity.

Why don't efficient business men
Enslaved before their love of ten
Simply indulge their whim for neuters
By changing things on their computers?

Even the children in their school
Lightly skip around the rule –
What teacher says is not so vital
As newspeak in a sporting title.

Two furlongs out! Cry commentators
To comprehending race-spectators.
80! In heatwaves, newsmen write
Still wedded to their Fahrenheit.

We stay, for all of Europe's fix
Still multiplying twelve by six,
Wedded to what is old and dear
We buy in pints our milk and beer.
Contented, as the cosmos lurches
With miles and rods, with poles and perches.

1990

TRESPASSERS UNWELCOME

No man's soul is a harsh proud place where he walks his way in
    splendour,
But sometimes it's a cosy house where he wants for nothing more,
Or a happy impecunious haunt with a view of field or shore,
And much more often a small bare room with a burnt out fire in
    the fender
Where a small thin nobody crouches close because his heart is
    tender.

Kindly stranger, do not harm.
Do not come here to disclose
Meagreness that no-one knows,
Do not sound the house alarm.
Please don't press the steaming cup
And do not throw the window up.
Turn your back, and in my shell
Let me live my private hell
Undisturbed by forms to fill,
And by help against my will,
Or by welfare's personnel.

1958

THE PET

Darling Grievance, sit by me,
Fed on cake and cups of tea,
Lulled with honey-dew, caressed,
Never by neglect depressed.

Eyes alert and features glowing,
Look how splendidly he's growing!
Large and larger day by day,
Never suffered to decay.

Husband, children, sister, brother
Bore me, one way and another;
Only little G exhales
Total charm that never fails.

Others wilt for lack of love;
I and Grievance, hand in glove,
Company that cannot tire
Sit and warm us by the fire.

1963

SHORT STORY

Red sunrise slides across the sleepless bed:
The morning after is the great disrober
Of fantasy from fact, of heart from head –
She loves him drunk, she cannot love him sober.

COLONEL AND WIFE

Their happiness is combat, and their joy
A kind of tender quarrelling, most dear
And stimulating to both girl and boy.
There's no exasperation, but a clear
Knock-for-knock tennis, where their thoughts entwine.
'I am eighty-six, she's in her eightieth year.'
'Don't rush it, Humphrey, I am seventy-nine:
Quite different from eighty.' 'Too much sugar
Is in this salad.' 'Say so if you must;
Yesterday there was too much vinegar'
She counters. It's not easy to define
Who most enjoys this gentle cut and thrust.
The absence of all bitterness and malice
Transforms their cottage to a kind of palace.
Never will he allow his sword to rust;
She turns from him, almost a mental shove
As who should throw his arguments to dust;
A sparkling energy that does but prove
How live and deep and constant is their love.

1981

AN OLD FRENCHMAN IN THE PARK WITH HIS GRANDSON

This is he
Who'll wear my manhood in the stony places,
Look with my eyes into the tigerish faces,
This is he.

The after-life is hid;
This single immortality is true
This hobgoblin who in my flesh shall do
All that I never did.

BOWLER HAT

I keep within the law: I come to pay
Knee-service every Sunday to the Name
All other names above; and when I pray
My lips confess his glory and my shame.

I talk to Mrs Robson after church
I'm more or less unspotted from the Foe.
I never left an orphan in the lurch
I listen to old Samson's tale of woe.

Is Ultimate Reality to me
Enshrined in stocks and shares of solid rank
Golden unquestionable property
The holy chink of money in the bank?

Who knows? In humbleness I take the Cup.
Lifting my trouser legs, I bend the knee.
With manly tread I take collection up:
The answer is between my God and me.

Perhaps I've little of spirit, most of letter;
But when they come to fetch me in the hearse
Though my report may say, He could do better,
Please add, He could have done a damn sight worse.

NILE ISLAND

At eight years old I dreaded afternoons:
I knew the lassitude of savage beasts
But not their sleep; I prowled the sultry dunes
Huge with uneaten feasts.

Night came at length and sudden; moon would rise
Jupiter blazed, out sprang triumphant Mars.
Fear had arrived, the glint of leopard's eyes
Shone in the pricking stars.

Skin of the leopard lay across the floor,
All day I knew his nothingness, I went
Carelessly where he lay beyond the door,
Glass-eyed and impotent.

At nightfall I'd remember how he'd housed
In life an evil spirit, preyed on men.
My father shot him, but with dark he roused
And wore his flesh again.

Rigid, I lay and listened every night,
Unswerving eyes gazed through mosquito net
To where would come, square head against the light,
His dreadful silhouette.

I knew the very lashing of his tail,
I smelled the catty harshness of his breath,
Helpless beneath his spring, his forelegs flail,
I died a nightly death.

Infinite leagues away in a jewelled city
God reigned among his towers of chrysolite,
But here the powers of ill were sitting pretty,
Here leopard ruled, and night.

Amazingly, the morning always broke –
Day more resplendent than a festival,
And God returned; the shouting songbirds woke
Tunes like a waterfall.

Joyful, I trod the dusty road to school
Past the kind jungles of the sugar cane;
Happily played, and learnt the lesson rule;
Leaping, bounced home again.

For six uncounted hours the magic held.
But heavy from the Citadel, how soon
The mid-day gun rolled menacing, and knelled
That shadowless forenoon.

BEING EIGHTEEN

Love me for more than sea-blue eyes
For silken voice and lively mind
Love me without expectancy:
Love me for more than mirror's gleam,
A looking glass where you may find
Reflections of a self-esteem;
Love me for me.

Love me for all my soul's confusions
For thoughts of which I would be free,
For thunder moods and rose illusions,
Love me for me:
For sudden laughter, folly's spree,
Ludicrous hopes, and shame's contusions,
Through teasings and inconstancy
Love me for me.

For hopes to which I vainly press
For dreams I never could confess,
In deeps you neither know nor see,
In glooms and in uncertainty
Love me for me.

Even for all my vain pretences
My haunting fears, my thin defences,
Love me for what I hope to be:
Beyond the sweet dance of the senses
Love me for me.

1959

FIVE-YEAR-OLD

Stay five;
With something yet of the nestling still unflown
In hands that seize, that strive
For food, warmth, love, a central place in the sun.
And even more of the grown,
In subtlety, audacity, surprise,
In the lightning gleam of the eyes,
The strong desire for choice.
Yet something too of the baby in the run,
The rounded limbs, slow voice,
The unashamed self-will.
Stay still.

Stay five:
Tremulous still,
Ready for tears, yet joyful at the thrill
Of finding yourself alive.
In full command of speech,
Laced with the pleasing error –
'That was the smallest church I've ever sawn.'
Too eager still to wait
For the next event to be born;

Stumping ahead with independent gait,
Yet needing a hand in the dark forest's terror –
All of a sudden forlorn.

Stay five;
With those round questioning eyes
Where light and clearness thrive;
With that unstudied charm without and within;
The guileless candour, all those innocent lies,
That liberal quota of original sin;
That cool and flower-like skin,
So feather-soft, so clear;
Halt here.

Spring can't for ever be.
The dew is parched by noon; and calling faint
The soft-voiced cuckoo fades from hill and tree.
On the fresh woodland floor
The bluebells float no more,
Snow of the hawthorn withers into taint.

Over the earth's hot crust
Slowly invades the serpent of mistrust,
And the huge world is no more friend and brother.
Full summer aches all day on field and fold,
On the deep green of the woods, on harvest gold –
Beautiful, but quite other.

1976

GRAND-CHILDREN

Incalculable, wilful, satin-skinned,
Sinning all day, yet never having sinned;
Knees bending for the leap of joy, and eyes
Brilliant with the excitement of surmise,
Or glazed in some impenetrable dream.
No mix of what you are with how you seem –
Wide eyes, and seizing hands, and open soul.
Wrath undissembled, grief without control,
And joy without the shadow of a cloud.
Now silent as the tomb, now wildly loud,
Impatient, and indifferent to the weather,
Lost in the wonder of a fallen feather;
Absorbed in some obsession of your own,
Marching eyes-front into a world unknown,
Part dancing, part advancing, part afraid,
Now halting, now defiant, undismayed,

Watching, the ancient heart will miss a beat
At the immortal impulse of those feet.

YOUNG MAN IN THE LIME-WALK

This is the sum of summer afternoons
Through which he walks so cloudily, so lost,
Unmindful of its evanescent gleam.
This is the sum
And summit of extravagant high summer
That never counts the cost
Of leaf, of flower, of sunlight, bubbling stream –
Such riches, lightly tossed.

Heavy with silence, or the bees' long hum,
Shadowy, English, green,
This is the lazy, lime-enchanted sum
– Hay harvest over, corn not yet begun –
Of summer afternoons
That ever yet have been
Or are to come,
Through which he walks un-seeing, scarcely seen.

As if the honeyed air
Never could reach his lungs
Or activate a heart so drowned in care.
The bees hum ever, and a wave of scent
Swims lightly from the fully-flowering limes.
He walks as if there never could be better

Nor could be, ever had been, darker times;
Beauty itself the mock
– In its bland carelessness –
Of his rejection, of his grief, his shock;
Beauty itself the haze
To hide from him the impermanence of days.

Pity him not, sad mother;
He will be married, well within the year,
To someone other.

July 1963

ALICE IN LONDON

Incurably convivial and assured
With round ingenuous face that has allured
Many to misconceive the rogue within –
That cheerful packet of original sin.
Sturdy, and neat, with hair as fair as tow,
Playful and sociable and full of go,
With will of iron and appetite most hearty
Where I arrive becomes a cocktail party.

Though sometimes I precipitate disaster,
Complain, assert, and throw my weight about,
My own persona is the sticking plaster.
As a third daughter, I'd to sink or swim
Under the odium of not being him.

Charm is the spell to put such thoughts to rout,
A strong determination helped me out –
Never you fear, I'll swim, without a doubt.
I fell, with great conviction, on my feet;
Never a son could turn out half so sweet.

DAUGHTER
ON HER ENGAGEMENT

Mocking and considerate,
Brusque, affectionate and true,
Loving to the un-admired –
Let me warm my hands by you.

Laughter cures; a reconciling
On the troubled water pours;
Lightning wits and loving kindness –
Let me warm my heart at yours.

Charming and compassionate,
Gently judging, free of range,
Friend to many – may another
Do the warming for a change.

In your going I should weep,
Family and love be riven,
Laughter lessened; but to you
So long giver, would be given.

August 1960

PARENTHOOD

Parents, when tempted to forgive your children
Seven times seventy, and then again,
It doesn't always do.

You note with pain
How very rarely they've forgiven you
That once you left them standing in the rain
From two till five past two.

Stiffen the sinews, give them once their due.
Bring them up some day with a quick round turn,
So that they learn
Forgiveness isn't always automatic;
Forgiveness is a thing they have to earn.

1998

Part IV

Places & Seasons

THE ORANGERY
MOUNT EDGCUMBE

Sound the long trumpet call, the winter's last
Sound and resound, the wild Atlantic blast!
The valiant wings of gull and cormorant fail,
Rise, flutter, and are vanquished in the gale,
And far on inland hedge and beechwood bent
The wind-flown curtain of the spray is sent;
On night-black rocks the sombre waves spill white
Whilst over dark seas falls the darker night.

Fast in their Adam house of stone and glass
The orange trees have watched the winter pass,
Now spring's reversion sends them forth from there
To breathe the summer's mild Atlantic air.
Here in this grove they bear their precious sheaf
Enamelled with bright bud and shining leaf,
And show to man's enchanted nose and eyes
The very smell and look of Paradise.

Stokehill, 1936

FROM A TRAIN WINDOW
WEST COUNTRY

These fields of green forever and forever
Compass the heart; these lighted trees of spring,
The stillness of the pools beyond the weir
Silent in evening light, serene and clear.
And though, beyond the flesh, the greed of men
With concrete worms these lovely scenes devour
Yet in our many bodies, sown apart,
They shall forever burgeon with new flower –
A consciousness, in distant lands entombed
Under a tropic moon, or northern star,
Within those worthy lovers, scattered far;
Deep in the fibres of each buried heart
Whose fleshly love for beauty that they see
Endows the sight with immortality.

1973

QUERY

Sweet blackbird, singing fit to bust
Do you just sing because you must?

Although you sing indeed
As if millennium had arrived
And everyone were fed and freed
And human grief dissolved in dust,
An end had come to need.
Flooding the evening with delight
Making a sullen sunset bright
In cheering us you do succeed –

What do you feel in your bird heart,
Nothing but lust and greed?

Snowdenham , 1985

GENEROSITY

Late, lovely, and extravagant spring
Your lavish riches still lay by –
Your spending spree of bud and flower,
Transparent leaf and cloudless sky.

Store up awhile, azalea's jewels,
Prodigal snow of the lilac tree,
Your scattered coin of king-cup gold,
Your bluebells flowing as the sea.

All of the winter's hoarded wealth
Spent now – close curled in a narrow corm
The iris flaunts for a single day
Her lovely, light, extravagant form.

Stokehill, May 1956

MAY AT FONTHILL

Sea-country, all awash with summer foam
Where the green wave breaks on the hawthorn tree;
Like spray along the road, the Queen Anne's Lace
Edges a verdant sea.

A sea with all the richness of the land –
Deep silent woods, new-lighted by the dance
Of young translucent leaves, and bluebell oceans –
Spring's full exuberance.

And cuckoos, calling, calling, from the woods
Cease not to tell their ancient mocking story;
Their gentle ribaldry and repetition
Hymns the day's glory.

Their voice all day in this enchanted season
Holds more of sweetness than of accusation –
Loved, lazy bird of spring, whose private life
Bears no investigation.

ELY: A WATER COLOUR

Great clouds as soft as down, and luminous
As light itself, go gently sailing by
Seeing themselves in pools unvisited
That still unruffled lie.
The scene's as silent as eternity;
Cloud after cloud reflected in slow streams
Broken in reedy shallows where the willows
Sadly, remotely, lean,
Dipping their long green hair to weep unseen
Beside inverted sky.

Out of the west, behind the great cathedral
Comes cloud on cloud, as luminous as glory,
To float awhile aloft,
A misty air, so far away, so soft,
They gently pass, fading, and rolling by,
Endless procession, touched by evening light,
Till the dark earth of the fen
Echoes itself in evening dark again,
And late rooks somewhat lumberingly fly
To harbour for the night
Through the enormous light-enchanted stretch
Of the East Anglian sky.

PORTRAIT
FONTHILL IN SUMMER

Haphazard June, whose waterfall of leaves
Splashes in green cascades from every tree
And breaks in hedgerows foaming into rose;
Up-ended, spumy country all at sea,

Top-heavy caravels, the lime trees tower
Spice-laden with the riches of the Ind,
Leaning on rippling oceans of ripe hay
That rise and fall at the sickle of the wind,

And, summer-dark, the woods are full and breathing ...
Last bluebells float the hidden rides along,
And nightingale, his silver flute unsheathing,
Pierces the coloured evening with his song.

1962

JULY – COLLINGBOURNE DUCIS

Lanes now are sweet with honeysuckle
And no less sweet, the pale wild rose,
And every elder bush and tree
Thickly wears its crown of snows,
The cranesbill plants along the hedge
Their blue unwinking eyes disclose;
Through warm green fields where barley stands
Yellow of harvest faintly shows.

The hay is in; under great trees
Warm workers broach the cheerful cask;
Bare-backed upon a sunlit roof
The thatchers glory in their task.
With scent intoxicant as wine
The lilies open their white flask,
On every cottage wall there bloom
More roses than we dream or ask.

1983

BECKFORD LODGE
one dark July evening

There are too many birds knocking and banging on the windows
    of this house,
Something unquiet about;
There's some parts doubled, some troubled twitter of spirit,
Somebody wants too much to get either in or out.

I don't so much mind the ghost that goes tramping around –
Much better ghosts than thieves,
Than razor-gangs and such. But all these birds!
I wish they'd stop this thudding and crashing around the eaves,
And fight their wars elsewhere
Far in the forests, among the ocean of dark and silent leaves.

THE EXILE

I would return again
To the west country where I am no stranger,
Where soft incessant rain
Falls gently into streams that splash and tumble
Between their rounded stones
As grey as mammoth bones;
And oaken woodlands hang
Under the windy ridge where the beech trees cling,
There the hills swell and fall
Softly to lambing valleys deep or small
Where ewes can browse and suckle far from danger
And the red Devons feed from a granite manger.

And I would leave
This flat rich arable land of wheat and pine,
Where slow and leisured waters scarcely move
By fields of carrot and beet,
And the gold corn stands splendid in the heat,
Where sunlit evenings smile
At mile on tawny mile
Of country thick in crops and short on kine,
Beautiful in its way, but never mine.

Euston, 1974

SUFFOLK

As in a dream, the milk-white Charollais
Move to their trough across an emerald field
And slowly, slowly drink; the fated gnats
Dance on above a scarcely moving stream,
And fallen fruit lies gold about the way.
The plane trees, with their yellow fans agleam
Stir not a whit; no lighter leaves will yield
To breezes through this still and soundless day.

Autumn so warm, so perfect, so serene,
Breathing so soft an air, so calm a peace,
Such dropping plenty of deep-coloured apples,
So full of yielding of the earth's increase
Held in a glow of such transcendent light
That the lulled heart believes it cannot end;
No storms could rise, no winter's wrath be seen,
The sun could everlastingly befriend.

Move to the east a furlong – to your woe.

Constant, oppressive, comes the engine roar
Along the motorway.

Loud nose to louder tail the lorries go
Destroyers of the day;
Moving too fast, too far, for no good reason,
Traitors to this sweet season.
Are they all blind to nature's ebb and flow?
Can they still feel the richness and the glow?

STARLINGS AT NIGHTFALL

From far the starlings gather
Above the wood at night,
Their thousand wings turn homeward
To join the evening flight.

Like spray they soar and quiver,
They float, and spread, and change,
Like furnace smoke wind-driven
Along the sky they range.

What wind of heaven blows them
About the windless sky,
What pride, what flame consumes them,
What secret sweeps them by?

Celestial armies hastening
They wheel in swift intent,
Their dark array wing-starring
The evening firmament.

O calm, O winter pallor,
Stillness of waiting trees,
And arrow flying movement
And rush of singing breeze.

Belsay, Northumberland, October 1938

NOVEMBER

Beauty of lights along the street
Wet pavements now reflect;
Nor can the north wind through the square
Their glory quite reject.

Like homeless millions, fallen leaves
Reft from their parent tree
Dance lonely down deserted streets
A rustling restless sea.

From many and many a thousand homes
Shines out the cheerful light,
And may all welcomes be as warm
This night, this winter night.

London

SO WOULD NOT I

The heavy lorries trundle down Cow Lane
Raising a spray of muck as they go by,
Hedgehogs and mice sensibly hibernate
And so would I.
The autumn gales are on, and luckless rooks
Are blown like thistledown about the sky
Whence brighter birds have gathered to migrate
And so would I,
But that the frosts and snow are still to come
On field and hill and wood, where underneath
The buried bulbs their miracles create,
And starlit nights on silent naked trees,
Or the moon riding high.
To miss
All this
So would not I.

FOREST UNDER THAW

If it were not for these
Blown oak leaves gathered into sodden mats,
Half-fallen branches, and a raw dank wind
Ruffling those hidden pools as dark as bats,

Soundless dim paths with none but pheasant noises
Where only the untrodden moss is bright,
Tattered bleak hedges, where forgotten swathes
And pennants of old snow reflect the light,

The pale despairing green of lichened limbs
Scattered on marshy ground, the broken trees
Aslant like fainting spirits on their neighbours,
Gale-broken stumps, airing a jagged splinter,
– If it were not, if it were not for these –
Sad wreckings and calamities of winter,

Less clearly, less triumphantly would ring
The trumpets of the spring,
Less sweetly in the dusk of summer nights
The nightingale would sing.

Euston, 1974

THE DARTMOOR STREAM

This is the forgiveness of sins
This voice of water moving over stones,
This sound of falling pools
Where the mind's fever cools;
This is the holy place where Love atones.
Here is the absolution
And the remission,
Return to God,
The sealing of the spirit's fission,
The moving into the land where truth begins,
Where every face befriends
And the long exile ends.

PART V

Mortal & Immortal

SUBCONSCIOUS

Dark under forest trees the levies muster,
Swift along mountain tracks,
In the slow dawn the helm and spearhead cluster,
The sword, the sombre axe.

To what assize of sentence or acquittal
Moves this mysterious host?
Whose banners wave, in promise, or committal,
What's to be won or lost?

On cloudy plains, groups of the armoured tide
Thicken and rise and flow,
Led by a nameless ancestor who died
A thousand years ago.

How can we tell which way the fight will go
Driven by rage, lost in a sudden fluster?
The moving impulses are all we know.
Dark under forest trees the levies muster.

DOG

He halted suddenly in the woodland track,
Ears pricked, and nose alert,
Sat down, and willed me firmly to come back.
I shouted at him, 'Don't be so absurd,
It's only mud. You've never been afraid
Of any lump of dirt!'

He sat quite still.
'You can't pretend you're lame,
It's nonsense.' But I went back all the same.

He was still rigid. 'What's the matter *now*?
You stubborn devil!' An enormous bough,
Rotten, decayed, yet hidden amongst green
Fell heavy on the place where I had been.

TRAVELLERS

Joy, the wayfaring man,
Attends us for an evening, for a day,
And then away.
Happiness comes to settle for a span.
Content will stay.

PASS, FRIEND

Go free of me, now; free of any hate
Anger, resentment, malice, or affront;
Dismissed the guardians and unlocked the gate;
Now walk unarmoured, not for you the brunt
Of long suspicion that the world has taught;
No voices challenge, no alarums sound,
The dusty drawbridge grumbles to the ground
And sleepy sentries drowse along the fort.

WOLF-BEING

Do not imagine, there among the mountain's
Giddy resorts, where eagle wings are soaring,
You will be free of me; or where slow fountains
Fall to the valleys in a cool out-pouring;
I will go to you.
In waters calm and blue
My gales pursue you
And drag your harboured ship from off its mooring.

I am no hound of Heaven, but Illusion,
Dream of a many-splendoured self, besetting
The path to truth with self-imposed confusion;
The thoughtless pride of youth, that unforgetting
Comes to imbue you.
I will go to you
Whatever change of heart
Tries to renew you;
And suffer you no peace, no quiet regretting.

Since I'm that wailing haunting ghost – nostalgia,
That hums and whistles like a rising gale
And winds around the spirit like a shroud
Persistent haunt that knows not how to fail,

Do not imagine there are sounding shores
Where ears may deafen to my strong behest,
That where the drum and fife of the city roars
I'll cease to follow with my louder zest.
If truth dawn to you
If hope renew you
I will pursue you
And steal the wakening heart from out your breast.

Harmless and dear, there's no escaping me
By grassy rides, or the cloud-shadowed plain.
In between you and your humility
I can impose – in happiness, in pain –
The image that's not you.
And when you pause, in rue,
I can possess; and do.
I am the Giant Delusion, and I reign.

WATCH IT

Love is a killer,
– And not the old kind
Whether normal or gay –
The utmost blood-spiller
Is love for the hopeless
Drugged child gone astray,
For the dribbling old husband
Who grumbles all day,
For the chill, the un-warmed,
For the nagging, the heart-less,
The infant deformed,
For the wandering, unhappy
Incurably mad.
For these love is blind
Is helpless, is doting,
Frustratedly sad,
Its whole life devoting
To what can't be mended
Until life is ended.
Although it can't find
A reciprocal love,
And somehow won't ask
For help from above,
Then this is the killer, inordinate love –

The love that's most blind
The dread quintessential
Enslavement of mind.

Love is the killer.
And if we survive
Spavined and battered
Barely alive,
Limping and empty
Of all that most mattered
Walking and wounded,
It's still a close call –

Best not love at all.

June 1998

PERSIAN PATTERN

O passionate exactitude
That sowed a silver field
With roses and ranunculi
All evenly revealed –

With peacocks and with parrots
Among the willow tracery,
With ibexes and cypresses
And lion and leopard chasery,

The arrows and the chivalry,
The bending bows in line,
At dragons dying twistily
To balance the design –

O subtlety of symmetry
That circumscribed their vision
And gave the shape of beauty
Such exquisite precision –

The amulets enamelled
In azure and alizarine,
With emerald for emerald
And tourmaline for tourmaline.

The gardener of their fantasies
Had curbed imagination
And twisted into order
Each poppy, each carnation –

And capturing the sudden,
The free, and the ecstatic,
Made all capricious nature
Divinely mathematic.

Persian Exhibition at The Royal Academy, 1931

THE PAGAN BURIAL

Come not with flowers to bury me,
Nor songs, nor holy panoply,
Nor lay my head
In some well-ordered city of the dead.

Nor to the sounding sea
Commit the dust that is no longer me,
Neither to air
Scatter the ashes of this flesh I wear,

Grave no memorial stone
Over the place where I shall lie alone,
Nor raise above
The emblem of God's sacrifice and love,

But in some woodland slope;
So shall I hope
Some solace in my dying;
Deep in the forest may be my last lying.

That from the well-loved earth
My useless flesh may give a fairer birth;
Flowers I'll not see
Of my decay shall so much richer be.

1932

EXILES

Understand me: I am you
Loving and expatriate,
Driven from the place I knew
To the place I execrate
Oh, believe me: I am you.

Dunned the same old human due,
Fettered to a feral past,
Serf to all the lies of time
Hoping to be free at last.
Look more closely: I am you.

Heir to thoughts I never knew
Subject to the ancient dread,
Groaning to primeval gods
Living somewhere in my head,
Stay and hear me: I am you.

Passionate and contrary,
Laughing in the jaws of death;
Haunted by mortality
In the glow of summer's breath.
Like or loathe it: you are me.

Rebel members of each other,
Hating husbands to our soul;
Strongly centred in ourselves
And yet dying to be whole
In the warm embrace of brother.

Understand me: you are mine
In this country of the blind
Where I'm yours, and both divine.
In the world beyond the mind
Listen, stranger; you are mine.

From such curious regions flying
We demand to be our own –
Singular, inviolate ...
But your death must be my dying,
And my kingdom you enthrone.

COLLECTIVE UNCONSCIOUS

Remember, soul, the dream and thunder
The Adam pangs of birth,
The thick of the tide as breath went under
Great ocean's shuddering girth.

Remember seas that swell within
The hearts of drowned mankind,
Unfathomed draughts of general sin
Deeps of unconscious mind;

Tides of confused and manic anger,
Ripples of humbug long accepted,
And hermit shells, that folk in danger
Creep into, lest they be rejected;

The lifelong heritage of fear
That perils, seeming laid to rest,
Will rise and threaten our most dear;
That life will never give us best.

Remember, too, the Sun in Splendour,
The Sun that draws and trawls the sea
And filters murky depths to render
Life to the drowning souls like me.

As the Sun catches love and laughter
From some wide oceanic swell,
So happiness, in time, comes after
Misery's storm; and all is well.

May 1960

EARLY MORNING

The worst of grief is its unwearied guilt
That drives the knife of sorrow to the hilt.
Not the remorse for some dramatic sin
Known and condemned, repented and forgiven,
Seen, almost, as some part of the grace of Heaven,
But guilt for limping insufficiency,
For lack of grace within,
Negative, nagging guilt
For bright occasions spilt,
For all that we so feebly failed to be.

For discontent, a stubbornness of mood
Almost a self-indulgence in unease –
Ludicrous fusses over small dismays
As petty storms lashing the summer days,
The blind and stupid eye that never sees.

Some manifold disgrace,
Wildness of passion, or a king-sized sin
Could be of God forgiven
Through blushing penitence, and the soul shriven.
But these, the petty sulks and grievances
The turning away of the face
From love's encounter,

From love's friendliness
For these, forgiveness has no time, no space.
The sorry, silly meanness of it all
Returning to appal.

It's not exactly sin
Simply a dullness, worn day out, day in
With an un-loving air that takes for granted

Cheerfulness, self-denial offered free,
A mood that's flat, lack-lustre, self-enchanted,
That can't, or more profoundly, will not see
The slow light creep along the morning wall
Or hear defiant birds begin to sing,
Or ponder what is large and what is small
In fate's decree.

This never lasted long – but why employ it?
What cussedness could hold so strong a pull
Seeing life's beautiful, so fair and full,
Why not enjoy it?

This tyranny of grief combined with guilt
Leaves hope an alien, love as nothing much.
While life's still lent
Mourn not as such,
But exercise the kindness you forwent
On lives that in sore ills are vainly spent.

Time is your ally, sleep the constant friend,
And the calm rise and setting of the sun
While, in new life, forgiveness is begun.
There's no forgetfulness in dream or dope
But in the end
Whatever we have done, not done, ill done,
There's always, and imperishably, hope.

1962

THE SHIP DISCOVERED

So, after twenty years those bars of gold
That know no transformation under seas
Still neatly ranged and newly-minted, gleam
And all their beauty and their value hold.

The proud ship falls apart, and shells encrust
The sharp line of her bows, her shapely side,
The valiant metal crumbling into rust
Where slow weeds wave and falter in the tide.
Bones of drowned seamen are forever rolled,
All else is sadness and disintegration,
But through the tarnished years the gleams abide
As full of lustre as the fish that glide –
Seas having no dominion over gold.

Still gleaming and unconquered in worse deeps
Of silty regions ever out of sight
The sunken gold its tireless splendour keeps.
Silence uncheered, and centuries of blight
Enshroud the bannered galleons blessed by saints
In dark and unimaginable cold;
Where sightless creatures innocently grope
Through their dim realms of everlasting night;
In fathoms without stars and without hope,

Spaghetti forms who desperately strive
Their insufficient shapes to keep alive ...
Till dooms their tiny turgid lives enfold.

Still gleam the shining and unsullied bars
Supreme, un-nourishing, unsearchable,
Among the rotted decks and broken spars –
Death having no dominion over gold.

DOUBLE LIFE

A curious image still pursues me
Different from me as chalk from cheese

Her silly antics still amuse me
Her fantasies beguile and tease.

She acts more clever than she should
Essential verity forgot,

Utters the boast I can't make good
And spends the money I have not.

Never quite lying out of hand
In statements that could be disproved

She simply gives to understand
How she's admired, how well she's loved;

Holds forth, a vigorous debater
On matters she has failed to grasp.

I know her, and at times I hate her,
Yet cannot shake her sticky clasp,

Nor ever hope to understand her,
Why she is on this lifelong spree?

This strange *persona*, smarter, grander,
A million miles from being me.

1966

REDUNDANT PLACE

There is no need for Hell; since we must burn
In our own fires, kindled and blown upon,
And banked by coals that our illusions earn
Through long un-seeing years
By the brisk bellows of our self-esteem
Nor ever dampened by repentant tears,
Stoked and replenished, steadily re-fuelled
By one or other self-deceiving dream.

Don't lay the task of torturer on God
That universal goodness we enthrone.
We torture most efficiently ourselves
And manage our damnation on our own.

1992

ST JAMES'S PARK

Under one tree the loving and the unloving
Stood, and the morning smouldered with their grief,
Above their heads the moving leaves accorded
With flowings of their rage and their relief.
Implacable they stood, the bored, the sighing,
Under one tree, the stolen and the thief.

The kill importuning the satiate hunter
With lies his waning hunger to renew,
Each with a strong concern, one for possession,
One for escape, their double course pursue:
How little differenced by the large eye of God
The cruel and kind, the traitor and the true?

In vain the singing birds assault their silence,
Deaf to all else, the sentiment and the scorning
Attend the stubborn beating of their hearts.
With separate woes, the loyal and the suborning
Cased in a tight predicament together
Forgo the strident glories of the morning.

Why do they stay so long? Are they unwilling
On new estranging worlds to make a start?

Who with an alien strong inertia cling
To this old woe, before at length they part?
Does some faint flicker of remembered fire
Enclose both straining and indifferent heart?

Under one tree the loving and the unloving
Stood, and their shadows shortened on the dew,
Stood, and the mackerel skies of April scattered
Their cloudy scales away across the blue;
Under one tree the conquered and the Caesar –
And which of them was I? And which were you?

1947/48

BACK TO THE BEGINNING

There is a game that children like to play
– Possibly for its dread reality –
Called Creeping Indians, or Grandmother's Steps.

Like those who love their God, the players reach
To union, moving cannily to touch
Unseen, the back of the appointed He
Whose face is still averted.

Suddenly he turns round and sends them back
To start again at their earliest beginnings
If he can catch them moving
In feintings, snatchings, grinnings,
Their faces creasing in a nervous smile.

And so we, crouching down behind each other,
And starting, running, dodging, falling over
With too much haste, or suddenly stopping, toppling
Fallen on grass, unbalanced in the clover,
Are halted into stillness in this race,
And sent again, humbly, to our beginnings
Right to the very start
In a sharp clutch of the heart –
By the appalling, brilliant, unexpected
And terror-striking turning of His face.

THE CHURCHGOER

Think of it as an opiate if you will;
I cannot do without the church bells ringing,
Music of ancient stone, familiar singing,
The voice of reassurance – 'Peace, be still

And know that I am God,' and that I rule.
I cannot do without the blessed freeing
In Christ's acceptance of my shallow being,
As learner in life's hard and lonely school.

I cannot do without God's power to save
So often in the daily round unheeded
Nor can forego the Church's badly-needed
And regular reminder to behave.

I cannot move without repentant prayer –
Where my exhausted batteries are charged
And soul refreshed, the heart as light as air
The petty compass of the mind enlarged.

In times of weakness, when the spirit faints
Seeing itself as loser, never winner,
I cannot do without – but I'm a sinner,
Probably all the rest of you are saints.

RELIGION

To worship is to play with fire. We pray,
But feelings full of hope go either way.

The devil waiting for the naked soul
Slips in between the creature and the Whole.

Bared by our aspirations, we are met
By new temptations worse than any yet.

Religion is a danger; for we see
How quickly God is made to look like Me,

Me with my plans – an intricate design
Unconsciously to make the cosmos mine.

Make clear our faith, and scatter our confusion,
Come between us, dear Lord, and our illusion
With love, the only ultimate conclusion.

SIGNIFICANCE

The thirteen shadows waver on the wall
Bend to one way, and mingle or dissever.
And two alone attend the silent call
That what is done this night is done forever.

Bitter farewell, that yet is no farewell;
The knowledge undiscovered by the clever,
A mystery no mortal man can tell –
Yet what is done this night is done forever.

This is my body, broken at God's will,
The bloom of life, borne to fruition never,
The gathered splendour that the years fulfil
For you and many is foregone forever.

This is my body – for the flesh is dear
And even God will lay it down in sorrow –
This is my body – and awake in fear
To pain and shame that shall be mine tomorrow.

This is my blood, my being, my delight,
This is my blood, the full and flowing river
That must be parched before another night,
Since what is done this night is done forever.

Do this in my remembrance ... On the wall
Twelve shadows only now converge and sever.
The silent footsteps tremble to the hall
To do what must be done this night forever.

The loud cicada shrieks his piercing ditty,
Above, un-numbered stars consume and quiver,
The very stones, unyielding, have more pity
Than he this night who sells his friend forever.

The midnight dust conceals the steps of sin
In that far city. And beyond endeavour
Awaits the field to bury strangers in
Where he, who takes his silver, hangs forever.

And strident feet, unconscious in their going
Move to betrayal. Purposeful and clever
And drunk within our dream, we move unknowing
That what is done today is done forever.

Rockingham, 1971 /72

THE PRODIGAL

There is no going back
To where we were; the turning of the world
Shoulders away the primavera being
To show a world of selfishness and strife.

There's no more seeing
Parents who loved, and gloried in their loving
The boys who loved, and gloried in their life.
Rough play, mild teasing from the elder brother
Turned into something other.

Harvest of grapes, hot days amongst the vine,
The juicy mumbling of the summer fig,
The crickets calling from the olive tree,
Family wealth, and due prosperity,
A love of all things fine,
A full moon rising, ruddy, low and big.

So much of welcome, so much that was sweet,
Family laughter, safe in stone-walled houses ...
Two healthy boys, a brave world at their feet.
To such there's no returning
From where we are. We have cut off retreat.

Where do we go from here? For underneath
The surface of these happy-seeming folks
There was a wild boy, and an envious brother,
Rebellion growing like a weed in one
And slow resentment swelling in the other –
Why do they laugh so loud at all *his* jokes?

They spoiled him rotten. And he opted out
Soon as he knew what life was all about,
Demanding, one fine day
'Give me my share and let me go my way!'
Grudging, I watched the money counted out
And belted round him. Surly, I decided
Good riddance. Now my father is all *mine*,
My mother's face will kindle towards *me*!
The full reward for toiling in the fields
Under a burning sun, is mine, is mine!
Bending from dawn to dusk, continual milking,
An aching back at pruning of the vine,
All is worth while, all will in time be mine.

How much the parents grieved there is no telling
As evening fell on the departure day.
Did the resentful boy
With ways of cheer illuminate their dwelling
While the rebellious drank his fill of joy?

After a spending spree, a jolly span,
He came to earth, eating the pigsty bran.
And staggered home, repentant and now starving,

Each painful step a dragging of parched limbs,
And scorching shame, feeling himself to be
A nameless waif, a hireling, and no man,
Dirty, dishevelled, scarcely to be known,
His every thought a groan.

Beyond the pale, he felt, of all forgiving –
To find a welcome blinding in its warmth,
While he was still a great way off, his father
Running to greet him, running to embrace
And give him welcome back to the land of the living.

* * * * *

The music sounded through the open window
The dancing pipe, the harp's rejoicing strings,
Where the whole household stretched their merry wings –
Set leaping in relief;
The feasted prodigal in gorgeous fullness
Forgiven, cleansed, and clad in sumptuous dress,
The mother weeping in her happiness ...

The furious home-boy, halted on the threshold
Mouthing his grief.
While music floated out on the evening air
His soul went parched and dead,
Fumes of resentment smoked
In his indignant head.
He stood, still coated with the long day's muck

All his contentment fled.
Why should this ullage collar all the welcome –
The shining garment and the fatted calf –
Why should this useless sod have all the luck?
Why is there nothing done on *my* behalf?

'Son thou art ever with me
All that I have is thine ...'

'Hasn't he had his share
Shouldn't the rest be mine?'

But this my son is *found,* who once was lost
Alive, who once was dead.

Maybe the prodigal changed his ways; his brother
Forgot that life should owe him a special living,
And ceased to feel, in time, that life was rough,
Maybe, drinking at nightfall under trees
That murmured of satiety and calm,
All was brought back to ease
By the Father, understanding and forgiving
Whose power was strong enough.

But sometimes, feeling older and undecided,
The elder son would stand in the field and stare
At the young green-budded vines in hopeful rows –
Why is our life eternally lopsided
Why is it irretrievably unfair.

AS A CHILD

He was a boy more real
Than other little boys. Yet this is nonsense
Since every mother's son is real to her,
A boy like other boys.
But how he made her feel!
Every least sense astir.

But he was more. Sometimes he gave himself
So wholly and entirely to his love
For me and for my husband, even until
Nothing of self was left,
His skinny frame bereft
His laughing face alight.
And then at other moments he was still,
And infinitely distant and remote,
Adult and wise. The words of admonition
Were halted in my throat,
(Until his absence made me sick with fright.)
He'd leave us for some transcendental height
His soul afloat.

So how can I believe
His dread and pitiful death,
The slow blood trickling down the wooden post

The agony of every indrawn breath,
The indifferent soldiers, and the mocking host
Of passers-by. A stony unbelief
Locks me awhile from the extreme of grief.

June 1990

ULTIMATE

It is not death we fear, but the hard dying
When pain has done its worst
Against defenceless flesh.
We are soothed no more by lying
And the bubble of courage has burst
When fear has darkened faith.

How will it be – the meeting face to face
With the bared teeth of unimagined death?
The ultimate time and place
And the lost fight for breath?

Oh Christ, oh gallant forbears, oh brave saints
Be with me when the conquered spirit faints.

THE BURIAL

I am thy shroud,
Who bury in myself thy blazing light
With layers of dull lassitude, with pomp,
With pangs of nervous fright,
With sullen grudging thoughts that riot and romp
Through the mind's maze,
With scuttling errands of self-interest
That fill my days
And rob all life of zest;
Giving my graceless being
The very feel and texture of a shroud.

Till all thy light
Hidden by such a cloud
In me lies quenched and dim,
No longer filtered those life-giving rays
Music in me no longer cries aloud
Its graceful hymn;
I am thy shroud
Hidden and lost in me is Heaven's blaze.

IN THE DRY PLACES

This is the country that the psalmist knew –
The vale of misery, the place accurst.
Stones scrabble underfoot, a parching wind
Tightens the throat in a hard knot of thirst.

Treeless the weary distance, and hope fails
As miraged water trembles into drought.
Only the tiny clatter of loose stones
Sends back an answer to the heart's wild shout.

Oh fountain love, fall now, fall green and full
Here, where heat licks us with the breath of hell!
And turn our shales and deserts to bright pools
That we may use our dryness for a well.

1973

PRAYER AT MORNING

Oh loving Father, minimize
The ill this day I do.
Help me to see with clearer eyes
Help me to hold to You.
Keep in my head a civil tongue,
Help me to sink my prejudice
And not to cavil at things new,
To comfort, with a heart still young,
Never to judge, or misconstrue,
To love and celebrate life's bliss
And to rejoice in all there is.

ASCENSION DAY

The holy and relentless bell
Rolls from the church beyond the lea;
Oh do not let me tire of You
Who never tire of me!

Here, to an organ thinly wailing,
With trembling hearts and voices failing,
Old ladies cry their meagre fears
Knowing He hears.

The backs that bend at age's rod,
The poor whose only wealth is God,
Arthritic fingers knit in prayer
Summon Him there.

Oh not the clever, good, and brave,
Only the fools He came to save
Only the sinners and the sore
Knock, and are answered, on His door.

IN MY FATHER'S HOUSE

The many mansions glitter on the hill
Caught in the furnace of the setting sun.
Wide stand the doors to welcome finishers –
But I have just begun.

The many mansions – ah, the many mansions!
Could they be fairer than the mansions here
The known and lovely mansion of the world
The faces known and near?

Christ was the poem that I learned by heart
And barely understood, saying by rote
Line upon line, never indeed discerning
The true deep note.

Oh God, the distances, the whirling worlds
In space unending! All those shining mansions
Hotly indifferent to the poor heart's shrinkings,
Cold to the heart's expansions.

Worlds within worlds, and worlds beyond each other,
An awesomeness and splendour still unfolding!
But I am settled in a tiny town
Myself withholding.

Is love enough? Even a minnow love
Starting and darting through enormous streams
Hither and yon, a prey to all distractions,
Ever seduced by dreams?

The mansions shimmer in their warm mirage
And as I near them, will they be the same?
My hope of entering them can only be
Under another Name.

1987

Part VI

Love, War, Loss & Reconciliation
PN to TMN

THE RECOGNITION

Suddenly, it's a gallop out of control,
The sliding forth of the immortal soul.

This should be joyful; and is otherwise –
A breathless drowning in a sudden sea.
A heavy love, like chains on liberty
Hangs on the first shocked meeting of the eyes
That should be riches, and is poverty.

'Blessed are the shoulders to love's burden bent,'
'Happy the pride blown bare by winds of scorn.'
I only know that all I have is spent,
Riches of solitude, the dear content,
All the long hoarding of myself foregone.

And well I know, stormed by a sense so new,
All I shall suffer, all I lose in you.

1931

MEDITERRANEAN

This is the sacred sea
Of triton-haunted foam,
Sparkling and rich as wine,
Poseidon's home.

Shadows of worshipped hills
Lie on the morning sea,
And dark against the evening stands
The templed promontory.

Behind the stony shore
There grows a blessed tree,
And streams that water all the world
Flow down from Calvary.

Magnificent, the sea-birds call
Along the cliffs of moly,
And all night long the breakers fall
Holy, holy, holy.

Lapad Peninsula, Ragusa,
July 1933

MALTA

Here's no impermanence.
Nothing gave warning;
And this, our zenith, felt like morning.
A tale scarce told,
Not making sense
An age of gold.

The lights along the ships are paled to nothing
By the illumination of the dawn
The ensigns rise, brazen the bugles call
Echoes from cliff to cliff.
New day is born,
Tuesday, but no less golden than them all.

Pale, honey-pale above their sparkling seas
The yellow bastions rise.
The harbour quickens: there are market cries.
Some fond illusion of perpetual joy
Turns this to paradise.

All through the baking noon a bird keeps singing
Loud in this tree-less land where few birds dwell.
And the harsh bells, for sunset vespers ringing
Sound as no earthly bell.

Sleeping or waking, we are locked in love.
Sleep on, my love, shutter your cheerful eyes,
For, like the warm unclouded sun at morning
Hope in our hearts will rise.

Move leisurely across the star-filled sky,
Move slowly, white and rounded moon, move slow ...
So shall our time, our happiness, our love
Never be called to go.

Time will not hear; nothing will heed, or halt,
No clock of fate will falter, and no bell
Will cease to mark these silken hours in passing,
Nor distance that slow knell.

Ambush is set for lover and for giver,
A total love teases a total hate.
We are disarmed: and in their horny quiver
The world's dark arrows wait.

1933

THE SKIRMISHERS

Here's the opponent worthy of the steel;
The darling foe who has the power to summon
All that is in our stubborn hearts to feel.

On either side the skirmishing's begun.
Let us enjoy it: it will soon be done.

Nothing we tell each other is the truth;
Our careful words, like dancers in a set
Pass and re-pass, forget each other's faces
In decorous, indifferent minuet.

Nothing we feel is said;
Pride, like a climate where no life endures
Seals us within a city of the dead;
And a sad wisdom, like a glacier, pours
Between my truth and yours.

Terrible pangs there may be, and suspense,
The turning upside down of common sense.
And yet the while, when all is said and done,
Deep down, these sorties are but part of the fun.

Only the traitor eyes
Suddenly glint with ambush and surprise
Suddenly speak in language of the dove,
Tell envy, and enchantment, and relief,
Torment, and certainty, and searing grief,
All the sharp dividends that passion earns,
The death-knell partings and the warm returns,
And the full range and orchestra of love.

1936/37

IGNORANCE

Holy and slow
As if for some perpetual wedding day
The bells of Florian chime.
All through the bright forenoon
As the ships come and go
The hook-necked bird sits on the stone break-water
The cormorant of death
Biding its time.

It may be that you caught a glimpse of him
At sea, where he'll abide,
The bird I never saw, pre-occupied
With love, with pleasure, the pursuit of fun,
With the sweet present and its time and tide
That swiftly run –
Night with its starry glim,
Sunrise, slow spreading morning,
The baking shine of noon
Veiled with its haze of light
Sweetly concealing him
The bird I never knew,
Black on the stone break-water.

Not knowing was a boon.

DECEMBER ON DARTMOOR

How deep on moor and mountainside
The cloaking fog swims like a tide,
Drowned in a still and weeping vapour
The shrouded seas forget their caper,
Night and winter lay their pall
On love, on levity, on all.

Fog on lane, on road, on fence –
No telephone can call you hence.
In this guarded interval
Fog becomes a fortress wall,
Fog becomes a glorious weather
Holding us secure together.

Never moon nor planets' sheen
Can through all the murk be seen.
While willows lower mourning heads
And sheeted rivers crawl their beds,
Let naked alders drip their tears,
Lie close to me and shut your ears.

Stokehill, 1936/37

THE SPIRIT OF THE AGE

All greatness is unease; all fame is war
Waged without quarter from a stony heart,
The angry soul's revenge; seizing the more
Out of a world that has denied the part.
All headlines cry despair; and every page
Of history is loud with shouting men
Whose triumphs spring from pre-historic rage
Baring its teeth beside an empty den.
Foul-weather coasts and sounding misted seas
Spew out the ships that wallow down the world,
Double the wild capes of Antipodes
And scour the oceans with a sail unfurled.
And are we blessed, we the obscure and craven,
Nursed by the sea-wall of a happy haven?

1938

SEPTEMBER 1938

A little peace
A little time for dreaming in the sun,
Another song before the blackbird cease
Before the summer and the day are done;

This lull, this glow of brightness to remember
Throughout the inescapable December,
A day of morning joy and evening sleep
An hour to see the river willows weep,

A time to laugh, a time to gather flowers,
To see the city's unbeleaguered towers
Raising their stony beauty to the sky,
A time to hear the flying swan's wings sigh,

And music, and delight, and glowing love,
And high clouds moving gloriously above,
A moment to run free,
A time to get the sons we shall not see,

This happiness above the mountain's shaking,
This quietness before the tempest's breaking,
This antiphon to strife,
This splendour, this warm life,

This respite, this deliverance from fear
Is bought too dear:

Brief festival before the looming fight,
Another hour to hear the singing lark,
This little light
Before the dark.

This lovely, this desired, this transient gold,
For this our honour and our pride are sold,
For this are we forsworn:
For these bright pence do we betray our brothers,
For this we sell the liberty of others,
And bow to shame and scorn.
Now for another year or two of youth –
Do we deny our hearts' most cherished truth,
For this do we surrender
Our loyalty and faith, the spirit's splendour.

This moment, this reprieve,
This time to laugh before the time to grieve,
These harbour lights, the dancing and the song
Before we sail upon a voyage long,
Before the fall of night
When we embark,
This little light
Before the dark,
This respite, this deliverance from fear
Is bought too dear.

EASTER 1939

This is forever,
These un-lit beech trees leaning over Teviot's stream,
Where you, with rod and boat
High in reflected tree-tops float
– Figures in some absurd, celestial dream –
Over the river running emerald deep.
These distant shallows whose sweet roar comes faint,
This ceaseless silly, innocent complaint
Of lambs still crying to their mother sheep;
These primrose leaves un-wrinkling at my feet,
This child with eager hand
Tirelessly drawing patterns in the river sand,
And the red field green-shadowed with young wheat,
This holiday, this love,
This Easter sun above,
This carelessness, this peace,
This heavenly springing of the earth's increase,

This has no finish, no catastrophe,
And death's disruptive hand
Cannot blot out this picture in the sand,
This is for ever,
And no ephemeral headlines we may see
Screaming their deathly sentences abroad,

No shock, no agony of spirit can sever
This timeless moment from the spread of time,
Though war unsheathed her adamantine sword
And howling dogs run free.
That noise, that tremor has no potency,
Those tortures will grow shadowy and pale,
This love, this moment of spring was all our tale,
This orchestra, this rhyme,
Not written in language of mortality.

Taken from 'Sheet Anchor'

COMING HOME FROM SEA

The arch of heaven narrows,
And night unbends the bow
That shot those glittering arrows
A million years ago,
Dark, dark, and still, that multitudinous burning,
The giddy firmament forgets its turning,
Alone we quicken and live, at your returning.

No wind upon the mountains,
The unviewed snow dishevels,
Time holds the tumbling fountains
Fast frozen in their revels,
The caracoling seas forbear to churn,
The singing stars their harmony unlearn,
Alone we live and move, for you return.

Taken from 'Sheet Anchor', 1939

RETURNING TO SEA

Sing, nightingale, and summer birds, arise
To drown the recreant music of farewell –
The midnight dockyard where the blue light lies,
The moment when there is no more to tell,
The long look, and the brave anticipant eyes,
While the sea waits, and the dark waters swell.

There will be spring again – the young leaf lent,
The blossom lavished, and the rose revealed,
The calm enormous star, the young bow bent
At evening in the cuckoo-calling field,
The squandered beauty that is never spent
And all the matchless wealth that summers yield.

The spring was ours: sorrow no more to lose
That long abundant summer of the heart.
Should we love's sharp eternity refuse
Because the end crowds in upon the start?
We were alive, we loved, now let us choose
To live as if we never had to part;

To love, and to relinquish love's possessing,
To feel the joy more instant than the pain,
All ardours of the greedy heart addressing
Towards that past incomparable gain,
And from the fountain of remembered blessing
To drink the stream, and never thirst again.

Taken from 'Sheet Anchor', June 1939

DESTROYER WAR: 1939–1940

I am resolved
Never to tremble with prophetic woe,
Never to think of you with clinging fear,
Most loved, most deeply dear –
Through the dark nights, the storms of wintry nights,
The crash of water, icy hiss of spume,
The rushing through the dark seas without lights,
The tensity and endlessness of watch
In danger's grip;
Never let loose imagination's flow,
Never to glimpse with the scared eyes of the mind
How near they rise and go –
The waiting jaws of the sea,
Never to let them find
The last plunge of a swiftly sinking ship.

Resolve is one thing
Keeping it another.
Too well we know
The hurrying feet that will not let us go –
Fear as the wolf, pursuing
Through the dark wood, over the waste of snow,

Mounting, infectious fear,
The strong tide in the throat,
Fear as death's echo, brother not much younger.

What whirring menace do such moments shed
While death, the kestrel, hovers overhead.

I am resolved to think
Only how much and totally I love you,
Only of our nine years and maybe more,
Of all the strength those happy years endue,
Of sigh of summer ripples on the shore;
Only how often we've been on the brink
Of comprehending why such things should be
As war at sea.
Though there's a part that bitterly rebels
Against such fate, against such sacrifice,
A part of us has crossed the deadly waters,
The storms, the seas of ice,
And the long deserts of our separation
To drink at last at the immortal wells.

SEEN FROM A TRAIN

Go plate yourself in armour
Boy in the summer field,
With yellow flags for arrows
With willows for your shield,

With cool of summer rivers
With fall of summer waves,
With sound of oars in rowlocks
With glint of weed in caves,

And, link on link, with August,
With bracken fronds unfurled
Enchain yourself in coat of mail
Against the hate of the world.

June 1940

JUNE 1940: GOING WEST

Here's the June week when every river iris
Flies a brief banner of flamboyant gold.
And here's the week when France is falling, falling,
Her lilies droop, and Europe's blood runs cold.

Never more bright, the fields of buttercups
Glow and are gone, beside the speeding train,
A dazzling blaze of riches seen no more,
Deep and opaque, as though that solid gold
Plunged underground in layered streams of ore.

The sun is past his zenith, a faint breeze
Fans down upon this brilliant trembling day ...
Now too, in France, sun rolls towards the west
So deadly near, and half a world away.

The shades of night on innocent small towns
Will fall, and on the sad defeated men.
Are we all started on the march of sorrow
As the warm sun fades over field and fen?

Exeter now, and the sea never far;
The sea that is our moat and our salvation.
For how long will it cut us off from all
The aching pain of a defeated nation?

Only the English Channel, and stout hearts
Come between us and imminent damnation.

Along the silver Channel, if Drake's drum
Sounding for England's danger, shudders clear
Under red cliffs, grey headlands storm-beset,
It sounds in vain; a note grown ever stranger
On stubborn ear-drums not prepared to hear,
On politicians scarce awakened yet.

The heaven that we seek so constantly
So fervently, so doggedly – is vain;
The summer fields, the winter cosiness,
The simple certainties of wife and child,
All the mild hearts fast closed against distress
Will soon be drowned in cataracts of pain.
Freedom from tyranny, escape from hate,
Music and art, and all we celebrate,
Every sure pleasure that we take for granted
Dies with the spell this week has dis-enchanted.

Alas for eyes that still refused to see,
The eyes of France, and ours, who would not hear
Menacing march of thunder in the mountains
Encroaching waterfalls of pain and fear.

Past Dartmoor rivers falling, tuneful, free
Within their secret woods, stunted and oaken,
Where moss and lichen cling on every tree;

Past the Osmunda ferns and quiet pools,
Late bluebells, in a solitude unbroken
Grow shaded, and the river tumbles on
Falling in silver past the rounded boulder;
Whilst along every stretch and curve of the line,
With every mile, the menaced heart grows colder.

Plymouth awaits us, with her darkened port,
And the broad Plym, pale under evening tide.
A hundred sailors ranged along the station
In the grey dusk. What fate looms near for all,
Through the warm night, what doom or destination?

THRESHOLD

What do they see, what do they see
When death draws close,
And they're impatient
For more than love, for more than me?

Far past the fever and the desperation
That strong men feel in weakness, far beyond
The voices hushed, the distant consultation,
Dying he seemed to me
More than mortality;
And seemed to hear
A sweeter sound than ever
A skilled conductor drew from violins
A sylvan sound, and clear.
Music of the forgiveness of our sins?

So fierce a war – the rigor and the trembling
Might turn one blind; and yet I saw him see
Some view beyond the power of dissembling,
Vision that had to be;
Past restlessness, the strong and sweating hour,
Exhaustion, and short sleep,
The fever tide in all its terrible power
That draws into the deep.

Past racing temperature, that rose again,
Past loss of voice, and the dark powers of pain
That long cool look, through people and beyond
A calm gaze, no more burning
So deeply thoughtful, so intensely yearning,
That is no longer feverish, nor fond.

What do they see, what do they see
Who step into eternity?

TO TREVIE, DYING

Soft night, soft coolness of the evening quiet,
Sweet healing hand of summer and of sleep,
Stirred, murmuring trees, that past the instant riot
And tumult, their caressed perfection keep;
Aloof unravaged country for whose peace
A total happiness is well forsworn,
And splintered cities for whose far release
The torment and the loss is fairly borne –
For these the sternest pain
We do in full accept, and would accept again.

You that were strength itself are weakness now,
Stretched in long fever of the wearied heart,
You that with resolute and smoking prow
Endured through winter's rage the heaviest part;
You whom no clamorous seas could overleap,
The mounting waves of poison overwhelm,
And fiercer tides to vaster oceans sweep
The rudder of your proud and steadfast helm,
Against whose vicious spate
With calm and mocking courage you yet navigate.

Not in the thunder and exhilarance
Of surface action wounded; but in these –
Perennial days of stony vigilance,
Interminable nights in the scorpion seas,
In the long roar of storm's besieging rumpus,
In the black minefields and the fog's eclipse,
Straining past mortal stature to encompass
The enormous ocean with the too scant ships,
On without sleep or rest
Till the worn flesh defaults before the will's behest.

You that are life itself draw near to death,
Life's very being fails, while the warm land
Murmurs and shines with summer's lavish breath;
The quivering oats are reaped, the corncocks stand,
And blue with afternoon, the slope hills run
Their feathered promontories in Tamar's gleam,
The valleys mist and clear, the glowing sun
Lights the curved haunches of the reaper's team,
And evening rings the cry
Of garrulous homing rooks, night-blown across the sky.

A comfort and a strength that never sleep
Delirium cannot change nor death disarm;
Even in this extremity you keep
Each weapon in your armoury of charm:
Kind hands, the gentle and deliberate voice,
The matchless smile, the blue discerning eyes,
Such lordly looks as most the heart rejoice

And did my mind long since emparadize,
Who wore in your brief span
Bearing and truth to vindicate God's hopes of man.

O strong ambassador from God, who held
His richest gift, the understanding heart,
And lively mind whose openness expelled
The narrow rivalries in which men smart,
Whose interest and sympathy were keys
Of laughter, that unbars the guarded mind,
The lubricant of toil, division's ease,
Laughter that is affection, that is kind;
By the heart he dies
Whose province was the heart's continual exercise.

Wisdom and strength are streaming from the earth,
Burning away in unavailing fight,
Laughter and friendship, truthfulness and mirth,
Are vapoured up into the hood of night;
All judgement, and all seamanship, all skill,
All coolness, all command and enterprise,
And all the sturdy qualities that fill
Men's hearts with reassurance. Spent he lies,
Whose courage could not swerve,
Whose greed was love, whose only avarice to serve.

Burning away from summer and from light,
Away, away, from unaccomplished good,
Far from this battle that he longed to fight,

From all he guarded, helped, and understood;
See, see, their banishment – love's noontide blaze
And long serenity, the sweet parade
Of fireside joys, the hill and garden days
With sunny lawns and orchards flecked with shade
Or sprayed with April foam,
The cheerful liveliness of children and of home.

Whatever comfort waits, it is not this:
This suckling paradise of you-and-me,
This kindergarten love whose narrow bliss
Shutters the world from out its sanctuary.
What comfort in the chill angelic wastes
To set against this kingdom of rewards,
This lollipop affection that yet tastes
Joys more extravagant than Heaven affords,
This passion and this pleasure
Whose warmth the trudging years must now in bleakness
    measure?

Who is this eyeless creature, who is she,
Moving along the summer-gilded lane,
This breathing torment, walking agony,
Wrapped in a fog of frenzy and of pain?
I am God seeing, and I recognize
The fiercest pangs, the bitterest tears unshed,
I am the pain, and I am God that lies
Spent and immortal on the fevered bed:
This is a flash, a moment,
And I the timeless peace behind the present ferment.

You, that long ceased to pray the name of Christ,
Yet men called Christian – loving, true and just,
Whose own entire endeavour well sufficed
To serve that God in whom you put your trust,
Whose courage and whose calm death cannot rout,
Who lie amused, irreverent, and unshriven,
Whilst all your strength and all your quietness shout
The glory and the certitude of heaven,
Unchastened by pain's rod,
Proclaim the spinning and reverberate love of God.

Death crowds on us, the fevers mount and gain
Above the clear vitality of youth,
Death bares his brazen countenance, makes plain
His strident and irrevocable truth.
Death cataracts about us, death is rife,
Devours the cities' splendours, drives his blade
With iron hardness through the heart of life,
And thunders his tremendous cannonade,
And fulminates above –
Yet there is nothing breathing in this room but love.

Taken from 'Sheet Anchor'

DEATHBED

All is told, Trevie,
All's settled, all's said:
Long I've been left alone
Long you've been dead.

Not in this darkened room
Or this drawn hour
The sharp seed was planted
That now comes to flower.

All days are judgement days,
Year in, year out,
Whisper of sentence
Swells to a shout.

While the first wind of love
Burned hot and cold,
Remote and unlikely
The bell always tolled.

The young, the surprised kiss
Made this last greeting,
A bitter au-revoir
Said at first meeting.

This arrow, this anguish,
This breaking of days
Is the fair tribute
That mortal love pays.

Strain for no words, Trevie,
With voice grown weak,
In a full music
The happy years speak.

But pay me a last kiss
Dear love, as full dues.
Death's still the dark river
For all he's no news.

1943

LEAVING IN AUGUST

He went away on a day of blazing summer,
Burned by a fever skill could not control:
Cool are the streams by which he walks in freedom
And cool the waters that refresh his soul.

Still are the pools along that living water,
Clear are the streams by which he walks at ease.
But coldly here the summer shadows fall,
Cold the warm wind that murmurs in the trees.

Though here a sky still cloudless and unflawed
Smiles on a field of corn serenely gold,
Just here and now the God who is loving Father
Loses awhile his hold.

Stokehill, 1940

THE ONLY CONSOLATION

Since one of us must walk alone,
Let it be me.
Rejoice that it is me.
In this still place, as silent as a stone,
Where I, at length, have found a kind of mooring,
Happy alone in this –
That after so much bliss
Cheerful companionship of many years,
Never for you fell these redundant tears;
And thankfulness, that it's not you enduring
The loneliness of which there is no curing.

1941

ANOTHER COUNTRY

Oh in some other country
We will return and see
The willows and the river,
The lark, the leaning tree,

And live so long together
That all our sons are born,
Our cattle on a hundred hills,
Our valleys thick with corn.

And live so long together
That we may drain the cup,
And see our children Christianly
And virtuously brought up.

And live so long together
That all our streams are seas,
And all our thoughts are voices
Borne clearly on the breeze.

Oh in some other country
The tale will be fulfilled –
The tale of your returning,
The time you are not killed.

1960, begun 1942

194

DAYS AFTER DEATH

Far down, from this deep well
This empty well, I see a round of sky,
From depths that I could never guess or tell.
Far up above, a different world goes by.

Evening and morning gather into one
Since time has lost its range;
Hours undiscovered by the visiting sun
Float by me without change.

Nothing that's recognisable remains –
Rooms, trees, the flowers and streams, beloved faces
Are insubstantial, faint as empty veins.
Strangers inhabit the familiar places.

It may be these dark walls will crumble in
Leaving the living spirit crushed and bent,
Walls strong as iron, and as severe as sin –
But time's too static for such dire event;

Too weary, and too limp, and too un-meaning
To find me. Time's a theory not for proving.
Time is a spiral tower of Pisa, leaning
This way or that, but never indeed moving.

Yet from this well, this nullifying well,
More clearly seen than ever seen before
The round of sky above the dark brick cell
Lit with faint stars, and lit for evermore.

1943

NOT THAT WE LOVED

Not that we grieved, but that our grief was written
In stepping stones across a sea in spate,
Not that we loved, but that our love was smitten
Out of a world stone-bastioned in hate,
For loving out of reason
In a divorcing season,
When anger breathed about us on each breath,
For living through a death,
When minutes had to count for more than years,
For being out of time,
People will catch our echoes, breathe our fears,
Will laugh to hear your mocking voice, and weep
With my abundant tears
While the earth turns beneath the scimitar moon.

1943

BLITZ

Night after iron night is loud,
The overwhelming bombs are hurled
The terrors crowd.
Looking on all those craters ploughed
Through harmless streets, obscure or proud,
At times there is a thought that greets –
Is this the hunger of the world
Opening great mouths in London streets?

1944

DARKNESS IN MAY

I have been brave for long enough
And for long enough alone.
My love of life is shrivelled away
My sad heart turned to stone.
Where I would be is six feet down
With the green grass live above
And no more need for courage
And no more need of love.

AFTER THE STORM

After the storm the clear forgiving morning
Shines over sodden fields; along the shore
Seaweed and spindrift glisten, and the hulls
Upturned, lie gleaming – those once splendid ships
That will to sea no more.

After the storm every young tree refreshed
Preens its sharp leaves, and all the forest glows –
Bright bark and striving sap and singing birds,
And in the sun, once huge, once widely shading
The fallen oak tree shows.

After the war the happy flags are flown
The guns are silent and the cheers resound,
The running feet of children clatter welcome,
The glad wives tremble love. The best men lie
Forever in cold ground.

For those dear landscapes made of trees and corn,
Flowery felicities that charm the day,
For families, and music, happy passions,
For poetry, for pictures, grave stone churches –
There is a price to pay.

INDIAN SUMMER

We walk towards each other down a vista,
I and my love who died seven years ago.
Under an infinite archway of high trees –
A yellow world whose sapless flowers fall slow.

We move towards each other in a stillness
Over a Persian carpet of spent leaves
That rise and drift like water past our feet –
We whom no seasons lull, no time relieves.

The casual flames fall soft from fiery trees –
Our veins are trembling with a silver fire,
The silence burns with our expectancy
Swiftly we move on limbs that never tire,

On urgent limbs that are the limbs of dream,
Limbs light as flame – yet never can approach;
Pastoral figures in a painted landscape
Where never passion comes, nor griefs encroach.

The light and stillness of another world
Float in this bubble hour of afternoon,
Rounded and clear, hung in the autumn hush,
Blown on the echo of immortal tune,

For this still moment I'm outside myself
Not looking in, nor back, nor making moan;
Not fearful of that other, darker vista
Of fifty years, maybe, of life alone.

This bubble moment, full of colour, gleaming,
Blown out of heaven into time and space
Reflects the misty beauties of the fall
To wear upon its brittle shining face.

The tender willow leaning on the hill,
The flame of the tulip tree, the night-dark yews,
The old horse grazing in his dust-white coat,
The grass re-emeralded with morning dews,

The pallid elms, the autumn-darkened rose,
The sombre bees droning around their hive,
All substance, all reality. Dear love,
Who died? And which of us is still alive?

Rockingham, 1947

DERBY STATION

The winter rain cascades through broken roofs,
Over the shuffle of feet, the weary backs.
The rain falls darkly – this is Derby Station –
Where black rain squibs along a gleaming platform
And inky pools deepen along the tracks.

Attention, travellers! This is Derby Station;
Attention! The next train from Platform Five
Will be the Seven-Two,
Calling at Egginton and Tutbury,
Calling at Marchington, Uttoxeter,
Creswell, Blythe Bridge, and Mier,
Calling at Longton, Stoke-on-Trent, Etruria,
At Langport, Kidsgrove, Alsager, and Crewe.

This the Here and Now, the rain falls steady;
Depleted faces glare in the waiting room
Bleakly illuminated by a ten-watt lamp
That mitigates but can't disperse the gloom.
With the unseeing stare of souls in hell
We gaze at anything but each other's eyes
Heavy with lateness, with the homeward plod,
At odds with January, at odds with rain,
With life, with Derby Station, and with God.

No charm invades the features, to enhance
The apologising, justifying glance
Between grey missus and her greyer man;
A weary couple shift their smudgy baby,
Hoarding him closely with a thin defiance
As if the assembled company were Herods,
As if infanticide were all their science.

Since war, have we forgotten how to greet?
If this is victory, what price defeat?
Oh desolation past the desolation
Of desert, mountain, or the cratered moon,
Past empty ocean, or deep jungle's gloom,
The stony look of faces on a January evening
In a Midland waiting-room.

Where are you going with your neutral faces,
Uttoxeter, Etruria, or Crewe?
And you, drawn-featured neighbour in a trilby
Warming yourself by a non-existent fire,
And damsel dressed in imitation leopard
Upon what dismal mission are you set,
Blown on what wind to Cresswell or to Mier?
You by your pallor and your pouchy eyes,
By your demobilised and rationed look
You, by the set of shoulders too soon bent
Are bound on errands drearier than mine,
Blown towards Tutbury or Stoke-on-Trent?

This is the Here and Now and this is all;
The ceaseless rain falling through blackened air
On a chill platform – this is all of life
For waiting insects crouching in their lair:

Nothing encompassing but Derby Station
Red signals hanging in their dark trapeze,
A senseless and mechanic universe
Compact about us, smelling of smoke and cheese.
There's no reality but Derby Station
The porter's trolley grumbling down the ramp,
The scattered ashes of the meagre fire,
Meanness and January, the ten-watt lamp,
Uttoxeter and Marchington and Mier,
Tight little vistas of smoke-blackened houses
With thick lace curtains, riding the Derby hills;
Dun mornings rising yet and yet again
On brief intoxicants, the certain ills,
Cancer and cozenage and pride and pain –
This is the Whole, and we are set about
Only by Derby Station and the rain.

Great leagues away there's love and delectation
The silent garden and the distant light,
The dulcet fall of rivers over pebbles,
The cypress and the jasmine-breathing night;
Infinite miles away there's warmth and kindness,

The mirrored moon caught in the lily's mesh,
The scent of pinewoods and the sound of music –
The world, the devil, and the darling flesh.
But speaking-close immediate and sure,
Between the dead fire and the broken cup
From jet-black water and red signal light
Heaven pyramids her sumptuous glories up;

Absolute beauty and eternal truth
Jostle each other on the spitting ramp,
And, brimming vessels of felicity,
Trilby and leopard glow beneath the lamp.
Joy in the melting of compassion's bowels
In no more enmity, no more retreat,
Joy in the augmentation of a sweetness
That is already infinitely sweet;
Joy in the stirring of the stubborn heart
In benediction for its long accurst,
Prodigal rapture as from tumbling fountains
Forever pouring wine for an unslaked thirst.
Teasing our sullen spirits with its flame,
At one with rain, with the delayed Six-Seven,
The dripping, the drawn faces, and the dark –
The mammoth inescapable blaze of Heaven.

Listen, beloved, this is Derby Station,
Heirs and joint-heirs with Christ, Attention please;
Turn your mild eyes to where, on Platform Two,

Gleaming like sunrise through the forest trees,
Moving like Jove across primeval dew,
Comes rolling in oppressive majesty,
Smoke-garlanded with tumbled cherubim
(And, really, not so badly overdue,)
Light-heralded, rose-wreathed, the train for Crewe.

January 1948

THE SAILOR'S WIDOW

Thunder and cataract, advancing seas,
Unfurl your foaming standards up the shore,
Crumple and surge and hunger through the rocks –
There is no longer menace in your roar
      Nor terror in your tide;
      Keen arrow-shafts of spray
      Wind-flown, fall wide,
      Scatter and glance away.

Never again the nostrils of the storm
Blow tigerish on my spirit, I'll not fear
Loud round the house in winter's wickedness
The drumming horses of his charioteer;
      Their wild dark manes
      No more I'll shake to hear
      Drumming the window-panes;
      Nothing's to fear.

Oh vanished love, whose going could un-danger
Enormous hounding waters, and make tame
The fell and tireless anger of the sea,
All has been honoured of that savage claim;

No more can sun and spill
Grace or torment the day,
All weather now is still
All weather grey.

1948

AUTUMN

Atlantic drums the window.
The evening gathers wet,
Dark flies the flag of winter
And the young moon is set.

Five thousand times the world has spun
With cirrus banners flying,
And fifteen years have spun away
The evening you lay dying.

And still it's you that live and breathe;
I walk with pallid hosts.
The world turned over once and ever
And all live men are ghosts.

1955

AS I CAME DOWN FROM FARINGDON

As I came down from Faringdon
The rainy wold was slant with sun,
Blue were the eyes in a sudden face
And blue the clear of sky begun.

Enchanted valleys thick with corn
Laugh under burning skies,
The harvest of remembered years
Ripe in a stranger's eyes.

The sound and movement of far streams
Falling as in eternity,
The echoes from the yellow rocks
Of stern bright places fringed with sea,

A stranger face, and yet the eyes
As blue as yours, as straightly seeing,
Awoke an echo of your look
To sound within a sleepy being.

A stranger face that came and went.
But kind endowment from another
Affection's well-learnt habitude –
Gave us a kindness for each other.

How sweet when one long serious look
Splinters the ice of love's negation,
His, 'How I'd love you if you would,'
Warming the heart with admiration.

In a chance flash I saw your look,
Brown visage briefly recognised;
The stubborn heart was smartly lifted
The buried memories surprised.

This is the pith of all we know
Of joy within a mortal span –
The bliss that comes of being woman,
Triumph inborn in being man.

This happy moment was as fleeting
For both of us, as unconcerned;
No lovers' parting, nor none meeting,
No ships were launched and no boats burned.

The clouds came rolling off the down
The bus went lurching up the hill.
Passengers left, the bus ground on,
Now lightened by its overspill.

As I came down from Faringdon
The rainy wold was lit with sun,
The larks now tumbled overhead
The corn was green, and spring begun.

1943, Written in 1958

THE PRISONER

Truth in the inward parts – but how's the seeing
Through heavy mists of sentiment and whine?
Truth is – you were of all men the most freeing:
The chains I wear, the chains I wear are mine.

You of all men the mover, the releaser,
The least encourager to sigh and pine,
The forward looker, and the range-increaser –
The chains I wear, the chains I wear are mine.

Last of the race of man to claim possession
Beyond the grave, oh never your design
To lock me in this fortress of obsession:
The chains I wear, the chains I wear are mine.

1958

HAMOAZE

The noon is harsh with wind and light
Blue water sharpens on the strand,
The pennants harden, and the dust
Stings on us as you come to land.

Blood tumbles in the arteries
In throat and ears the tumult roars,
The trees are yellow loud with spring –
Another time, on other shores.

Sun lashes on the waterfront
The same bright ripples shoot their dart,
While twenty years of loss and grief
Ransack the unforgetting heart.

1960

30 AUGUST 1961

Come between me and sleep,
In that mysterious moment when the mind
Rolling between oblivion and full sense
The gleam of truth may find.

Come between me and care,
And prejudice, and littleness, and blame,
Come between me and my malignity,
Come, as in life you came.

Come between me and fear,
And solitude, and want and deprivation,
The creeping Indians of old age and loss,
Love's long negation.

Come between me and time,
And come with all your panoply about you,
Come in full blaze, that so I may forget
Twenty-one years without you.

ICE IN THE RIVER BREAKING

Spring breaks the sea of ice.
The dragon, still asleep, his breath releases,
A burning blast, to blow away in pieces
Mind's cool advice.

Up-ended floes are grinding;
And in the dark of those subconscious deeps
A slow upheaval, as the dragon sleeps
No more, his freedom finding.

Dragon has held his fire
All winter; body slumbered, shamming dead.
But now from that banked furnace wakes the dread
Power of desire.

But cold discovery
As the mind clears, breaks like an arctic spring
Bitter and slow – that there is no such thing
Ever, for you and me.

1964

FIRST YEARS

I loved you with no limit but the fence
Surrounding my own frail capacity –
The stucco walls of youthful lack of sense.

For love is wisdom; not at first to be
Unselfish in its purpose and its flow.
Love is a knowledge, not a cleverness.
Its first step is to see
How far it has to go
How prone to shallow woe,
How long its thorny journey into wisdom
And generous understanding;
How ready to expect the easy landing
From passion's undertone,

How very slowly we begin to know
That we must seek and slowly find each other
And in this knowledge very slowly grow
And steadfastly indulge while flags are flying,
Or love may cease to glow
Its warm light palely dying,
Its ardour dumbly groping for another.

* * * * *

But I was not like this
Slowly and wisely learning,
But stumbled undeservingly to bliss
Without its earning.

RECONCILIATION
WELLAND VALLEY
30 AUGUST 1970

Thirty years on,
In the green stillness of this oak tree's shade,
Loss is still absolute, but better weighed.

Our life here, its long happiness foregone
Becomes of lesser worth
Held in the balance of this sylvan peace
And this unconquered earth.

However hardly earned
This standing corn untrampled in its gold
By foreign armies, these slow kine un-driven,
These homesteads, made of stone tawny with iron,
Cottages never burned,
Show a wide countryside as calm as heaven,
A cruel destruction stopped.

These spreading trees no conquering axe has lopped,
These backs unburdened, and these hearts at ease
With woes of conquering tyranny unlearned –
Are gold new-turned.

And all this, fairly bought;
By many a worthy lover
Whose lives were cut in half.

Only their own immediate families
Will never quite recover
However well they know
– Standing at ease under a great tree's shade
In summer's downy warmth –
This bargain was well made.

Within this strange and complicated whole
We call ourselves, and used to call our soul,
A hidden sanctuary
Of intermittent gleams of truth and light,
We know that this was right.

TERMINUS

Life, after all, is one long station platform,
Chill winds of parting whipping round our legs,
Hoping, obscurely, that the train won't go,
Time will run slow,
Life will not leave us with the tasteless dregs.

There will be happiness, and gleams of sunlight
Out of a sullen sky
After the train rolls off into the night.
Even, there will be, at long last, content –
Yet something here must die.
No more the glory and the blaze of heaven
From a blue sky, because
The sun itself is shuttered, and has left
Only the mellow pleasure of remembering
How bountiful life was.

No more that close commotion, and no more
Delight in its full flood:
No more shall violent beating of the heart
Let loose that fevered coursing of the blood.

No more will every fibre of the being
Quicken to full employ.
There will be gladness of a gentle kind
But no more joy.

1976

DEPARTED

Had I first left, and you the one who tarried
You'd have been sad awhile.
But then you would have sensibly re-married,
Retrieving that large smile.

Wholly involved in life
And mostly unconcerned with resurrection,
You would have thought of me with warm affection
Sometimes, on summer evenings, in the dusk,
Though well contented with your second wife.

Oh love, how quickly do we pass, how lightly.
We are regretted little more than slightly
In patches of nostalgia, interspersed
With long forgetfulness,
(A mood in which we're all of us well-versed,)
Lost faces growing fainter, ever less,
Recaptured with diminishing distress –

Until we no more see.
This is as it should be;
Since life is here for living,
And time, for all its faults, keeps on forgiving
That luxury, as in a dream to lean
On all the happiness there once has been.

Yes, you'd be right
So to re-marry and renew the name
Of loving teasing husband.
Just the same
Possession's not relinquished overnight,
If my ghost lived, I'd love you with delight –
And sometimes come and tweak you in the night.

1978

WHAT GOES ON?

One would have thought that matters of more moment
Would fill your lively mind and active frame,
Wider horizons would engross your gaze
And dazzling matters your attention claim
In that far country that you now inhabit
Than grace this little purlieu whence you came.

Surely there must be other things to do
Further enormous landscapes to look over?
Wonders more vital must your soul absorb
Deep secrets that the living mayn't discover.
And yet you never really leave my side
Nor ever cease to be my constant lover.

And is that world indeed all milk and honey
A land devoid of partings, fevers, strife?
Maybe. For I'm confiding in God's promise.
Although we never more are man and wife.
We'll live together, by some means or other,
Whatever way – a joined eternal life.

AUGUST THE THIRTIETH

Night fell on such another day as this
Of open windows, honeysuckle air,
The smell of mignonette and of sweet peas,
Of oak leaves dark upon the spreading trees
Heavy with summer, and as soft a breeze
As left those leaves unstirred –
When death walked in, silent and undeterred
As any thief of night; unfaltering death.
Forty years on, I yet can feel his breath.

By cloudless skies, although the year was turning,
The distant Tamar river gleamed again.
In fields around, earth broke before the plough,
On the huge haunches of the plough horse played
A late indulgent sun, and neatly stayed
The corncocks stood, beside a lengthening shade
Blue as a far horizon after rain.
Here were the deeps of pain;
Never relaxing, never a while delayed.

Yet no sad catalogues of time efface
The way it was. Let wiser tongues explain
How, when these piercing hours of doom arrive,
That *here* the spent despairing mind can trace

226

The fathomless uprising of God's grace.
With your flesh dead and mine but half alive
How did the truth of both ourselves survive
On airs of glory borne from that high place,
And goodness hold us in its sure embrace?

1981

FOREST

Once we were there, afloat on those green seas
That summer evenings make of forest rides,
When myriad leaves are quiet on stirless trees
And silent as an ocean under tides.

There would I live, if living could be dwelling
In a green land beyond suspense or care,
Where once we walked in a delight past telling.
If love be anchorage, I shall be there.

But love's the long translation out of dream,
The heaving up of anchors and their chains,
In the committal to the flowing stream
With all its misadventure and hard pains.

Out of the light, and the trees' sweet confusion
Under dark cliffs, to oceans yet unknown
Love leads the luckless dweller in illusion
On perilous journeys he must take alone.

1983

WINTER

In the dark silence of the early mornings
I recognise the country and its people
More real than ours;
Sometimes, inside those strange abstracted moments
I set a tentative foot across the threshold
The magic world of those believed-in powers.

And then, as soon, withdraw.
I fear the song of its birds,
The brilliance of its flowers,
The whisper of strange trees,
Eternity's long hours,
Love, with its inexplicable decrees.

Here, there's the bath in the morning, piping hot,
Coffee, and safety, the streams flowing still
Cleanly, from every hill,
Reading, with all its choices,
The sound of friendly voices –
The undeserved, the happy happy lot.
The distant trees, the long-loved slope of the down,
The humble joys that cannot be forgot;
Loss of all this I fear –
Here are the fearless buds of spring beginning

Long daylight slowly winning,
The evening fireside and the tea and toast
My darling children, inexpressibly dear,
And all those lively beings I love most.

This the immediate, the well-worn Here
Set against unimaginable There –
I fear the iron hand in the velvet glove;
Difficult to embrace a lightning love
Flashing from one horizon to another.

I stand at nearly eighty
Over against the dazzling huge unknown
That I must meet alone.
The puny heart cries out
Let me stay here!
In this small world that's still within my range,
These baby pleasures here are all about.
I don't feel like resigning
For that starred world I can't begin defining.
Old people find it difficult to change.

1986

THE VOYAGE

Enchanted islands on a sea of sleep
Old moments surface, and their resonance keep.
Yet soon enough they mock us with the glow
And gleam of other feelings, other days,
Other horizons, certainties, desires,
And ecstasies only the youthful know.

Far have we journeyed from those distant shores,
Long has it cooled, that well-remembered blaze,
Dowsed, the devouring fires.
The pain of love, the agony expires
– Thank goodness – and from those lost furnace days
Whose burning seemed eternal in our eyes
Merely a wisp of smoke can slowly rise,
A smudge against the haze,
A breath of warmth, as past the islands flow,
Into the mist where all our memories go,
A kindling, from that fifty-years-past glow
Leaving us to the calmness of the sea
All that is gone, that will forever be.

1990

8 AUGUST 1991

Your death was an illusion
– Bitter and hard, and cruel to contemplate –
But an illusion I am slowly shedding
Fifty-one years too late;
Happy with nothing much
Of mingled work and play
This August day like any other day,
But this I celebrate;
Deep in my heart I hold the diamond wedding.

END OF YEAR

I have enjoyed a long old age, and yet
There are discrepancies I can't forget.
All through the sunlit days of late October
I gloried in the pleasures of each day
And a kind of peace I had not known in May,
And yet
These last ten years of fall and of November
Have taken far too many friends away
Well known, and deeply valued;
As evening gathered to their last December
I understood dismay
In realising none would now remember
The wisdom, the light heartedness, the play,
The warmth of heart, the glory, of your day.

1994

ADDICT

I am as hooked as any on cocaine
Working in dullness, not, thank God, in pain.

Oh haunt beloved and eternal haunt
Whom slowing arteries can never daunt,
Impervious to time's autumns, dropping slow
The yellow leaves of age, those crumpled shapes
Of leaves once green and glowing. Even though
The limbs move heavily, and feelings grow
Daily more careless of the world's events
And hearing fades away, to all intents
And purposes, in a remote distress –
You move untroubled through my consciousness
Equally certain to disturb and bless.

1996

AN AFTERNOON AT BIDDESDEN

Come celebrate the second age of gold –
The comfort and delight of being old.

Tumult, and war itself are grown remote
From the unworried haven where we float

No longer tugging at those stubborn anchors
Free of those old dislikes, and ancient rancours,

Not stiff, not deaf, still seeing, (but again
A little bit forgetful now and then;)

With grandchildren that tumble on the lawn
On summer days, who are ourselves re-born,

Behaving just as wildly, with the same
Shouting and tears; but we are not to blame;

No more responsible, no more involved,
Loving, not judging, all old pains resolved.

Oh blessed age of sky, and bird, and tree,
And leisure to be still, and time to see.

NINETY YEAR OLD

Silently, silently,
Still I sigh and grieve for you
Loving no less longingly
Knowing end is well in view.

Where's the use, where's the use
Of a love that cannot be?
Where's the help? Since so long
You have been a part of me.

Sixty years, sixty years
Nearly, since you went away.
In the lastingness of love
Sixty years are but a day.

Far astern, far astern,
Still astern I lag behind you,
Slow, yet hoping, I will grow
As much goodness as can find you,

As much flexibility
As can bend, as can change,
As can love with different love
In that world where now you range.

February 1998

TAVISTOCK – A FANTASY

When you come back it will be Tuesday morning;
Arriving at the station on the hill
And walking down, because there were no taxis
Among the railway's usual overspill.

Grey clouds low overhead, and rain impending,
The cheerful faces, far from war's alarms,
The leaning bicycles and whistling boys,
A moderate bustle round the Bedford Arms.

Sixty years on, the same heaped vegetables
Fresh on the stalls in all their rich array,
The same mauve dresses flapping on their hangers –
A day like any other market day.

The same grey splendid church, late summer trees
Still unsusceptible to autumn's touch,
A troupe of happy people buying clothes
Tuned to Apollo's words, 'Nothing too much.'

And you, the man in prime, home from the sea,
With lengthened stride crossing the market place,
'I wonder, now, who that old woman was?'
So he would muse. 'I seem to know her face.'

Rewritten 1998

ROCK MY HEART
EMMA NICHOLS

First published in 2021 by:

J'Adore Les Books

www.emmanicholsauthor.com

Copyright © 2021 by Emma Nichols

Books by Emma Nichols

Other books by Emma Nichols...

The Vincenti Series:
Finding You
Remember Us
The Hangover

Duckton-by-Dale Series:
Summer Fate
Blind Faith
Christmas Bizarre

Other Titles:
Forbidden
This Is Me (Novella)
Ariana
Madeleine
Cosa Nostra
Cosa Nostra II
Elodie

To keep in touch with the latest news from Emma Nichols and her writing please visit:

www.emmanicholsauthor.com
www.facebook.com/EmmaNicholsAuthor
https://twitter.com/ENichols_Author

Thanks

Without the assistance, advice, support and love of the following people, this book would not have been possible.

Bev. Thank you, as always, for your insight and wisdom. Sue, thank you for your expertise with horses. You've saved the day for me. Kim, Gill, and Doreen. Thank you for your feedback. I'm delighted you enjoyed this story. Mu. Thank you for another amazing cover. This one wasn't easy to find, but you've nailed it.

Thank you to my editor at Global Wordsmiths, Nicci Robinson. It is a pleasure to work with you and your team to get the best out of my writing.

To my wonderful readers and avid followers. Thank you for continuing to read the stories I write. I have really enjoyed writing this story of loss, love, and family.
I hope you enjoy it too.

If you enjoy my stories, please do me the honour of leaving a review on Amazon or Goodreads as this helps with visibility so that other readers may discover my stories too. You can also subscribe to my website at **www.emmanicholsauthor.com** for updates on my book releases.

With love, Emma x

Dedication

To my darling daughter, Amelie.
Your passion for horses inspired this story. I love you.

1.

THE CONTINUOUS MONOTONE ALARM was poor harmony for the measured voices in the surgical room at Bellevue Hospital.

"One more time?"

Maddison Hernandez watched the thin white line move across the monitor, then studied the lifeless body on the bed. The sense of familiar peace chilled her bones, something she'd never managed to adjust to in her years as an emergency physician. As a specialist heart surgeon, she knew instinctively when someone wasn't coming back. To try again would be futile and the next patient would be compromised, the time wasted. It was a delicate balance, a judgment call beyond the red tape and protocols that dictated procedural necessities. She closed her eyes for a moment to confirm her decision. An internal check that she would be accountable to both herself and to any inquiry that might be forthcoming if she was perceived to have screwed up. The sanity check she'd always deferred to with unwavering confidence before seemed to take longer now, and there was nothing more crippling and potentially ruinous than indecision. She took a deep breath and opened her eyes. "No. I'm calling it. Time of death," she looked at the clock on the wall, "twenty-two, fifty-six. Can someone follow up with the police, please?"

"I'll take that call," the senior nurse said.

She didn't need to give any further instructions. Her team would shift seamlessly into action, clearing away, cleaning down, completing paperwork, and moving onto the next urgent case. She left the room, removed her gloves and gown, washed her hands, and stared at herself in the washroom mirror. She hadn't replaced the lipstick that had worn from her lips within an hour of her starting work or repaired the foundation cream that she used now to hide the deep shadows below her eyes. In what little time she'd had between patients that hadn't been taken up with completing paperwork, attending meetings, or dealing with departmental issues, she'd chosen to sit and rest, to close her eyes, to block out the busyness that surrounded her. If her mamá could see her, she would say she'd stopped caring about her appearance, that she lacked pride, and more pointedly, that she would never attract un corazón if she looked as though she'd just fallen out of a whorehouse. She rubbed her eyes. It was already almost three hours since her shift should have ended, not that time meant a great deal anymore. The hours merged into days, the days into weeks, the weeks into months.

It'd been two years since she'd taken more than a long weekend break from work. Twenty-six months and three days since Lizzy had died in her arms. A shiver passed over her as if someone had stepped on her grave, and the vision of the woman on the ER table taunted her. She'd been someone's child and possibly someone's mother. Had she made the right call? She tried to piece together the scenes to tick the procedural boxes, but her recollection was obscured by the woman's image, and she was slow to reconstruct the string of events into a cohesive and affirmative operation. She had to trust that she hadn't fucked up. Sudden cardiac arrest was responsible for more than half of the total heart disease deaths in the US, and the wealthy and the famous weren't immune. Judging by the woman's Balenciaga crewneck sweater and the white gold, diamond-encrusted Rolex she wore, she appeared to be one of those women who had enjoyed wealth. The heavily wrinkled skin that aged her beyond her years and pale puffy cheeks were clear indicators that she'd consumed a significant amount of alcohol, probably cocaine too judging by the slight disfiguration of her nose. Her faded perfume did little to conceal the smell of tobacco. She'd collapsed in a bar, and Maddie wouldn't be surprised at what the toxicology report revealed given the

2

woman's apparent tendency to self-medicate. Delays getting to her because of the sheer volume of Friday night traffic had significantly reduced her chances of survival, but Maddie couldn't stop worrying, not for the first time these past months, that she'd missed something. Yes, they were overworked, but that was nothing new, and every doctor was in the same position. They had to be resilient to tiredness. Fuck-ups just didn't happen at Bellevue. One strike and you really were out.

"Hey, Maddie."

She stirred from her self-doubts and smiled weakly. Her colleague Lee approached with a spring in her step and a broad smile. She looked as though she was just starting a shift rather than finishing it. "You make me feel old."

Lee shrugged. "You are. Old enough to be my mom."

Maddie laughed. She was nowhere near that age though she felt it. "Geez, thanks for the uplift."

Lee slapped her on the back. "Always here to help. You heading to the bar?"

Maddie hesitated. If her eyelids became any heavier, she wouldn't be able to keep her eyes open long enough for a shot, let alone a couple of beers. A yawn confirmed her reservations, but she needed some downtime and a sedative before trying to sleep. She needed to forget this day, if only for a couple of hours.

"Ah, come on. Don't be a spoiler mom-type. Who needs one of those?"

Maddie stifled another yawn. "Sure."

"Cool. I've got a couple bits of paperwork. I'll be there shortly."

Maddie nodded, and Lee turned toward the nurse who approached them. Maddie made her way out of the main entrance and walked straight into a wall of humidity. If she'd wanted a spa experience to end her day with, she wouldn't pick a New York street for the occasion. The contrast with the A/C inside the hospital made walking feel like wading through molasses with a respirator mask on. She hated the feeling when working in full PPE, though sometimes the pollution levels in the city seemed to warrant greater protection than her work. She side-stepped two guys moving toward her as if they were late for an important date and broke out into a sweat.

Moisture had coated every millimeter of her skin before she'd made it fifty yards up East 29th Street toward Paddy Reilly's, and breathing in the warm, damp, fume-filled air didn't make the walk any easier. She looked up to where she expected to see the stars. Even though it was a cloudless night, the sky was painted in a haze of soft light. *New York, the city that never sleeps, bustling by day and hustling by night.* A man nudged her shoulder as he passed. There was no time for stargazing anyway. Walking against the flow didn't create any airflow. It just took her longer to get to the bar and added to her irritation.

Maybe there had been a time when she'd been entertained by the active city life, the heady rush that came with playing hard, and the relentless pressure that came with working in the ER. She couldn't recall the point at which the highs and the lows had merged into a kind of unconscious existence. Nothing had meant anything since Lizzy's death. Any happiness was superficial and fleeting, happening just often enough to give the illusion that it was attainable, just sufficient to keep her from the doors of depression. Who was she trying to kid? If she were the patient, she'd have prescribed Prozac already. Damien Rice's haunting voice made its way past her thoughts and added a little lightness to her step. "She Moved Through the Fair," one of her favorite songs, was a sad, profound ballad that always seemed to touch something inside her and transport her to another time and space. To a place where love lasted a lifetime.

Paddy Reilly's would be packed, as always. The promise of the cool Guinness, the best beer in the city, quickened her step. Or maybe she'd choose the soft warmth of the Bushmills Black Bush with its subtle woody and malted barley flavors to lift the day or reduce the stress. Hopefully, both. Paddy Reilly's was the choice hangout of the Bellevue physicians. She would lose herself in its bustle, escape from the events of the day, and find solace in the gently numbing effect that came with slowly getting buzzed.

Patrons milled around in the street outside. Some sipped their drinks and chatted animatedly, laughing raucously, while others sang along to "The Hornblower's Daughter," badly. Their downtime had probably started a good number of hours earlier. Maddie stepped inside and picked her way through the crowded room to the bar. She lifted her chin and smiled to catch the attention of the bartender, a slender-hipped twenty-something with a beaming white smile and a designer hairstyle that suggested he would be better placed on a Hollywood set. The landlord and bar's namesake approached from behind the young man. He said something to the kid, who changed direction and went to attend to another customer.

"Well, good evening, Doctor Hernandez. Will it be a Guinness or Bushmills this fine evening?"

It was the same welcome every time, with his soft Irish lilt that he hadn't let go of in his fifty-plus years of residency in the country. Which was good, since authenticity was vital to the success of a traditional Irish pub in the city.

"A Guinness, Paddy. It's so damn hot."

"The A/C is trying its best."

She laughed. If it *was* on, she couldn't feel it. She swept her bangs from her cheek and looked around the room for a familiar face. Finding none, she waited, pressured by the bodies around her that stood too close for comfort.

"Here you are." Paddy passed the drink across the bar. "Tough day?"

"Always." She gulped down half the beer. So much for the slow route to inebriation. It was too crowded to bother going back and forth to the bar. "I'll take another, Paddy." She took another long swallow and savored the bitterness and silk that cooled her throat. She'd almost finished it before Paddy returned with a second Guinness. "Thanks. You're a lifesaver."

Paddy laughed. "I'll leave that job to you."

She didn't feel like a lifesaver at all, especially not today. It was a crappy way to end her last shift before the vacation she'd had to fight so hard to get approved. Her stomach soured the Guinness. She took another swig and headed around the bar to a vacant stool. She sat with her back to the bar and tried to give her attention to the soft ballad that had quieted conversation inside the pub. It was one of Lizzy's favorite songs. The white head on the black beer quivered as she gripped the glass. She took a deep breath and closed her eyes but all she could see was Lizzy. Peaceful. Asleep. Gone.

"Hey."

Maddie opened her eyes. "It's packed," she said, not missing Lee's gaze focused on her trembling hand. Lee didn't respond to her inane comment, and Maddie ignored Lee's quizzical expression. The bar was packed every night of the week, and with Damien Rice in the house, doubly so tonight. She lifted her glass. "Cheers. Here's to another crappy day in the office."

Lee raised her glass. "Some we win, some we lose, huh? Don't be too hard on yourself." She took a sip of her drink and glanced around the room.

"I guess so." Maddie swallowed down the bitterness that rose in her throat. The trembling inside wouldn't abate. It would take more than a couple of drinks for that to ease.

Lee leaned toward her. "You'll soon forget about it. I still don't know how you managed to negotiate a month's vacation out of those fuckers."

Maddie didn't want to get into that conversation.

"Rumor has it you screwed the boss, of course." Lee smiled at someone across the room.

Maddie was too tired to care about hospital gossip or the inevitable criticism that would be levied at her for abandoning her colleagues. She'd been torn asking for the extended unpaid leave, but if she hadn't pushed for it, she might have ended up taking sick leave just to avoid making a devastating mistake. It galled her to accept that the standard long weekend wasn't going to give her the mental relief she needed, but saving her job was more important and that meant she had to go. As it was, she'd had to plan the vacation months ago and work around the hospital rather than her own needs. The truth was, she'd been hanging onto her sanity by a thread for too long now, and this day hadn't come quickly enough.

"Fuck what the rest of them say, huh? I think it's great, and Lizzy wouldn't want you living like this."

Maddie stopped short of rolling her eyes. She was sure Lee meant well but recently she'd gotten the impression that Lee just wanted Maddie around so she had someone to hang out with while she scoped out other women. They'd had the "Lizzy wouldn't want" conversation more than once in the past six months. Why did the living always think they knew what the dead would want them to do? It was a crappy attempt to alleviate survivor guilt that only made matters worse. Overworking had kept her sane, but her delayed reactions were noticeable. She was processing information too slowly and questioning her decision-making when she should be confident and incisive. She'd been hiding her grief behind the demands of the job. She hadn't messed up and she never would, no matter what it took. But it was taking too much of her now. Her anger had dissipated quickly when she'd finally accepted she was struggling. It didn't make leaving the hospital easy though and a big part of her wanted to stay.

Still, what was she supposed to do with four weeks off? Jostle with the thoughts in her head, wrestle with negativity, relive her irritation with her own inadequacies, and be consumed by sadness and regret. It was possible the break could be more damaging to her sanity and destroy her confidence. It was too long to be out of the fire. Nevertheless, she didn't really have a choice.

"Honestly, you're burned out."

Maddie shrugged. "Aren't we all?"

"That's not the point."

"Then what is?"

Lee shook her head. "You need to work through your shit."

Maddie sipped her drink. She didn't need Lee telling her what she already knew. "Thanks."

Lee huffed. "What if you end up making a serious mistake? You'll never live with yourself. If you fuck up, it affects us all, Maddie."

Maddie allowed the spark of anger to fizzle out and lowered her gaze to the drink in her hand. At least Lee had the integrity to talk to her directly. There were other colleagues who would simply raise their concerns with her boss and watch her be called on the carpet so they could jump into her position as she vacated it. The pleasantly numbing effect of the Guinness didn't touch the painful truth. Her hesitation could cost a life, and Lee was right, she wouldn't be able to live with herself if that happened.

"You'll be fine once you get away. God knows, you need it. You've had a crappy few years."

Maddie took a long slug of the drink and thought about the retreat at the Wild Horse Ranch in Austin, Nevada that she'd booked. An ex-patient had spent time there. He'd been so vehement about how wonderful it was while she'd treated him that the location had stuck with her. It was a living ghost town off US 50, the loneliest road in America. She wasn't a huge fan of horses, and the Nevada terrain, with its high plains and arid desert, couldn't be more different from New York. A million miles from this soulless city, certainly cooler, *and* she'd be away from people. If she broke down there, no one of any significance would know about it. Lee was right, she needed to take advantage of this vacation to get herself back on track.

"Hey, maybe you'll find yourself a nice cowgirl." Lee laughed.

The thought of getting involved with someone caused the Guinness to turn in her stomach. "No, thanks." She would take the time to reflect, to mourn the loss of Lizzy, and chill out, and she would return to work refreshed and refocused.

2.

"YOU GOING TO THE dance next Saturday?"

"Nope." Devin swung the lump hammer over her head and down hard onto the stake Cody was holding, nudging it an inch deeper into the rocky surface. Devin swung again and landed the metal head with a force that should have resulted in more than another half inch of movement, but it barely shifted. Working the canyon's arid terrain was backbreaking on the best of days, but with two miles of fence to repair in the driest summer on record, it was painstaking. It would take weeks until fall for them to get it finished. She landed another hit and smiled as the post shifted a good inch. "That son of a coyote's going nowhere." She straightened her back and rubbed her forearm across her mouth.

"You know Ella's gonna be there?"

Devin swiped at the sweaty streak of dust and dirt that stuck to the hairs on her arm. "Yep." She ambled to her truck and pulled two bottles of water from the cooler in the front. She threw one across to Cody and downed the best part of the other bottle in one long steady slug.

"She likes you. A lot."

Devin leaned against the front fender and rested her heel on the rail behind her. She nudged the brim of her hat up a fraction and closed her eyes, savoring the sun and its late evening warmth. "Yep." Nothing could beat the sound of almost silence, with just an echo of a breeze that moved through the canyon.

"She's hot. You should give her a chance."

She opened her eyes and squinted at Cody. "She's a friend, Cody, nothing more. You want to try your luck, go for it." She laughed. Cody wasn't brave enough to approach Ella, even though she clearly had strong feelings for her.

"It's you she's crushing on," Cody said, though it sounded more like a question than a statement.

Devin shook her head. "It's not happening." She looked out across the high plains at US 50 in the distance. Nothing but desert and grassland between them and the main road leading to civilization. This place was perfect.

"I thought you were into her?"

Devin frowned. Surely Cody knew there was nothing between Ella and her and never would be. She'd considered the idea briefly when she'd been feeling lonely one winter a few years back but decided that if they got involved, it would most likely destroy the friendship they had. Mind-blowing sex wasn't worth losing that.

Ella was attractive, with long blonde hair and baby-blue eyes that caught the attention of many an unsuspecting male passing through Austin. They didn't stand a chance of getting near her, of course, and she always let them down gently. She was like that, gentle and caring. They'd been friends since school, and they got along in the same way an old married couple might. She was a teacher at the local school, was great with kids, and even shared Devin's passion for classic cars. It might be natural and simple to slip into a physical relationship with a few women of interest locally, but what would happen when it didn't last? She knew it wouldn't because seeing Ella didn't cause her breath to hitch, and she didn't think about Ella every hour of the day or night. "You don't give up, do you?"

"You two look so easy together is all I'm saying."

"I look easy around the horses. Doesn't mean I'm gonna marry one."

Cody threw her empty water bottle at Devin. "Ass."

"I won't be marrying a mule either." Devin laughed. "Help me with these crossbars." She walked to the back of the truck and lifted a half-moon shaped six-foot pole from the trunk.

Ella threw herself into Devin's arms, her long skirt becoming wrapped around Devin's legs. She smelled like a powder puff out of a woman's restroom.

"Right, feeding's done. I'll catch you tomorrow," Cody said, coming out of the barn.

Ella released Devin. She had a beaming grin and color in her cheeks that hadn't previously been obvious. Devin turned to Cody. She looked pissed. She'd probably misinterpreted their embrace. "You sure you don't want wings?"

Cody strode toward her car, parked on the other side of the house, and lifted her hand in the air as if waving Devin off, cursing as she went. She'd reassure her tomorrow. She turned back to Ella. "So, you want to tell me a bit more about this kid?"

"Her name's Alice," Ella said.

Devin didn't miss Ella's gentle chastising tone. "Alice. Sure." Devin lifted her ballcap and scratched the back of her head. "So, let's eat. Do you want a beer?" She certainly needed a very cold drink to reconcile her commitment to Ella and this Alice kid.

3.

ASIDE FROM THE THUNDEROUS crack that seemed to split the sky as four military jets flew overhead just outside of Fallon, the long drive from Reno to Austin had been virtually silent. Even Maddie's thoughts had quieted a little as she'd become entranced by the expansive sandy plains and the road that stretched into the distance, seemingly heading to nowhere. She'd stopped once for gas and a Coke and enjoyed the dry desert heat while stretching her legs. She'd wondered what was happening back in the ER. And then weariness struck her, and she'd slept in the car for twenty minutes. She'd woken in a haze with a sense of urgency calling to her and felt overcome by anxiety. She'd turned around and started back to the airport, back to New York and the reassuring comfort of Bellevue, but stopped herself.

She turned off the highway just outside Austin and followed the wooden handwritten sign that said, *Wild Horse Ranch 'n Retreat*. Dirt and dust rose up from the road as she drove toward the higher plains and the elevated green oasis in the distance. This place really was in the middle of nowhere. She thought again about New York, the high-rise structures that dominated the landscape and the overcrowded streets, the constant noise and pollution, the hustle and bustle that indicated life, and a wave of fatigue passed through her. The desert started to transform, and the cacti and shrubs became more infrequent in the lush green terrain of the higher plains. She turned the A/C down as the temperature dropped. The sky was an expanse of deep blue, clear and intense. The ranch appeared on the horizon, and her stomach trembled.

The familiarity of home called to her, but was it still home without Lizzy? She stopped the car and wiped the cold sweat from her brow. Her heart pounded and her pulse raced.

She flung open the door, stepped out of the car, and strode the open plains. Where the hell did she think she was heading? She put her hands on her hips, closed her eyes and took long deep breaths until her heart rate slowed. *Come on, this is crazy. What's wrong with me?* She settled her breathing and opened her eyes. The air was pleasantly a few degrees cooler here than in the lower valley along the highway. And, if complete silence was possible in anything other than a soundproofed chamber, then she'd found it in this vast abyss. She felt the absence of the city, the draw to return and lose herself in the noise and her work. She'd only felt this alone, this inadequate once in her life and that was in the aftermath of Lizzy dying. She wiped at her cheek, but it didn't stop the tears from flowing freely. She got back in the car, turned on the radio, and headed on.

The wooden sign set against a large boulder outside the ranch's entrance looked like something from the Wild West. She expected tumbleweed to come flying past her on a gust of wind, though there was no breeze of note. This really was cowboy territory, wholesome and free. She drove slowly through the open gate and up the dirt road toward the buildings that were still some distance away. Horses grazed in the fenced fields. Lush green trees lined a large corral with four barrels set out in two rows. A large wooden two-story house stood proudly at the end of the road with a white painted porch and shuttered doors and windows. Several outbuildings were dotted around either side of the house. In the smaller corral to the right, a woman exercised a large horse on a lunge line. Next to the hay barn on the left, closer to the large enclosure, were a couple of cars and what looked like a stable block. She parked next to the other vehicles and turned off the engine. She'd expected to see more people milling around. No wonder the area had the reputation of being a living ghost town. Where was everyone?

As she approached the house, the door opened and a rosy-cheeked woman greeted her with a broad smile.

"Hi, there. You must be Doctor Hernandez." The woman stood squeezing her hands together in front of her body. "Welcome. Please come in."

"Thank you."

"My name's Rosie. How was your drive?"

"Long."

Rosie laughed. "That road sure goes on."

It did, and given the hours with her thoughts, it had drained the life out of her. Rosie moved at an easy pace that made Maddie feel as though she was holding back. Irritation spiked as she followed her inside, and she had to remind herself she was on vacation, not heading to an ER room.

The sweet smell of dried grass carried into the house, which reminded Maddie of her grandparents' house as a kid, warm and homely. "Please call me Maddie." She followed Rosie up the stairs. "I can see why they call it the loneliest road in America."

"The highway runs a good four hundred miles to Salt Lake City from here with winds like a rattlesnake further down. You can spend a long time driving and feeling like you're not moving very far forward."

Rosie opened a door and ushered Maddie inside a cool room. "I hope you'll find this place to your liking. You're from New York?"

"Yes. It's very quiet here." Maddie smiled. A quiet that came with a sense of unease.

"Wait till the coyotes start howling."

When Rosie laughed, her body jiggled in a way that made her look jolly and motherly.

The large double bed invited Maddie to rest with its puffed-up quilt and pillows. She imagined the soft cotton against her cheek and stifled a yawn. "It's perfect. Thank you."

"I'll leave you to unpack. Come and go as you please. Take a wander around. There're horses out back, or you can relax in the garden, or take a walk. You'll see the house from most parts you can walk to. There's a path down to the lake on the west side. There's cultural trips daily if you want to go with other folks, or you can take yourself, of course. Do you ride?"

Maddie shook her head.

"Ah, well, Devin can help you with that if you're interested in learning. Horses are powerful healers, and you'll not find a better teacher outside of Texas than Devin."

Rosie grew in stature beyond her five-foot-two-inches and beamed with what Maddie could only assume was immense pride. "It sounds delightful," she said, although the thought of riding a horse couldn't be further from her idea of relaxing.

"I'll leave you to settle in. Supper's at seven."

Rosie left, and Maddie took a moment to explore the room. A picture of a shimmering silver-white horse with pale blue eyes hung from the wall, and a wooden carved statue of a dark brown horse standing on its hind legs took up most of the space on the bedside table. Her gaze was drawn to the picture, and it almost stared back. There was something quite majestic and powerful about the fascinating creature. She went to the window. Open plains, dirt tracks, and fence lines extended into the distance, shrub bushes dotted all the way to the mountains, and the highway snaked across the desert. It was so very different from her condo view: high-rise buildings and the sound and sight of people that reminded her she wasn't alone in the world. The expansiveness and the absence of familiarity here left her feeling isolated, vulnerable, and weak. A sinking feeling settled in the pit of her stomach at where her thoughts might lead her. She should never have come.

She went down the stairs and out into the yard. The cooler air was fresh, and she filled her lungs, inhaling slowly. She needed to give herself, and this place, time. She watched the woman leading the horse around the corral, swishing a long whip lightly at his heels and calling to him, encouraging him to follow her instructions. The horse's dark chestnut coat shone, and he held his head high. He looked happy, if that was possible, as though he was enjoying the workout.

She had the urge to explore and stretch her legs, so she went around the back of the empty stables block. An ancient-looking car was parked half in and half out of a large barn. It resembled something out of a nineteen twenties movie. More intriguing was the pair of light tan leather boots with a steel rim around the toe sticking out from beneath the car engine. She watched from a short distance until the tranquility was intruded upon by the clash of metal on metal.

"Ah, shit."

Maddie smiled at the curse. The image of a woman's face splattered with oil came to mind. "Do you need help?"

"Can you pass me the ratchet?" The woman reached out from beneath the car and wriggled her fingers.

Maddie searched the tools scattered on the ground, picked up the ratchet, and placed it in her hand. More banging and groaning followed.

"Six-inch wrench."

She held out her hand again. Maddie was reminded of working in the ER, only it was usually her making the demands, and the urgency was much greater in the hospital. She searched through the tools scattered on the ground, studied the stamped measurements on their handles and handed over the correct wrench.

"There should be a six-inch bolt there somewhere. Can you see it?"

Maddie couldn't see it. She moved the tools and looked underneath. How can anyone work in chaos like this? She would have everything laid out in exactly the order she intended to use it. She looked inside the sack from where the tools had clearly been spilled onto the earth and searched through it. She handed over the bolt.

"Thanks."

After more clunking and a sigh, the woman eased out from under the car, revealing toned legs in battered Levis. Holding the jeans on her hips was a leather belt with a large silver buckle and a horse insignia on it, then a red checked shirt and then the woman's head appeared. Oil decorated her face as Maddie had imagined.

"Oh, hi." She got to her feet and brushed the dust off her. "Sorry, I thought you were someone else. I should've picked up on your accent."

"I didn't say much."

The woman rubbed her hands on her jeans before holding out her hand. "Pleased to meet you. I'm Devin."

"Hi, I'm Maddie." *So, this must be Rosie's daughter.* She saw the resemblance between them in the way their mouths turned up at the edges as if they wore a permanent smile and their dark brown wavy hair, though Devin's was a lot shorter than Rosie's. Devin's eyes were a lighter blue, and her mom was well-proportioned, whereas Devin could easily be mistaken for a cowboy at first glance. "Interesting car."

Devin wiped the front wing with a cloth. "She's an old lady now. A Dodge convertible touring car, built in nineteen-fifteen. I was lucky to find her a few years back. I restored her with my dad."

Cars had never been Lizzy's thing and living in New York, they hadn't needed one in the time they'd been together. Maddie had always voted for a fly-drive holiday so she could enjoy being behind the wheel on the open road, but if she had a passion for cars, it would be the sports-convertible variety rather than an old classic. She'd named their family car Mavis as a kid because it was slow and dull, but then she'd always been in the back and at the will of her parents' ultra-cautious driving styles. "Does she have a name?"

"Sally-Ann, after my great grandma."

"That's sweet. Does she still run?"

Devin smiled and, in that moment, looked as proud as Rosie had when talking about her daughter.

"She sure does." Devin ambled to the driver's side, climbed in, and started the car.

It sounded like one of those irritating scooters whose noise seemed to compensate for their lack of speed. Maddie cringed at the loud grinding sound, the crunching of gears, but smiled as Devin reversed the car into the barn.

Devin walked over to Maddie, picked up the wrench she'd discarded, and threw it into the sack.

Maddie picked up a tin of grease and handed it to Devin. She rubbed her hands together to get rid of the residual stickiness. "Do you take her to rallies?"

"Sometimes." Devin gathered up the other bits and packed them away. She grabbed the sack and headed deeper into the garage. "You like classic cars?"

Maddie didn't feel anything about classic cars. She just liked the fact that someone would spend time restoring something old and preserving a small piece of history. "My padre was a clock collector. He used to take them apart and repair them. I guess it reminds me of him."

"So, you're the doc from New York, right?"

She nodded and drifted off to thoughts about her padre, how he was and what he might be doing. It had been twenty years since she'd last seen him and her mamá, and she wondered if she'd recognize them now. She had no doubts that they would still put their archaic beliefs before their daughter's happiness. How divisive cultural and religious principles could be in the wrong minds, such that they gave someone the power to destroy all that should be good and loving. She couldn't remember either of her parents looking at her with the immense pride and joy that she'd seen in Rosie when she'd mentioned Devin's name. Not since she'd told them she was a

25

lesbian and refused their suggestion of engaging in some form of corrective therapy. How could a parent not see how barbaric that suggestion was? She was relieved Devin hadn't pried into her personal life.

"I've never been drawn to cities," Devin said. "Reno is about as far as I've been and that's enough for me."

Maddie looked around. By New York standards, this place was a deserted island. On a bad weather day, she was sure it could be a hellhole. It would be too isolated a place to live. Too serene, too. What did people do here all day? "Nevada is very pretty," she said. That much she couldn't deny. This wasn't her kind of place, though, and these weren't her kind of people. The impression exhausted her. Her legs failed to respond to her command to move as the last trace of the energy that had gotten her to the ranch drained from her. She discarded the idea that she might fall or faint as foolish, even though the possibility was more than a hallucination.

Devin stepped toward her and grabbed her arm. "Are you okay?"

"I'm fine."

"You looked kinda dizzy there."

Maddie's mouth was as dry as the desert she'd driven through for the best part of the afternoon, and she had an overpowering urge to sleep. "I'm just tired from the drive." The lie came easily, not because she was apt to deceive but because she couldn't break down in front of a stranger. A good sleep would resolve the problem.

Devin let go of Maddie's arm and took a step backwards. She set her hands back on her hips and nodded. "You're the doc. You'd be the best judge of that, I guess."

Devin didn't look convinced. Maddie gazed toward the house.

"You're free to do as you please here. There's no fixed schedule."

Maddie nodded. "I think I might take a rest."

"For sure. If you miss supper, breakfast starts at seven."

Maddie smiled weakly. "Thanks."

"I'll take you for a ride in Sally-Ann when you're up to it."

"I'd like that," Maddie called over her shoulder. As she stepped inside the house, she started to tremble. She wouldn't be going anywhere anytime soon. She needed to sleep more than she'd realized.

4.

MADDIE DIDN'T MAKE IT down to dinner, or breakfast, and if it wasn't for her rental car parked outside, Devin might've thought she'd upped and left the ranch in the middle of the night. She'd come close to knocking on Maddie's bedroom door, just to check she was okay or if she needed something. That she'd considered encroaching on the doc's privacy was against their way of operating. Every guest was entitled to their own space and encouraged to come and go as they pleased. Even more disconcerting was that she hadn't stopped thinking about Maddie since looking up at her from under the car. Maddie wasn't the first guest to arrive looking totally exhausted, but she was the first that had caused this level of concern to stir inside Devin. She'd seen such sadness in Maddie's eyes, and when Maddie had tried to smile, it looked almost painful. A troubled look like that didn't come from nowhere. Despite it being against her own rules, Devin had wanted to talk to her about it but didn't want to make a nuisance of herself. It was none of her business, but just like with the children she helped, a mix of concern and compassion drove her to want to find out more.

Maddie didn't look like any doctor that Devin had come across. She reminded her of an auburn-haired version of her friend Ella, but quieter where Ella was sociable and outgoing. Maybe Maddie was a deep thinker, an introvert, one of those women who observed rather than talked their way through situations. She'd sure looked lost in thought when she'd introduced herself yesterday.

She spiked the loose hay with the pitchfork, lifted it, and threw it close to where Rocky stood. He stopped craning his neck over the fence, gave a short nicker then dived his nose into the pile and started munching. "Hungry, eh?" She thought about Maddie as she tipped another flake of hay farther down, close

29

to where Cookie was tied up. He too was quick to dive in. Maddie should be eating to gain her strength. She looked toward the house for any sign of movement. If Maddie didn't make an appearance by mid-afternoon, rules or no rules, she'd knock on her door and check she was okay.

"What you looking out for?" Cody carried two buckets of water and tipped them into the trough.

Devin raked at the ground with the fork. "What d'you mean?"

"You've had your eyes glued to the house all afternoon, like you're waiting for something interesting to happen."

Devin shook her head and strode back to the barn. Maddie wasn't her problem to solve. She thrust the fork deep into the hay and continued feeding the horses.

"And you're all keyed up." Cody leaned against the fence.

Devin threw the hay onto the pile for Cookie. "I'm not."

"Is this to do with that kid who's coming?"

Devin frowned. "Nothing's wrong, and no."

"Well, you sure are acting a lot like a coyote in heat. All jumpy and uptight."

Devin put the fork inside the barn. "I'm going to the bathroom."

Cody held out her hand. "See, that's exactly what I mean."

Devin strode toward the house. "Make sure Taco's ready for Alice in the small arena. Brushes and tack."

"Alice?"

"The kid from school."

Devin entered the house and glanced up the stairs. The place was quiet. After going to the bathroom, she wandered into the kitchen. Her mom turned to face her from the central island where she was pulling strips of pork from a large joint.

"Come and taste this for me."

"I'm sure it's fine, Mom." She went to the fridge and pulled out a bottle of cold water.

"What brings you in so early?"

"Nothing. I just needed a drink." She took a sip.

"Your fridge stopped working?"

"Nope." Devin would have gone to the fridge in the garage for refreshments but wanting to see Maddie or find out if she was up and about had driven her inside. "Any sign of the doc yet?"

Her mom looked up and half-smiled. "No. She'll be down when she's good and ready. Don't you go worrying."

Devin bit the inside of her lip. "Sure." Trouble was, she couldn't stop the itch that unsettled her. The urge to check on Maddie was still there despite her mom's confidence. She'd been disappointed not to see Maddie at supper after her arrival. She'd gone to breakfast at seven and hovered around for an hour when she would normally be up and out with just coffee to kickstart her day. She'd been distracted all morning, wondering about how Maddie was feeling and wanting to chat with her again. She'd see her soon enough, of course. And then what? She wanted to know what it was like as a physician in New York, because all she knew about it was what she'd seen on the news. She couldn't imagine living in that hellish environment with all the stress, chaos, and sirens. "Do we have any of those peanut butter cookies left?"

Her mom pointed to the shelf on the other side of the kitchen, and Devin plucked a handful of cookies from the jar.

"You hungry?"

"They're for Alice and Cody."

"Best you put them on a plate."

"They'll be fine."

"You know where the plates are." Her mom shook her head as Devin juggled the cookies onto the plate. "You're like a cow with a gun."

She smiled. Working with Alice and Taco would take her mind off the doc for a bit. "Thanks, Mom." She ambled out of the kitchen, hovered at the base of the stairs, then went into the yard.

"Awesome, your mom's cookies. Now you're talking." Cody grabbed one from the plate and ate it in a couple of bites. "Taco's tacked up." She pointed down the road toward the main entrance. "And Ella's here." She wiped her mouth and rubbed her hands down her jeans.

"You look fine." Devin patted her on the back. "Why don't you take Ella out for a ride while I look after Alice?"

Cody blushed. "You think she'll go for that? Doesn't she have to hang around while you're teaching the kid?"

"I'm sure she'll be fine as long as Alice settles."

Cody lifted her hat, ran her fingers through her hair, and buttoned up her shirt.

Devin laughed. "Chill out. It's not a date."

Cody's cheeks flamed red, and she shoved her hands in her pockets. Devin headed toward the smaller enclosure with the plate of cookies. She set the plate on a tree stump, away from Taco. She climbed through the fence and approached the horse with an outstretched hand. He pressed his nose into it and twitched his lips as if searching for food. "Treats come later," she said. She rubbed his nose and lightly scratched the side of his face, holding his gaze. "You gonna be a good boy for Alice, eh?"

He lifted his head upwards and nickered softly. She scratched his neck and ran her hand over his shoulder, turning as Ella approached with Alice. Cody remained with Rocky, against the larger corral fence.

Devin smiled. "You must be Alice. I'm Devin. Pleased to meet you."

Alice stood close to Ella's side, almost matching her in height. She stared at Devin, unblinking. Her skin looked sallow, and her lips were set in a thin line as if she'd forgotten how to smile. Ella took Alice's hand.

"Do you like horses?" Devin asked.

Alice nodded.

"That's good. This is Taco. Taco, this is Alice." She ran her hand down his neck and looked from the horse to Alice. Taco whinnied and nodded his head. "He says hi."

Alice gave a half smile and her cheeks colored.

"You want to pet him?"

Alice moved closer to Ella.

"He won't bite you." Devin pulled out a treat from her pocket and held it out in the flat of her hand. He nibbled it away. "Do you want to try? He likes lots of treats. We can't give him too many though or he'll get gassy."

Alice chuckled. Devin handed Alice a treat, and she held it out to Taco. She drew her hand back quickly after the horse took the treat.

"He needs a good brush. You think you can help me?"

Alice looked at Ella, who smiled and nodded. "Sure." She climbed through the fence to join Devin.

"Shall we let Miss Ella go for a ride with Cody?" Devin asked. "We have some work to do here and then you can have a ride on Taco, if you like?"

Alice glanced at Ella again. "Sure."

"If you're sure?" Ella asked.

"I think we'll do just fine, don't you, Alice?" Devin handed her a brush, picked up another, and started to move it across Taco's hind quarters. "Brush along the line of his coat, like this."

Taco flicked his tail, and Alice brushed along the line of his neck. Ella headed back across the yard toward Cody.

"So, Taco is the same age as you. He's an—"

"Appaloosa. That's why he has this spotted back and a brown neck and face."

"You know about horses?"

"A bit."

"Well, like you, he's courageous, smart, and he has a great personality. He's also loyal and friendly. If he likes you, you'll be best buddies for life."

Taco nudged Alice's arm. "Does that mean he likes me?"

"You hear that chuffing noise he's making?"

Alice nodded as she scratched his neck.

"It's called a nicker. That means he likes you. And you scratching him like that is one of his favorite things."

"He has hazel eyes like me."

Devin's heart warmed as she watched Alice making friends with Taco. She seemed at home with him, as if she'd been around horses before. Alice brushed along his back with long easy strokes and talked to him with tenderness and affection. He stood perfectly still for her, occasionally flicking his tail in gratitude. Devin took the hoof pick and showed Alice how to encourage him to lift his leg and dig out the dirt from his hooves.

When Devin looked up from finishing his last hoof, she saw Maddie at the front of the house. Devin's heart skipped a beat. *She's okay.* Now Devin would be able to relax. She touched the bill of her ballcap to Maddie then gave her attention back to the task, releasing a long breath that relieved the tension that had crept into her neck.

"Can I give him a treat?"

"For sure." Devin handed Alice a couple from her pocket. When she looked back toward the house, Maddie had disappeared, and a dull ache emerged behind Devin's ribs. She took a deep breath and settled the unwarranted urgency that had driven her to want to talk with Maddie. There would be plenty of time to chat during her stay. She turned her attention to Alice and patted her gently on the shoulder. "You've done a great job. Shall we saddle him up and take a ride?" The pure joy and excitement in Alice's expression warmed her heart. Devin was blessed to be able to have a positive impact on Alice's otherwise troubled life. She ruffled Alice's hair and the warmth in her chest expanded. "Come on. I'll show you somewhere secret."

5.

MADDIE STOOD ON THE balcony at the rear of the house and sipped chilled lemon tea as she watched Devin and the young girl ride out. A gentle tremor still flowed through her hands. The combination of a sudden withdrawal from the habitual drinking she'd used to numb her feelings and the effects of extreme tiredness wasn't a good one. Another twenty-four hours and she'd be feeling something closer to human.

She'd never slept for sixteen hours straight before, and she'd woken with a splitting headache. Two Tylenol and a couple of glasses of water had taken the edge off the throbbing and the fresh air as she wandered around the ranch had reduced it to a dull ache. Enjoying the serenity had quieted her obsessive thoughts about the hospital, and she'd started to hear the birds chirping and the horses snorting as they grazed.

She'd talked to Lizzy as she'd walked, told her how much she would have loved it here and enjoyed the stillness in her mind and softness in her heart. Rosie had offered to make her a sandwich, but she still hadn't rediscovered her appetite. The lemon iced tea was totally refreshing though.

Devin looked at ease riding the tall dark bay horse without a saddle. She held the reins in one hand and pointed and gesticulated with her other hand. Maddie followed Devin's animated directions to see if she could work out what she might be referring to. That they were too far away to be heard was frustrating because she wanted to discover more about this way of living. *What did they talk about here apart from horses and classic car renovation?*

In New York, she would discuss medicine, politics, and science, and occasionally religion and ethics with her colleagues. Whenever they went for a drink after work, they talked about the events of the day. It was an easy way to educate the residents. The culture at the hospital was evident in where certain personalities sat on the organization chart. Those who gave their life to the job rose the highest. She might not be as intelligent as some of the consultants she'd worked with, but she'd chosen one of the toughest medical disciplines to work in and she was one of the best at her job. Status and intellect meant everything and in the absence of both she had nothing. She was nothing. *Damn it.* She missed Lizzy so much.

She watched Devin and the girl, and mild irritation riled her thoughts. *Didn't they have more productive things to do?* She sipped the tea and, reminded of her need to chill out, she tried to settle with the tranquility that surrounded her. If she were honest, and maybe this was a part of the reason she felt unsettled, she was a little bit intrigued by Devin. She had a quietly confident aura about her that was easy to be around. She had to be one of the most chilled-out people she'd ever met, and her family had been welcoming and appeared equally as laid back. Perhaps the next month wouldn't be so bad. It had certainly helped her relax a little already. Tiredness had struck her like a tornado yesterday evening, as if she'd literally run into a brick wall, all expectations suspended and with no place to go and nothing that needed doing. She'd barely been able to think by the time her head hit the pillow. *A month of this*, the driven voice in her head persisted.

You don't have time to sit around, Maddie. You're letting the team down. The movie that played out in her mind obscured the view out the window. A stretcher was being carried into the ER with measured urgency. Multiple voices, details, instructions, and the swift well-rehearsed actions that came together as the crew set to work on preserving the fading life before them. She should be there now, supporting her colleagues and helping to save that life. The lemon tea curdled in her stomach. *A month is too long to be away. Someone else will replace you.* Her heart thundered and sweat beaded across her forehead. "You deserve this break, sweetheart." Lizzy's whispered voice was gently encouraging but the anxiety lingered in the tight ball in her stomach. This was exactly why she hadn't wanted to take a vacation. She didn't need her conscience reminding her of her fears. She put down the cup and fought the vivid impression that she should be in New York to draw her thoughts back into the moment.

The girl's horse was smaller, and she rode with a saddle. She sat stiffly and bounced up and down whereas Devin moved lazily with the rhythm of the horse's motion. She'd watched Devin showing the girl how to clean the horse's hooves and brush his coat in the corral. She'd seen tenderness in the way Devin had encouraged her protégé with enthusiasm and positivity, and it was clear she cared from the way she'd smiled. Maddie had studied the girl a little too. She seemed eager to take in everything Devin said. They seemed happy. Were people too busy to look that happy in New York?

As the horses changed direction, she noticed the lead line that attached the girl's horse to Devin's. Maddie would feel safe learning to ride with Devin at her side. Maybe she would give it a try in a day or two when she was feeling more settled. The horses started to trot. The girl bounced around like a rubber ball on a hard surface for a while before finding her stride. She rose and sat in a repeating pattern, and Devin applauded while riding alongside her. The horses shifted back into a walk, and they both turned toward the house.

Maddie exited the balcony into her room and sat on her bed. *You should be at work.* She stared at her shaking hands. What use would she be in this state? She laid down on the bed and the room started to spin. She closed her eyes and waited for it to stop. She would wait for the trembling to abate and take a long, cool shower. She lay for a while, drifting in and out of sleep, in and out of thought, and when she rallied herself, the sun had started to go down. She quickly dressed in jeans, a loose-fitting shirt, and her hiking boots and headed downstairs.

The delicious smell of sweet roasted meat stirred her appetite. She drifted toward the dining room and the sound of laughter, a little hesitant because she'd missed the first meals of her stay and not met any of the other guests—not that she wanted to meet anyone else. She hoped her absence hadn't come across as rude. Rosie and Devin had said, "Come and go as you please," and she didn't think they'd bear a grudge. Had she been staying at her parents' house, skipping meals would have been considered disrespectful. Her mamá would have given her a piece of her mind, and her padre would have studied her over the top of his newspaper with a look that Maddie could only describe as disappointment. No matter how hard she tried to rid herself of their influence, and even after twenty years of not having any contact with them, her stomach still knotted and the urge to justify her earlier absence to Devin and Rosie—God knows, to apologize for her existence even—pressured the tip of her tongue.

The conversations continued as she entered the room, and the occupants glanced to her and smiled. She took a deep breath and swallowed down the apology. Devin stood with a man and woman Maddie hadn't seen before and the woman who had been training the horse when she arrived. Two other women came and went from the kitchen and placed food on the table. An elderly man came in with a wooden tray carrying bottles of beer, glasses, and a pitcher of water, and he approached Maddie.

"Welcome to Wild Horse Ranch. I'm Joe, Devin, Jeana, and Ruby's dad. I think you've met Devin. Jeana and Ruby, there, are my other two daughters. They live in town with their own families but pop over to see their old dad from time to time." He nodded toward the kitchen where the two women who had been helping to set the table had gone. "God forgive me, I must've sinned real bad."

He laughed and Maddie didn't stop herself from joining him. He was a handsome, broad set man with a square jaw and a full set of white teeth. His six-pack rippled beneath his tight, white T-shirt. Devin had his physique, though in a cut-down way, where her sisters seemed cast from their mother's physique.

"You want a beer or water?"

"I'll take water, please."

"We have soda too."

"Water's fine, thanks." Maddie took a glass and poured herself a drink.

"I hope the coyotes didn't keep you awake last night."

Maddie shook her head. "I've never slept so well."

"That's what we like to hear. It's the air 'round here. Crashes you early on. Wait till a few days have passed, and you'll feel like a new woman."

Maddie tried not to choke on the water. She wouldn't know what the heck to do with a new woman. "I look forward to that." She caught Devin watching her. She hesitated to walk over to her, though she wanted to be near a familiar face, but Devin excused herself to the group she was with and walked toward Maddie.

"How're you feeling?"

"Much better, thanks. It's so tranquil here." She was being honest, though the tranquility was as disconcerting as it was relaxing, and sleeping well had nothing to do with the quietness and everything to do with her current state of exhaustion. She feared the more she rested and the freer her time, the stronger that nagging voice in her head would become. The shit she'd buried over the years would rear its ugly head. It had already started, and that voice wasn't going to quiet easily. But this was a process she had to go through to heal, and

41

the quicker she accepted the situation for what it was, the sooner she would be fully fit for work.

Devin sipped from her bottle of beer. "Sure is. We call it our piece of heaven."

Maddie wouldn't call it that. It was pretty, but it was too remote. "How long have you lived here?"

"I was born in the house, Dad was too. My great grandpa bought the ranch when he got married, and they moved up here from Tucson. He'd studied as a doctor there. He ended up in horse medicine here as well as tending to the local ranchers who couldn't afford to pay for treatment. He worked alongside a great medicine man for a time and learned some of their traditions, so he got a reputation as a horse whisperer after they settled here."

"He sounds like a wonderful man." Maddie couldn't imagine her padre having that level of compassion for another human being, let alone an animal. She could see that streak of kindness in Devin's dad and in Devin too. It explained the softness in their manner and their sense of rootedness. They were the people of the earth she'd read about, people who were at one with and in nature. She stifled a yawn and allowed the calmness to quiet her mind.

Devin nodded. "I never met him, but he was. It was during the great depression. Times were hard for a lot of folks. I reckon most of what he administered was a placebo but back then, people worked miracles with hope."

Maddie smiled. She guessed they did.

"Can I get you anything?"

"No. Thanks."

"I'm glad you came to dinner. I was beginning to wonder if you were ever coming out of the room." She picked a tortilla chip from the bowl on the table, dipped it in the sauce and popped it into her mouth. "These are good. The sauce is sweet chilli."

Maddie took a chip and ate it. "I was more tired than I realized." She didn't want to talk about that. She'd battled with her desire to return home for the best part of her waking day. She needed some respite, to occupy her time with a pleasant distraction, and to enjoy the evening as best she could. Maybe, at some point, she would feel she could talk to someone but not while the rawness and vulnerability was so close to the surface. She wasn't ready to break down. "The weather is glorious here."

"Hot summers and cool winters. You get the best view of the Milky Way in the whole of the US from here. Did you know that?"

Maddie laughed. "I did *not* know that, no."

"It's a fact. No one believes it until they see it with their own eyes. I bet you can barely see the moon in New York. There's no light pollution here. The night sky is as clear as spring water. It's an open door to the stars."

Maddie took another chip and dipped it in the sauce. They tasted good and her stomach reminded her she was ravenous. "It seems there's a lot to look forward to while I'm here."

"Spencer Hot Springs is twenty miles from here. Great views of the Toiyabe National Forest and the mountains. There's Toquima cave if you want to see the best pictographs ever discovered in North America."

Maddie smiled. Devin's regard for her home territory shone through in her enthusiasm. "Maybe when I can go more than a couple of hours without falling asleep."

"I reckon cities drain the life from you. Most of our guests come from the cities. Don't know of many folks from here who would head to Vegas or LA to de-stress. Mind, they go to spend their hard-earned cash on the slots and come back to recover."

Maddie laughed. "I guess I've never been away from the city long enough to notice."

"Well, you're here now. You'll feel like a new woman in two weeks."

"Funny, your dad said exactly the same thing."

The clanging of a bell caught Maddie's attention and the voices around her quieted.

Rosie smiled at the assembled group. "Supper's up. Fill your boots, lovely people."

Devin gestured toward the table. "After you. You must be famished."

"I am."

"Mom makes the best food this side of Vegas."

"I've been to Vegas. I didn't much care for the food there." Maddie stopped short of saying she could eat a scabby horse right now, in case she offended her hosts, though something told her Devin would be very difficult to offend.

Devin held out a chair for one of the other guests to sit, then held out one for Maddie.

Maddie grabbed at the seat and pulled it clumsily toward her before sitting. Chivalrous gestures weren't something she and Lizzy had engaged in for a long time. She felt slightly awkward and a little spoiled, and a lot out of sorts. "Um, thanks."

Other guests started to serve themselves and the man to her left asked her whether she'd been to the Lehman Caves at Baker yet and told her she must add it to her itinerary. He went on to talk about the historical steam train museum in Ely and managed to link that with the fact that US 50 was originally used for the Pony Express, which was only in operation for eighteen months, and later the Lincoln Highway, which was one of the first transcontinental highway routes for automobiles travelling across the US. He was a library of historical details about the area and seemed to love the sound of his own voice.

She didn't love it, so she tuned him out, picked up a serving spoon, and turned a good-sized helping of pulled pork onto her plate. She took a bread bun from the basket and started to fill it with the meat and toppings. The aroma was like a potent drug, and she needed to slow herself down or she'd look like some rabid wild dog scavenging for food. She took a deep breath and gazed at the people around the table. It was like one large, happy family with no differentiating who was related and who was just passing through. Devin dug into her food as she talked to her dad about Rocky, which Maddie assumed was the horse she'd seen Devin riding earlier. She looked up and winked.

Maddie took a large bite of the pulled pork sandwich and moaned in pleasure. Devin was almost right about Rosie's cooking skills. The food tasted better than anything she'd eaten before period, not just this side of Vegas.

6.

DEVIN DOWNED HER COFFEE and bit into a slice of heavily buttered toast as she walked from the dining room to the kitchen. "I'm headed into town, Mom. D'you need me to get anything?"

"More eggs and muffins, milk and juice. And there's an order of chicken wings and steak waiting to be picked up."

"Okay. I'm heading to Abe's to pick up a couple of things."

"Oh, and your dad needs something for the water pipe that keeps on springing a leak."

She smiled at her mom's exaggeration. "I'll talk to Cody and get it fixed. I'll be back around lunchtime." She plucked a strip of freshly cooked bacon in maple syrup from a plate on the side as she left.

"And don't forget beer and soda."

"Sure." The salty sweet taste tempted her back to the kitchen for a couple more strips but if she did that, she'd likely finish the plate and ruin her appetite for lunch. She licked the fat off her fingers, grabbed her ball cap, and headed to the truck.

"What kept you?" Cody asked, leaning against the back of the truck.

"Mom's bacon. I'm headed into town to get some feed and some things for Mom."

"Want me to come with you?"

"Nah. I'll be back by lunch." Devin picked a bit of bacon from her teeth.

"I'll get Alice mucking out the stables before her ride." Cody kicked back off the tailgate to stand. "You want her on Taco again?"

"Sure." Devin got into the truck. "Need anything?"

"No, I'm all good."

Devin turned the engine and leaned out the open window. "If you get a chance, can you help Dad with that leaking pipe around the back? Mom's on his case. There's a compression joint and bits in the garage. Just shut the water off and switch out the joint."

Cody patted the side of the truck. "Will do."

Devin made her way slowly down the dirt road to the highway. The wild mustangs that gave the ranch its name were grazing on the lower range. She never tired of admiring them. For their size, they moved with elegance and grace. They were one of the last remaining symbols of the Wild West and a huge attraction to the area. Those guests who visited the retreat and appreciated these magnificent wild horses had a good chance of healing from the stresses that had brought them to the ranch in the first place. Her grandpa had always said that to recognize the majesty in nature was the first step to being able to see the failings in a society hell-bent on destroying itself through greed and arrogance. It was a mantra that ran through her blood.

She drove straight down Main Street to the other side of town to Abe's Tack and Feed. Abe, standing outside and leaning over the porch railing, inhaled on a cigarette as Devin approached the barn store. "Hey, Abe. How're you doing?"

He blew out the smoke, crushed the stub into the ground with his heel, and made his way inside the store. "Still this side of the dirt. What can I get ya?"

"A sack of feed. And I'm looking for a riding helmet for Alice."

"The foster kid staying with Pastor Williams?"

Nothing went on in town without Abe noticing it. "That's the one. She's learning to ride, and I thought it'd be good for her to have her own hat."

"Size?"

"Six and five eighths."

Abe headed into the room at the back of the store. Devin wandered to the clothing stand. She didn't know what size feet Alice had but hazarded a guess at a five and a half. She could always return them if they didn't fit. She spotted a pair of light tan leather boots with a white feathered pattern down the leg that she thought Alice might like. A hundred and fifty bucks was a small price to pay for the joy they would bring.

Abe returned with a box and pulled out a black helmet with a narrow rim and a silver stripe across its top from front to back.

"That looks perfect. I'll take a five and a half in these."

Abe squinted as if struggling to see her. "Sure thing." He pottered back into the rear of the shop and returned with the boots. "That Alice is one lucky kid," he said, ringing the prices into the cash register.

"I guess that depends how you look at it. She hasn't got family, Abe."

Abe gave her a toothless grin. "How'd you get to be so smart, Devin? I remember when you were just a babe in your mom's arms. Now look at ya."

"A lot can happen in thirty-nine years. I guess I learned a few things along the way." She pulled out her wallet. "How much do I owe you?"

"The register says four-twenty but with a discount and given it's charity, let's call it three-fifty."

Devin smiled. "You sure about that? You know I'm happy to pay."

Abe pushed the boxes toward her. "And I'm saying it's three-fifty."

"I'll tell Alice you did me a deal because she's a special customer. It'll be good for her to know people are looking out for her."

Abe processed the payment and smiled. "You've got the soul of an angel." He coughed and spluttered, reached into his pocket, and pulled out another cigarette.

Devin picked up the boxes and started toward the door. "Best you go light on those, or you'll find yourself in an early grave."

"Ah, I'm long since past my sell-by date. Every day's a bonus. Ain't no stoppin' smokin' gonna save me from the inevitable." He laughed through a chesty cough. "Don't forget your sack of feed."

Devin laughed. He was right. He'd made his choices a long time ago and any drastic changes now would be likely to cause him more stress than they would add any value to his life. She put the boxes on the passenger seat and a warm feeling settled in her chest. She hoped Alice loved them. Ella would be mad at her, though only for a short while. This wasn't about Devin getting close to the kid, it was about doing right by her, helping her to feel good and know that she mattered. Feeling loved was what all kids in Alice's position wanted and maybe the gifts might go some way to helping Alice feel special.

She got a sack of feed from the pile at the front of the store, threw it into the back of the truck, and headed back toward the center of town. She'd pick up the groceries and grab a coffee before heading back to the ranch. She pulled up outside the convenience store and went inside, trying to recall everything on the list her mom had called out.

"Morning, Devin. How's your mom?" Frank asked.

Frank had owned and managed the family business since not long after leaving school. A widower for more than twenty years, he'd had a soft spot for her mom even when he was married and if anything happened to her dad, Devin suspected Frank would be the one to come calling with an offer to look after her. Her mom didn't need looking after though, so she didn't like Frank's chances much. "She's good. So is Dad."

"Anything you can't see that you need, just ask." Frank scuttled away as if chastised.

Devin moved up and down the store ticking off the items as she gathered them into the basket: eggs, bacon, milk, juice, muffins. She spied a box of pancake mix and threw that in for good measure. Perhaps Maddie would be tempted by them. She lifted the basket onto the counter. "Add me twenty-four beers and twelve sodas, Frank."

"Sure." Frank put everything into a paper bag. "That's a hundred and eight fifty-six. I'll bring the cans out to you."

Devin scooped up the groceries and headed to the door. She eased it open with her boot and stepped into the street.

"I thought that was your truck."

Maddie. Heat flooded her body. "Oh, hi. I didn't expect to see you here."

"I thought I'd do a little exploring. This is quaint."

Devin looked around at the familiar buildings and the quiet street. "The living ghost town." She laughed. "I was just going to grab a coffee."

Frank approached with the beer and soda and loaded them onto her truck. Devin put the groceries on the floor of the passenger seat.

"So, coffee. Can I tag along?" Maddie smiled.

"Sure." She'd been silent for too long, staring in a mindless state of admiration at Maddie's tight-fitting jeans and the dark blue shirt that matched her eyes. Maddie's appearance had changed a little already. She still carried her shoulders too high but the dark rings under her eyes seemed lighter and she appeared less self-absorbed. It was good to see her out and about. Hopefully the mountain air would do its thing and she'd be able to take full advantage of her stay. Devin jolted herself into action. "That saloon does the best breakfast—"

"This side of Vegas?"

Devin laughed. "It's the best in town, for sure. My mom's is the best this side of Vegas." She winked and heat moved up her neck and into her cheeks. Maddie was looking at her, and Devin couldn't read her thoughts. She turned away and led Maddie to the café, relieved at the light breeze that cooled her.

7.

"COFFEE COMES IN TWO shades, dark or light?" Devin pointed to a stool at a small round table.

"No chance of a macchiato or a cappuccino?" Maddie tried not to react to the sawdust on the floor, and the smell of dry grass, sweat, and stale beer. The bar stretched the length of the room, and small tables with stools were dotted around the remaining space. A fan that hung from the ceiling by a metal chain in the center of the room, turned precariously, wafting warm air. She would avoid the table directly beneath it and the other two tables within landing distance should the fan fall while rotating.

Devin pinched her lips as she shook her head. "No fancy coffee, I'm afraid. Comes stronger than road tar and straight out of the pot. The milk comes cold and straight out of the—"

"Cow." Maddie half expected one to be feeding at the other end of the bar.

Devin laughed. "Straight out of the jug."

Maddie laughed. "With a dash of milk, thanks."

"Tell me when?" Devin pinched her finger and thumb together then started to separate them slowly.

"Stop. That'll do fine."

While Devin went to the bar, Maddie took a seat by the window and smiled at the neon sign on the wall that flashed at her, *Free Beer Tomorrow*. Two men at the farthest end of the bar, wearing black Stetson hats, played cards. A jukebox in the corner made an odd scratching noise. She watched the vinyl record collected and positioned, and the needle lowered. Billie Jo Spears singing "Blanket on the Ground" came to life and sounded almost as good as Damien Rice's version.

In the far corner, a young kid, maybe sixteen or seventeen, played a pinball machine that competed with the jukebox. She couldn't believe saloons like this still existed. The dust on the inside of the windows made them opaque, and cobwebs spanned from beam to beam and in the corners of the ceiling. They clearly followed a different set of hygiene regulations from New York bars. Not that the tables appeared dirty, it was just that the place looked like the dust and dirt from the outside had made its way inside and that the wildlife were as welcome as the paying guests. It was an authentic Wild West-style saloon in the same way Paddy Reilly's was an authentic Irish pub. Locals drank here, and yet the atmosphere was different from Paddy's place in a way that she couldn't define. Maybe it was the sense of community linked to the history of Austin that was different. Whatever it was, it was wonderful.

Maddie drew her attention to Devin as she carried two mugs of coffee toward their table.

"Do you want breakfast?" Devin put the drinks on the table and sat.

"No, I'm fine with coffee, thanks." She cupped both hands around the mug and sipped her drink. The inside of her mouth constricted as if she'd just bitten into a lemon. "Wow, that is strong."

"Yup, like the kick of an angry mule."

Devin drank her coffee black with a single sugar cube that she didn't bother to stir into the drink. She didn't seem to bat an eyelid at the bitterness that had gripped Maddie's throat either. "How many people live in Austin?"

Devin tilted her head from side to side. "About three hundred. The tally goes down quicker than it goes up, what with the number of older folks."

"Austin is what, just under two square miles? That's a hundred and fifty people per square mile. Manhattan alone has thirty-five and a half thousand people in a square mile." Population density was one of the stats that had always stuck with Maddie. It was one of the factors that dictated the

54

probability and numbers of ER incidents on any day of the week. What did the local doctors do here to occupy their time? She couldn't imagine working in a hospital where the pace wasn't too fast to even have time to think about anything other than the needs of the casualty on the stretcher.

"That's insane. No wonder city folks are so beat." Devin shook her head. "That's too many people all sitting too close, like caged animals. That's not for me." She frowned. "How do you cope with it?"

Maddie sipped her coffee. "You just get used to it, I guess. How do you cope with living here?"

Devin shrugged. "What's there to cope with?"

"The slow pace of life. I mean, other than horses and restoring old cars, what do you do for entertainment?" She felt like a bit of a fraud asking the question, since her own social life had revolved around Paddy Reilly's pub for so long it could hardly classify as entertainment. She hadn't been to a concert or a ball game since a few years before Lizzy died but those events were a possibility in New York. Here, any event would involve a day of travelling to get to and from.

Devin laughed. "Let's see. There's the dance once a month at the school. We have the rodeo every other weekend at one of the ranches, with home cooked food and races for the kids. The fair comes around from time to time. There's the annual car rally in Reno, skiing in the winter if you like that kinda thing, and a lot of history to discover. And that doesn't include the activities put on for tourists. Thing is, no one here's in a rush to get anywhere. You can get involved or not, and no one judges you for it. Life rolls on faster when you're chasing a dream than it does when you're living the life you've got."

Maddie raised her eyebrows. "You dance?" She imagined Devin line-dancing or square-dancing with a piece of straw in her mouth. She thought about when she'd danced with Lizzy and how wonderful it was to hold her close, and then her thoughts drifted to the last time she'd held her in her arms. Her smile disappeared.

"Of course. Dancing's like riding. It's as natural as the wind blowing or the sun shining. Everyone here dances."

Maddie couldn't imagine everyone in Manhattan dancing, let alone in New York. There was something frivolous about the Country and Western style that she imagined took place here. The people she knew in New York were too serious, too intense. The idea of this small community enjoying themselves together, like one big happy family, awoke something inside her that she hadn't realized she'd been missing. "It sounds delightful."

"There's a dance this weekend if you want to come along. It's causal, so no need to dress up. I mean, if you're feeling up to it."

Maddie smiled. "Maybe I will."

Devin leaned back in her chair. "What's it like being a doctor in a city that busy?"

"It's tough. I work in the ER at Bellevue."

"Isn't that the place the President got treated?"

She nodded. "It has a reputation for being at the forefront of medical advances, so it's a popular choice. It's a public hospital funded by the government. We take care of the homeless and disadvantaged too, though I think the media prefer to focus on the rich and famous who visit." Now she was sounding serious and defensive when a simple yes would have sufficed.

"Helping those less fortunate is good. Have you treated anyone rich and famous?"

The image of her last patient startled Maddie for a moment. She'd been wealthy but not famous. "Yes, I have."

"It must be nerve-racking, all those expectations on you?"

Maddie had never thought about it that way. "A life is a life. The medicine is the same. We try not to think about who we're treating."

Devin shook her head. "Yeah, but when it comes down to it, some lives are still worth more than others. I think the pressure of trying to save a president's life would be a lot higher than for someone who isn't in the public eye."

Maddie had led the team who had treated Pope Benedict XVI when he'd collapsed with a heart attack while on a visit to the city a few years earlier. Medical procedures and processes certainly focused one's attention, but they didn't stop the heightened sensitization to the consequences if the important man on the table died in their care. The whole world would know, and the potential for being hauled into the spotlight and having one's competence investigated was frighteningly high. She hadn't gone into a career in medicine to be the headline news for losing someone perceptibly important to the world. "You're right. It is different."

"I couldn't do it even if I was smart enough, which I'm not."

Maddie smiled. Everyone had different skills and talents. "Passion is what drove me."

"My passion is horses."

Maddie smiled. "And helping people to heal."

Devin finished the last of her coffee. "Sometimes people have to learn to heal themselves."

The words jarred. Devin had no idea how close she was to Maddie's personal truth. The medical services she provided as an ER physician couldn't help her heal from the emotional and mental trauma that she'd suffered in her life and buried deeply. She'd always thought of herself as resilient, and on the surface, she was. Even throughout the whole thing with Lizzy, she'd been strong and never faltered in her work. But she hadn't let go, had she? Her parents still haunted her. And she still hated herself for losing Lizzy. Lee had said she had to deal with her crap. She was right, and so was Devin.

"We provide a space that gives visitors an opportunity to reflect at the ranch, but..." Devin stopped talking and lowered her head. "Sorry, I'm preaching and you're a guest. I didn't mean to imply—"

"No, you're right. My colleague in New York reminded me of the same point before I left." *Physician, heal thy self.* Maddie had failed miserably. She could stop someone bleeding and she could start a heart or set a bone, and she could administer drugs that might save someone's life, but when it came to emotional trauma, she was the wrong person to take advice from. "I think you know more about emotional healing than I do."

Devin half smiled. "I don't think so, doc."

Maddie stared at her coffee. If she drank any more, she'd end up flying back to the ranch. "Your mom said you teach riding."

"Mostly to the kids from school. Many of our guests come to take advantage of the facilities at the ranch, but they don't need lessons."

Maddie hadn't come on the retreat with the intention of learning to ride. She hadn't given the vacation much thought at all. Now she was here, she might as well make the most of it. She had reservations though. The horses were big and strong, and she didn't feel that comfortable up close to them. She looked directly at Devin and summoned the courage to ask, "Will you teach me?"

Devin smiled. "Sure. I didn't think you were too crazy about horses. Most folks come straight into the yard to see them as soon as they arrive."

"I'm not."

Devin's eyes widened and her smile disappeared.

Maddie sensed she'd disappointed her, and her stomach dropped like lead. "I mean, I've never been around horses before. I saw the ones running wild on the way into town. They were stunning, and there was something about them that was quite compelling. I'd like to see what it's like to sit on one."

Devin's smile returned. "That was the wild mustangs you saw. They're a different breed altogether. Alice is coming over this afternoon and then we have to mend the fencing, but I can show you around before supper, if you like?"

Maddie held Devin's gaze as her stomach recovered itself, and her pulse increased at the thought of a lesson. "I would, thanks."

Lizzy would think she was crazy getting on a horse, since she could barely ride a bicycle, but Maddie was in good hands with Devin, and she felt surprisingly drawn to discover more about the healing power of horses. Now that she was a little more alert and intent on chilling out, staying active would help to keep her mind off worrying about work. She owed it to the team back at Bellevue to return fully fit and focused, and given how laid back it was at the ranch, if she couldn't achieve that here, then she probably couldn't achieve it anywhere.

8.

CODY SNIFFED AND TURNED up her nose as Devin approached her outside the stables. "What are you smelling so sweet for? The dance isn't till Saturday. Anyone would think you just stepped out from one of those brothels off the highway."

Devin slapped Cody's arm. "I was hot and needed to freshen up. Maybe you could take a hint."

Cody sniffed at her armpit and shrugged.

"See what I mean? Anyway, there's only one of us here who knows what the inside of a brothel smells like." Devin raised her eyebrows and grinned.

Cody held out her hands. "Hey, I went with Jessie long before she ended up going down that path. That was more than fifteen years ago." She narrowed her eyes and shook her head. "I wonder what happened to her?"

Devin didn't want to think about what might have happened to Jessie. Nothing good ever came of that kind of career, from what she knew. Jessie had been a pretty girl too, and smart enough to have had other options if it hadn't been for her dad, who'd been a gambler and a drunk, and her mom, who'd left home when Jessie was just a kid. She hadn't had much of a chance at a decent life, poor kid. "You fixed the leak?"

"Yeah, I replaced the joint and the pipe."

Devin nodded. "Thanks." She looked toward the smaller stall where the grey dapple mare, Dolly, was pacing the fence line.

"She's heading into labor."

"Yeah, she's restless and pawing. I'll wrap her tail and keep a close eye on her."

Devin checked her watch. The birth would be a couple of hours away, possibly a bit less. "Alice will be here shortly, and I promised I'd show one of the guests around the place later."

Cody pointed down the track. "Alice is heading this way now."

Cody's smile grew and her expression softened as the car drew closer. Devin had experienced the same thing when she'd run into Maddie outside the convenience store. The time they'd spent drinking coffee had passed too quickly and when they'd parted ways, Devin hadn't been able to think about anything other than Maddie. She still looked burned out but at least she was up and about and eager to explore the area. Maybe she'd like to see a foal being born. She turned toward the house. Maddie's car wasn't in the driveway. She hoped Maddie would be back in time.

Devin went to the truck and pulled out the boots and hat box as Ella stopped the car in front of the house. "Good day to you, Miss Alice."

"Hi," Alice said but her attention was clearly drawn to the horses.

Ella glanced at the boxes in Devin's hand and shook her head. "Been shopping?"

Devin shrugged. She expected a hard time from Ella about buying Alice gifts, but these were more like necessities. She looked down at the sneakers on her feet. "They won't do for riding."

Alice followed Devin's gaze to her feet. "They're all I've got."

Devin nodded. "Hm, that's what I figured." She held out the flatter of the two boxes. "When I was in town today, I happened to find just the thing with a little help from a man called Abe. Here, see if these fit."

Alice took the box and stared at it in her hands for a long time, her frown deepening. "These are for me?"

"For sure."

"But…" She looked toward Ella. "I can't pay for them."

Devin shook her head. "I don't want you to pay for them. They're yours. This one too." She put the second box at Alice's feet. "It's for safety, and to make sure you have the right equipment that fits." The last bit was an exaggeration. They had a large range of hats at the ranch that Alice could have borrowed, and boots too. Heat flushed her cheeks. "They're for you to keep. Then wherever you ride, you'll have something to wear."

A smile spread quickly across Alice's face. She ripped into the box and lifted a boot. She stared from the boot to Devin to Ella and back to Devin with her mouth and eyes wide open.

Ella linked her arm through Devin's. She gave Devin her "That's a very extravagant gift," look, but the way she squeezed Devin's arm said that she couldn't be more thrilled.

Alice turned the boots in her hand, ran her fingers over the stitching, and worked the zipper. "Wow. They're awesome, and just like yours."

Devin looked down at her own boots. She hadn't intended on the resemblance when she was in the shop. The pattern was slightly different, but the tan color and the steel toed style was identical. "You'd better try them on and make sure they fit well. You've got a lot of mucking out to do today."

Alice held the boot close to her chest. "That'll ruin them."

Devin laughed. "That's what those boots are made for. That and riding. So, cowgirl, get your boots on, and let's get to work."

Alice kicked off her sneakers and put Devin's gift on. She stamped her heels to the ground and nodded. "They feel fine."

"Good." Devin pointed to the other box. "You'll need that too."

When Alice opened it, her jaw dropped and when she looked up her eyes were wet with tears. "It's beautiful."

She put the helmet on, and Devin adjusted the strap. "Fits you perfectly. You're ready to go."

Alice sniffed, wiped her eyes, and nodded.

"And what do you think about seeing a foal born?"

Alice gasped. "Really?"

"For sure. You see Dolly over there acting strange?" Devin pointed to where Dolly was rolling on the ground in the foaling stall next to the smaller corral. "She's in labor, so I reckon a foal is coming just as soon as we've finished mucking out. Come on." She turned and headed toward the barn. "We need the shovels and cart."

"I'll go and help Cody," Ella said.

Devin turned and smiled. "She'll like that."

Devin had kept one eye on Dolly as they'd made their way around the larger corral clearing horse muck. Rocky had shown an interest in Devin and Alice initially but wandered off and continued grazing with Taco and Cookie. They'd been working steadily for an hour, and Devin was parched. She leaned on her shovel and watched Alice strain to lift the muck into the cart. Her heart warmed at her enthusiasm and persistence. "How're you liking the school here?"

Alice continued to shovel. "It's good."

"Have you made friends?"

Alice shrugged. "Some."

"What about Pastor Williams's kids?"

"It's okay. They're all busy. I like to read in my room."

Something didn't feel right. "They're treating you okay?"

Alice smiled, though her eyes lacked the sparkle they'd had when she'd opened the boxes. Not every occasion was worthy of excitement, of course, but Devin would expect Alice to be a little more upbeat when talking about the pastor and his family.

"They treat me fine." Alice looked away. She walked toward the horse manure and shoveled it into the cart.

It was clear that Alice wasn't happy. It must be difficult for the kid, not being able to settle because she was going to be on the move again before she knew it. The pastor and his family were good people, but it wasn't the same as Alice being with her own family. And with five of his own kids, Devin doubted either he or his wife had any quality time to give to anyone else. "School's nearly out and there's the summer vacation to have lots of fun, but promise me, if you're not happy, you speak to Ella, okay?"

Alice smiled. "I promise." Her cheeks were red from the heat and exercise and her lips looked dry.

"Are you ready for a drink?"

"Yes, please."

"Come on." Devin led Alice out of the corral. She glanced toward Dolly who was lying down. Cody stood outside the stall with Ella.

"Foal's coming," Cody said as Devin and Alice approached.

Alice stood next to Ella and craned her neck to see the mare.

"I'll go and get some drinks," Devin said and headed to the house. She grabbed a couple of bottles of water and a few cans of soda. "Foal's coming, Mom."

"How wonderful." Her mom took off her apron and washed her hands. "I'm coming."

Devin stepped out of the front door as Maddie drew up.

She got out of the car and smiled. "I hope I'm not late. I went to the hot spring and lost track of time."

Devin's heart started to race. The lesson would have to wait. "You want to see a foal born first?" She motioned toward the corral.

"What, now?"

Devin chuckled, amused by the slightly horrified look that passed across Maddie's face. "Midwifery not your thing, doc?"

Maddie shook her head. "No, that wasn't my thing at med school." She laughed. "But I'd love to see it."

Devin started toward the foaling stall.

"Let me help." Maddie took the cans of soda.

"How were the hot springs?"

"Damn hot."

Devin laughed. "As advertised."

"And very relaxing."

Maddie looked incredible. Devin became aware that Ella was watching her. "Soda or water?" she asked, avoiding Ella's lingering gaze.

"It's coming out," Alice said in a stifled squeal.

Devin handed out the drinks. She'd seen plenty of foals born and would see plenty more. Devin saw awe in Maddie's eyes and when a tear slipped onto her cheek, Devin ached to wipe it away.

Devin waited for the moment the foal would break free. Dolly licked and bit at the tough sac that protected it from the outside world, finally splitting it. The foal tried to lift its head, a sign that it was breathing and alert. Dolly bit at the cord between them and sniffed at the foal's silky wet dark coat. It would be clear sailing from here. Cody would keep a watch over mom and baby until the placenta had been delivered and the pair had settled together. "What shall we call him, Alice?"

Alice didn't break eye contact with the colt who fought to try to stand. "It looks like a rain cloud."

Maddie smiled.

"It's because he's all wet. He'll lighten up when he's dry." Maddie pointed out the lighter colored streak down his nose and the marks across her back. "You can see some of his white markings showing through."

"I think he looks like a lightning storm."

"Lightning Storm. That's a great name."

Alice nodded. "He'll be fast like lightning."

Devin caught Maddie's glance, something in her eyes that she couldn't define. Whatever it was, it took her breath away. "Lightning Storm, it is," she said, a slight tremble in her voice. She drank her water and enjoyed watching the sun reveal the rich red colors that danced through Maddie's hair, and she wished Maddie would be here to see the Nevada fall. She bit her lip. She needed to refocus before they started their lesson.

9.

MADDIE COULDN'T TAKE HER eyes off the foal as it honed its instincts. It rolled and wriggled on the ground, cleaning its coat in the straw and dust. It found its balance and stood with a wobble and a sway. It looked around with quick, uncoordinated movements that caused it to topple, before it tried to stand again. She couldn't imagine what giving life felt like for the mare, but if it was anything like the exhilaration that came with watching the birth, maybe she should have considered midwifery as an option after all.

Her job was all about saving lives, not bringing new life into the world. Her heart had raced when the foal appeared, and she melted as the foal broke out of the sac. Something shifted inside her. The vulnerability she'd experienced watching the foal find its way into this life wasn't anything to do with the fragility of it being a living being in the physical sense. It was something deeper that had touched her, connected her with the magic of life, the inexplicable reality that no amount of logic or reasoning could explain to her fickle human mind. She felt the profundity of the moment in the gentle tremor that rocked her. She turned to find Devin smiling at her. "I've never experienced anything as special. Thank you."

Devin nodded. "It was something, huh? Lightning will be up and about in no time. He's strong willed, you can see it in the way he takes in the world. He'll be fearless."

Maddie studied the foal. "You can tell that?"

"Yep. He's frisky and curious. Dolly's reacting well to him."

Maddie saw genuine affection in Devin's eyes as she watched the horses.

69

"We'd better get going, Alice," the other woman said and touched Devin's forearm. "That was beautiful. Thank you." She turned to Maddie and held out her hand. "Hi, I'm Ella."

Her grip was light, and her hand warm and soft. "I'm Maddie."

"Nice to meet you. Are you here on vacation?"

"Yes." Maddie hadn't thought of the retreat as a real vacation. For that, she might have gone sightseeing in Europe, or to Las Vegas for the buzz. She wasn't going to say that she was on a retreat for a much-needed respite from her work and to de-stress after the mental and emotional hell she'd been through caring for Lizzy.

"I'm sure you'll have a wonderful time," Ella said before she turned to the young girl. "Come on, Alice. We need to let these good people get on now."

Alice looked at Devin with a slight frown. "Can I stay a bit longer?"

Devin put her hand on Alice's shoulder and looked into her eyes. "You know how new babies like to sleep a lot when they're first born? Foals need a little space and time to themselves too. You can come and see him again tomorrow—and the next day."

Alice grinned and nodded. "Can we come earlier tomorrow?"

Devin smiled at Ella, and Maddie sensed their closeness. Devin was different with her than she was with Cody, softer. Perhaps Ella was Devin's girlfriend? Maddie saw something akin to deep admiration in her expression.

Devin held Alice's gaze and unclipped her hat. "That depends on what else you've got going on, since school's out for the summer soon. You should talk to Ella and let me know. We're here, and there's plenty of work to do. Maybe Ella would like to go for another ride?" She winked at Alice conspiratorially, as if they were in cahoots together and creating a cunning plan to get Alice back to the ranch as early as possible.

Alice turned to Ella. "Can we?"

Ella lifted Alice's hat from her head. "Let's check with Pastor Williams when we get back."

Alice lowered her chin, her smile fading a little. She took her hat from Ella and looked at Devin. "Thank you for my gifts."

Maddie noted the quality of the boots and hat, and the joy in Alice's expression as she hugged the hat close to her chest. They were a very generous gift. Devin stood casually with her hands on her hips.

"You're very welcome. You be sure to wear them tomorrow. Would you like to ride Taco again?"

Alice looked toward the foal.

Devin laughed. "It'll be a while before Lightning can be ridden. He needs to get much bigger and stronger."

"Come on, Alice. We need to get you home."

Ella led Alice to the car, and they disappeared down the dirt road. Maddie became aware that Devin was watching her. "They're sweet," she said.

"Ella is Alice's schoolteacher in Austin. She's got a big heart. Alice has only just started coming here. She's in temporary foster care. Being around the horses helps kids like her with their emotional difficulties." She stared down the road. "They are sweet."

The tremor Maddie had experienced earlier returned. She wrapped her arms around her body. "You're very gracious."

Devin gave a thin-lipped smile and tilted her head toward the large corral. "Are you ready for your lesson?"

The horses suddenly looked huge, especially the dark chestnut one. The spotted one Alice had ridden was the smallest, and even that looked tall as Maddie got closer. She wouldn't describe the rush of adrenaline as a feeling of readiness. More like abject fear. She stood a short distance from the corral, watching the horses, her pulse racing. The lighter brown horse looked up from grazing then continued with its business. The other two made their way toward Devin as she entered the enclosure.

"This is Rocky. His full name is Rock My Heart." She scratched his neck as he nudged her. "He's seven years old and a bit of a handful, but he's a champion barrel racer."

He seemed to scrutinize Maddie through his dark chocolate brown eyes for a long time. His coat shone and his muscle structure was well defined. Aside from the fleeting thought that he could easily crush Maddie with his strength, he appeared quite gentlemanly. "He's striking." Maddie saw esteem and affection in the way Devin handled him.

"He's stunning." Devin patted the spotted horse's shoulder. "This here is Taco. Taco Bell is his full name."

Maddie smiled. "After the restaurant chain?"

Devin shrugged. "It was Cody's choice. She's a big fan. It's the only restaurant she'll eat at when we're in Reno."

Maddie laughed. "I'm a fan too."

Devin smiled. "Come and say hello."

Maddie was happier standing at a distance and asking questions. She was genuinely interested, just stalling from getting on any of the horses. "What's the light brown one called?"

Devin looked toward the grazing horse. "That's Cookie, or Cookie Dough."

Maddie wiped her hands down her thighs and crossed them in front of her body. Her heart thundered harder than the herd of mustangs she'd seen racing across the desert. She was running out of horses to ask questions about. "Who likes cookies?"

Devin grinned. "Me. Cookie Dough ice cream is my favorite too."

Maddie looked across to the mare and foal. "And you have Dolly."

"Yep, Dolly Parton, one of the greatest singers that ever lived."

Maddie stopped herself from disagreeing. Dolly wouldn't hit her top five best singers but that wasn't the issue. If she got into a heated discussion, no matter how trivial, she would likely find an excuse to stop her from getting on the damn horse. Avoidance was a habit she'd perfected to handle the unwanted conflict she'd been subjected to with her parents over the years. She didn't want to kick off her stay at the ranch by getting into something that might turn into an argument or lead her to distance herself. There was a danger she would clam up completely to avoid dealing with her shit, and the trip would have been an utter waste of her time. She took a deep breath to calm her nerves. She needed to seize the moment, or it might be lost forever, and besides, she was enjoying Devin's easy company. "And now you have Lightning Storm."

"There's another twenty-three horses on the range, aside from the mustangs that run free."

Maddie widened her eyes. "You name them all?"

"Sure do."

Rocky lifted his head and softly snorted through his nose. Maddie jumped and stifled a gasp. Rocky gave her a fleeting glance before moving away. An echo of disappointment left an empty feeling, as if she'd let Rocky down. She should've been braver and now the moment was lost. She lowered her head.

"Don't worry, he'll be back when you're ready. Say hi to Taco. He's more patient than Rocky." Devin rubbed Taco's nose. "Good boy. You're gonna look after Maddie here, aren't you?" Taco rubbed his nose against Devin's arm and moved closer to the fence. "He wants to say hello."

Maddie could barely breathe. Her heart thundered so hard she thought it might spring from her chest. Her mouth was dry, and her hands shook. She closed her eyes and took in a slow deep breath. She could hear what sounded like scratching, clicking noises and Taco snorting through his nose. She could mend people who were badly broken and yet she couldn't move toward a horse who stood on the other side of a fence from her. The thought of being crushed lingered. Alice had ridden Taco. Alice was just a kid. She'd survived. *Maddie, you'll be fine.* Lizzy's voice came to her, soft and encouraging. Her heart eased its attack on her chest, and she opened her eyes. Devin stood in front of her. She couldn't read the look in her eyes, though she felt comforted by it. Devin offered her hand, and she hesitantly took it. Devin's firm grip instilled confidence. "I didn't think I was this scared."

"It's okay. Relax."

Devin looked so still, so calm and unfazed by her extreme reaction. "I know this is totally irrational." She smiled, though it felt weak and disingenuous.

"Take your time," Devin said.

Her tone was softer than Maddie had heard before, and her focus was entirely on Maddie, and yet Maddie didn't feel that the look was intrusive or judgmental. She became aware that she was nodding and that she'd taken a pace closer to Taco.

"Sh." Devin maintained eye contact with Maddie as she stroked Taco's cheek. "There's a good boy," she whispered.

Maddie drew closer and put her hand next to Devin's. The coarseness of Taco's hair distracted her. She'd imagined it to be softer and less bristly. Taco stared at her and looked like he might almost be smiling. He nudged Maddie's arm, and she fought her instinct to move away.

"He likes being scratched," Devin said.

"O-kay." Maddie scratched his cheek.

Devin smiled. "How're you feeling?"

The trembling had abated though her heart still pumped as if she'd just run a hundred-yard sprint. "Fine." She held Devin's gaze, grateful for the fact that she'd been there for her. "I couldn't have done it without you."

Devin nodded. "You will."

Maddie had only once in her life felt fear as deeply as she just had. When her parents had disowned her for being a lesbian, she'd experienced intense anger and frustration. She'd felt misunderstood and condemned for a crime that was apparently so shocking and disgusting that it had warranted her expulsion from the family and her home. When she'd doubted herself at work, questioned her decision-making until the early hours to be sure she'd not fucked up, that guilt would still haunt her.

This fear had nothing to do with Taco or the thought of riding a horse, or her job or family. *This* fear was as gut-wrenchingly debilitating as the fear she'd felt knowing she was losing Lizzy. She took a deep breath, made eye contact with Devin, and smiled. "Thank you." She wouldn't ride today, but she would before she left the ranch. This wasn't about Maddie wanting to prove she was more than a city girl; she needed to do this for Lizzy, to deliver on the promise she'd made to her.

10.

"PASS THE SALT, DEV."

Devin watched Maddie from across the dinner table. She hadn't gotten into conversation with the other guests, her smile looked strained, and she'd picked at her food.

"Dev."

Devin jolted. "Sorry." She passed the salt to Jeana.

Maddie excused herself from the table and stood. They hadn't started dessert, and Maddie had barely touched her main course. Devin picked up her fork and prodded a chunk of steak to stop herself from jumping to her feet and heading out after Maddie. She glanced around the table at the other guests who were digging into their food. If she made an excuse and left, it would look oddly out of character. She'd never missed a dessert in her life. She chewed on the meat and hoped Maddie didn't go straight to bed.

"Hey, daydreamer, pass the fries."

It was Ruby this time. Her sisters had probably already noticed she was distracted and restless. She picked up the basket and passed it down the table.

Cody looked toward the door and back to Devin. She raised her eyebrows and smiled as if she'd discovered Devin's secret. She'd clearly picked up on the changes in Devin's behavior around Maddie.

Devin ignored her and chewed hard on another piece of steak, barely tasting it, aware that her desire to assist vulnerable people was also confused by her extreme concern for Maddie. She was normally good at being teased about her rescuer instinct, but for some reason, this time, it galled. It wasn't that she had an urge to help Maddie, it was more that she had a deep, inexplicable desire to protect her.

She wouldn't be able to settle until she'd seen Maddie. It wasn't just Maddie's response to the horses that had her wondering about her. She'd seen folks when they were unfamiliar with horses. A little anxiety was a good thing, and most new riders overcame it quickly. In the time she'd spent with Maddie today and the way Maddie had talked, she'd gotten the sense that work stress wasn't the only reason Maddie had come on the retreat. She was intrigued to find out more.

Horses were incredibly perceptive. They always sensed whatever it was that troubled a person or held them back, and they reflected it back to them in the way that they communicated. Rocky had remained calm and walked away. He wasn't disinterested in Maddie; he was being respectful. He'd sensed Maddie's fear and that his strength and power would have been too much for her. Taco was a smaller horse, calmer, and tolerant. He'd bowed his head to Maddie and stayed perfectly still to give Maddie the confidence to approach him. Maddie's extreme fear when coming close to Taco had come out of nowhere. It reflected some aspect of her life. And whatever that was, it was intense.

Resisting the urge to take Maddie into her arms and hold her, to chase the fear away, and for Maddie to feel safe had tied Devin in knots. She'd learned that for some people the offer of such comfort could be misinterpreted as affection or attraction, and that led to attachment problems. It was like her getting close to the kids she'd looked after. She'd been destroyed by the heartbreak when they'd left. But that had been her problem, and she'd gotten over it, eventually. It was hard not to get involved sometimes, especially with the kids. Maddie wasn't a kid though, and she wasn't like any other guest. Not even Jaynee. She didn't want to think about that time in her past, but she could see parallels with Maddie. That squeezing sensation in her chest was nothing to do with her desire to rescue. *That* feeling meant something entirely different. And the longing hadn't relented. If anything, it had gotten worse, and in Maddie's absence, it was driving her stir-crazy. She wanted to be around Maddie. She wanted to hold her, not just for Maddie's comfort but for her own. *Shit*. She ran her hand across her brow and through her hair. The pressure from the sensible voice in her head vied with the desperate ache in her heart. This wasn't good.

Maddie's healing needed to come from within, not from Devin's comfort. And given her feelings for Maddie, she needed to tread carefully. She wasn't prepared for complications, and she was pretty sure Maddie didn't need any either. Maddie would talk when, and if, she was ready to do so, and when she did, Devin would be there for her. In the meantime, she had to back off and give Maddie the time and space she needed. The itch that accompanied the longing made the patience she needed hard to find. Maybe she should take Rocky on a long ride and get her act together. A very long ride.

She ate the maple and toffee pie in three bites, excused herself, and stepped into the yard. The sun was slipping slowly into the horizon, providing a sliver of light that would soon disappear. The Milky Way would come to life in the darkness. Maybe Maddie would like to see it. So much for backing off. She couldn't settle. Her heart thumped hard and heavy, and she tuned into the cries of the owls and the chirping of the crickets. She scanned the yard for Maddie. Rocky and Cookie munched the hay in the corral. Lightning stood at his mother's side in the smaller arena. She couldn't see Maddie. *She's a guest. Leave her be*. She dismissed the thought.

Devin headed around the other side of the house and looked toward Maddie's bedroom balcony. The curtains were closed. Maybe, she'd gone to bed early or wanted to rest alone in her room. Devin headed back inside the house and took the stairs two at a time. She stood outside Maddie's bedroom door, listened for a moment, and raised her hand to the door. *What the heck am I doing?* The twisting sensation in her gut tightened. Knocking on a guest's bedroom door in the evening just to ask if they were okay was crazy. She was breaking the biggest retreat house rule, and she couldn't get away from the reason for it. Maddie had touched her heart. She'd felt it when she'd looked up from the garage floor, though she'd told herself it was the surprise that had caused her heart to flutter since she'd expected to see Cody. Again, when she'd bumped into Maddie in town, the warmth had spread in her chest and the tightness in her throat had made it a challenge to speak coherently. All of it was her connection to Maddie. She'd gotten lost in wonder as she'd watched her when they drank coffee together. Watching Maddie enjoy the foal being born had cemented her affections. Seeing Maddie struggle with fear when approaching Taco, a sharp pain had anchored behind her ribs. It had been purgatory letting her go back to her room alone after that.

Devin pressed her ear closer to the door, mindful that she could be spotted if a guest ventured into the hall. Silence. She took a deep breath and headed out into the yard. She'd work on Sally-Ann for a bit and try to take her mind off Maddie, not that she rated her chances of achieving that very highly. Some distraction was better than none.

As she went around the back of the stables and toward the garage, she caught the unexpected sound of crying. *Maddie.* She tracked the sobbing to behind the garage. Maddie gripped the fence and faced out across the fields, her head bowed. Devin's heart sank. She walked slowly toward her, her heart pounding, figuring out what to say and not wanting to unnerve her. "Hey," she said softly.

Maddie lifted her head but didn't turn to face Devin. She sniffed and wiped her face. "Hey."

She sounded frail. Devin leaned on the fence and looked out across the plains, trying to appear relaxed. Being closer to Maddie eased the ache, even if she couldn't find the right words or hold her and take away the pain. "You can just about make out the mustangs." She pointed toward the dark shapes in the distance that would be easy to miss if you didn't know what you were looking for.

Maddie cleared her throat. "They're so free."

Devin tried not to let Maddie's broken voice affect her. She swallowed hard. "And that's a great horned owl you can hear."

"We have barred owls in Manhattan. They sound very different."

Devin scanned Maddie's face. Judging by the puffiness around her eyes, she'd been crying for a while. "Is everything okay?" The tears welled in Maddie's eyes, and she wished she hadn't asked.

"I didn't think I'd break down this quickly."

Maddie laughed, but it seemed forced and laced with self-disgust. There was no shame in showing emotion and it was most often what their guests needed to do to start to heal. Devin nodded. "Emotion needs a voice. It has to be listened to or it turns nasty inside you."

Maddie smiled through the tears. "You're very clever."

"Not really. Horses are the smart ones. You know, they show us where we're at and what we need. We can deceive ourselves, but they know sure enough. Horses are like looking in a mirror." Devin looked away into the distance to give Maddie some thinking time. When she looked up, Maddie's expression had changed. It seemed softer.

Maddie took a deep breath. "Her name was Lizzy." Maddie's gaze wandered, as if she were gathering her thoughts or maybe considering whether she should say any more. "We'd been married ten years."

Devin remained silent, willing Maddie to continue.

She turned away and looked toward the plains. "She was an oncology nurse working in palliative care. She died just over two years ago of breast cancer. She was only thirty-nine." She sighed, though it didn't stop the tears that slid down her face. "She was so very brave, and there was nothing I could do to save her."

Devin's recent ex Cat came to mind, but that wasn't the same thing. They hadn't been together that long, and Cat hadn't died. Their split had been amicable, and in the end, Devin hadn't felt as though she'd lost anyone. Her relationship with Jaynee had been more intense, and they'd planned a future together. Devin had been hurt by her leaving. She was abandoned and betrayed, and for a time she'd hated Jaynee. But Jaynee was still alive, somewhere in the world, and there was comfort in that even if Devin didn't want to be with her. Death was so absolute, and everyone handled loss differently. It was hard to relate to Maddie's experience. "I'm so sorry," she whispered.

"Lizzy knew exactly what was coming to her, with the disease I mean. And yet she was always so fucking accepting and gracious. I was angry. So fucking mad." Maddie rubbed at her eyes. "And I let her down."

Devin frowned. "Because you couldn't save her?"

Maddie remained quiet for a moment. "Because I was so blinded by rage that I didn't give her the precious time and the love that she deserved. I was too wrapped up trying to find a solution that could save her. She'd been treated at Roswell Park, and they'd done all they could, and I wanted her to go to the Abramson Center in Philadelphia. I wanted her to try anything, everything. All she wanted was for me to hold her hand and be at her side, and I couldn't do it. I couldn't sit there and watch her slip away like that, not without fighting for her."

The pie Devin had eaten turned in her stomach. She couldn't picture watching someone she loved die either. "I can't imagine how hard that was."

"We missed so much together in those last few months, and it was all my fault."

Devin gritted her teeth and shook her head. She hated that Maddie blamed herself for doing what almost every other human being would do. The pain of loss was hard enough without a heavy dose of guilt. No wonder Maddie was exhausted. "You're being hard on yourself. I'd do anything I could to save someone I loved and get more time with them."

Maddie sniffed and thumbed a tear from her cheek.

Devin moved to Maddie's side and put her arm across her shoulders. "Hey," she whispered. Maddie sobbed. She turned to face Devin and buried her head against Devin's chest. She wrapped her arm around Maddie's waist and cradled her head. Maddie wasn't just fragile, she was devastated and heartbroken. Devin held her trembling body tightly, and Maddie wrapped her arms around Devin's waist.

She breathed in Maddie's sweet perfume and pressed a tender kiss to the top of her head. "God bless you." She had no other words to offer Maddie. Nothing she said would change the reality. Maddie needed to forgive herself. Eventually, Maddie shifted in her arms and Devin relaxed her hold allowing her to ease away.

Maddie swept her hair from her face and half-smiled. "I'm sorry I downloaded on you like that. I haven't spoken about this with anyone." She shook her head as if silently chastising herself.

Devin shoved her hands in her pockets to stop herself from tugging Maddie into her arms again. "Loss is hard to take." She stopped short of saying she was glad Maddie felt able to talk. *Give her time and space.*

"It is."

"Emotion always finds a voice," Devin said softly, recognizing her own struggle now. Her hands itched. She desperately wanted to make everything better, to stroke Maddie's cheek, to lift her chin and look into her eyes, and to kiss her. "You're shivering."

Maddie lifted her trembling hands and stared at them. "The cold has hit me."

Devin clenched her fists in her pockets to keep them there. "Would you like to stargaze for a bit?" It was a dumb question given Maddie was feeling the cold even though there wasn't a chill in the air, but she wanted Maddie to stay out with her a little longer. Maddie smiled at her wearily.

"I think I'll turn in, if you don't mind. Maybe another night."

"For sure," she said. When Maddie turned and walked away, Devin turned toward the plains and stared into the darkness, her eyes burning from the tears she'd withheld.

11.

THE GARDENS WERE ALWAYS at their best late in the spring. The flowers, rich with color, gave off a sweet aroma as they welcomed the warmth of another new day. She hadn't realized how uneven the grassy areas were but pushing Lizzy in her wheelchair across them broke her out in a light sweat. She stopped in the shade. "Is here okay?"

Lizzy tried to ease herself up in the chair. Her movements were slow and labored, as if making them required every ounce of her attention and more effort than she could muster. She pushed down on the arms of the chair with her frail hands, but her body barely shifted.

"Would you like me to help?"

She shook her head. "No, it's fine. Sometimes I think I need to move when perhaps I don't. It's no bother. It's just wonderful to be out in the fresh air."

Maddie knew it would be the last time. She thought Lizzy knew it too. The ache in her heart deepened, and she swallowed back the tears that threatened to spoil the day.

Maddie unpacked the bag they'd brought, laid out the blanket, and poured Lizzy a small cup of water. She wanted to tell Lizzy about the latest developments in cancer research, the DNA-based treatments that might help her. She held Lizzy's gaze for a long moment, wondering where to start the conversation. The wisps of hair that had replaced the thick curls Lizzy used to have clung to her head and lifted effortlessly on the breeze. The red blouse didn't lift the color of her cheeks or conceal their puffiness. She held her head high, and her eyes sparkled with more joy than Maddie felt as she watched the clouds passing. Maddie took a deep breath and abandoned her intended conversation. "Would you like a piece of cake? I got your favorite."

Lizzy's smile warmed her heart though she knew Lizzy wouldn't eat anything. What Lizzy had eaten in the last couple of days wouldn't fill Maddie for more than an hour, though now she'd lost her appetite.

As she bent down, Lizzy stroked her cheek. The tenderness screamed to her for things to be different. *God damn you for leaving me.*

Lizzy smiled. "You need to let me go, my love."

Maddie's heart sank like a stone. She shook her head, and the tears that had burned behind her eyes burst onto her cheeks. Not for the first time in the past months, Lizzy wiped them away as she smiled softly.

"I know it's hard. But I need you to promise me. You deserve to be happy."

Maddie eased Lizzy gently toward her, worried she might break her. "I want to be happy with you."

"Sh. I know you do. And I want that too. I'll always be close, but—"

Maddie silenced her with a tender kiss. "I promise," she whispered.

She pushed Lizzy the long route back through Central Park. She wanted to soak up the Metropolitan Museum of Art, The High Line, and everything the Theatre District could throw at them, to capture those last precious moments so that she could lock them into her heart and treasure them for her lifetime.

Lizzy's chin dropped and rested on her chest before they'd gone a hundred yards.

She lifted Lizzy into their bed, climbed in next to her, and held her hand. Her breathing became shallower with each passing hour until it stopped. "I'm sorry. I'm sorry." Maddie repeated the words and allowed the tears to fall as she lay with Lizzy until the sun rose and when the ambulance took Lizzy away, the abyss that her heart had fallen into deepened.

Maddie stirred in the bed, her pillow wet from the tears, her heart pounding. She blinked her damp, sticky eyes and forced them to open. She lay for a while, orientating herself to the white ceiling and the pictures of the horses, and her heart slowed. She closed her eyes again and snuggled the tear-stained pillow to her. "I love you, Lizzy." Already, she couldn't recall the dream in any detail and although she felt emotionally spent, she also felt lighter, as if the shackles of guilt had been loosened around her. It was something positive to grab a hold on. The idea of coming on the retreat and engaging in the process of letting go of Lizzy had scared her the most. She hadn't thought she was ready to move on. But something inside her had shifted during the dream just enough for her to believe that she could and more importantly, that she must. She owed it to herself and to Lizzy. Her thoughts drifted to the ranch and the previous evening.

After talking to Devin, she'd studied the stars until she could no longer keep her eyes open. She'd pondered which among the thousands of lights dancing to the tune of the night was Lizzy's star. She'd picked one, or it had called to her, and then she'd fallen into a deep sleep. She rose slowly from the bed, entranced by the events of the night, and stared out the window. She wished she could see Lizzy's star now, capture it in a locket, and keep it close to her heart. She would look for Lizzy again tonight and every night, and she would carve out her new life that Lizzy would always be a part of because Lizzy had a place in her heart and that would never change.

The sun had painted the horizon in red and orange hues and the spectacle captivated her in awe. The ball of fire rose quickly, turning the deep blue sky lighter. Devin had been right. Maddie had been too hard on herself. That had always been Maddie's default. It was what drove her to work harder and achieve more, to be the best. Lee had told her the same thing often enough. Maddie had known her negative thoughts about those last days with Lizzy were unfounded, but that hadn't stopped them taunting her into believing she'd failed Lizzy. She'd constructed an image of that time, skewed by her broken heart, to justify the fact that she hated herself for being the survivor. She wasn't perfect, and if she continued to analyze her actions, there would always be more that she could have done. But she hadn't neglected Lizzy. She couldn't have done that. She'd been there every step of the way, and Lizzy had never asked anything more of her than Maddie had given. It was time to let the past, and Lizzy, go. That didn't mean she didn't care about Lizzy or that she didn't love her. It was about accepting that she couldn't have done any more than she had, and she couldn't bring Lizzy back.

She would have swapped places with Lizzy back then without a second thought. Lizzy had always had a smile on her face and always seen the pleasure in life, no matter what. Lizzy had been the one person who could draw Maddie out of herself, put things into context, and pacify the stress. When Maddie's parents had disowned her, it had been Lizzy who'd stood at her side. Lizzy had always been the pragmatic one, the steadying influence, and she'd missed her. She wiped away the tears that accompanied her images of the joy and the sadness they'd shared. There was beauty where the pain had been. There was clarity where the fog had lifted. And there was still the rawness that came with feeling vulnerable and visible in a way that she hadn't been in a very long time.

"Emotion needs a voice," Devin had said. Maybe finding that voice had just been a matter of time. And perhaps being away from the stress of work in which she'd buried her grief had encouraged that voice to start to free her. Whatever it was that had caused the softness inside her, she welcomed it. What was disconcerting was the vulnerability that seemed more evident. It was something she needed to accept to be able to move on from Lizzy and create a new life. She had no idea what that new life looked like, but she was, for the first time since Lizzy had died, open to seeing it.

As she wandered out across the higher plains with her back to the sun, her skin tingled with the dry heat. The sky was the blue of a pure sapphire. A heat haze rose across the surface of the desert. It seemed denser hovering above the highway where the road split the valley floor. The air this high up was clear and cleansed her lungs with every breath. The mustangs herded and grazed. The cars seemed to crawl like insects along the highway. Dust rose with every movement on the plains, and the light breeze tossed it to a new home. It was a beautiful day, a day like no other, the tentative beginnings of a new life.

The simplicity and pace of life on the ranch was a world away from her frenzied life in the hospital's ER. Being at the ranch and without the relentless pressure of work in the past three days hadn't stopped her feeling as though she was letting her colleagues down though. Additional pressure on others in the department was when accidents and mistakes were most likely to happen. She didn't want to be responsible for that. They needed her in the ER.

She stopped walking and pressed her hand to her chest. Her heart raced, and her breath came in short, sharp bursts. Her body stiffened. The notion that she might not be missed by those she worked with was suddenly as frightening as the fact that she'd come too close to fucking up. Was that all she was? An ER doctor, with no life and an ego that needed the job to feel she was special. It had been that line of thinking that had led to her burning out in the first place. She needed to hang on to the softness that she'd woken with earlier, the reassurance that she could let go of the past and that she could relax and enjoy a break without feeling guilt or shame. She closed her eyes and took a few deep breaths.

Take time for yourself, Maddie. Lizzy was willing her, coaxing her, releasing her. The tension that always arose when she thought about work subsided a little. She opened her eyes and slowly looked around her.

It was hard to put her finger on one specific thing that made the living ghost town of Austin and its surrounding area so mesmerizing. She gazed back toward the house. Taco, Rocky, and Cookie grazed together in the bigger arena. The foal stood close to its mother in the smaller enclosure. The track that led to the house and separated the two corrals was cast from the dirt and rock. There was an easiness about everything at the ranch, and she would immerse herself in it and try to forget about her job.

Enjoying the mustangs' freedom, the bareness of the scorched earth, and the starkness of the contrast with her city life, she took a long deep breath. The weight of that New York life slipped a little from her shoulders, and she took a slow stroll back toward the house.

As she approached the large corral, Rocky lifted his head and stared at her. He really was the most handsome horse she'd set eyes on. She didn't know whether he was a stallion or not, but he certainly looked the part.

"Hey, Rocky."

He snorted lightly and flicked his tail. She smiled. He continued to watch her as she made her way to the end of the corral closest to the house and stood close to the fence. Taco ambled toward her. "Hey, boy," she whispered. Her heart thumped harder as he moved closer, then he stopped just out of reach and flicked his head up and down gently. She stared into his eyes until her heart rate settled into a more natural rhythm. "I'm okay," she whispered and held out her hand.

He moved his right leg toward her and leaned forward. His whiskers tickled her palm, and she resisted the urge to pull her hand away. A pleasant tingling sensation moved up her arm.

"He's looking for food."

Maddie jolted at Devin's voice, turned toward her, and smiled. "I don't have any."

"Here."

Devin handed Maddie two treats that looked like small cookies made from compacted dried grass. Maddie held them out, and Taco nibbled at them as though he hadn't eaten for a week. "He's hungry."

"He's the devil for treats." Devin leaned her back against the fence and looked up to the sun. "Did you enjoy a walk?"

Maddie acknowledged the sudden wave of heat that reminded her of their conversation the previous evening. She shouldn't feel embarrassed or ashamed about confessing to Devin, but she did. "I'm sorry about last night."

Devin frowned. "Hey, it's good that you wanted to talk. Must be hard being the one to fix people up all the time with no one looking out for you." Devin smiled. "Did you sleep okay?"

Maddie nodded. "I did."

Taco stepped up to the rail and nudged Maddie's arm.

"He likes you." Devin scratched his cheek. "Don't you, boy? You're gonna teach Maddie here how to ride." She winked at Maddie.

Maddie chuckled, dissipating the nerves that came with the idea of getting onto the horse's back. "One step at a time."

"You hear that, Taco?" Taco lifted his head and swished his tail before turning and ambling away. "There's lots of fine places to explore around here, if you can ride."

Maddie didn't doubt that. The terrain extended for miles beyond the horizon. "I'd like that." Devin was staring at her, and her stomach threw a somersault. "I need to get a drink," she said and pressed her dry lips together.

"There's beer and soda in the fridge in the garage." Devin looked toward the open doors, where Sally-Ann was parked.

Maddie set off before Devin had moved. There really wasn't any need to hurry, she just needed to get out of the heat. The problem was the cause of the heat was now hot on her heels.

Devin caught up to Maddie and matched her stride. "You're gonna start a fire walking that fast around here."

Maddie stifled a laugh. She caught a whiff of Devin's perfume. She couldn't look at her without being aware of how attractive she was. And now that she'd *seen* her, she couldn't *un-see* her. The kindness she'd experienced and the calmness and understanding that Devin had afforded her sat even more uncomfortably now than it had after she'd blurted out her crap to Devin. She snuck a peek at Devin who was looking at her through a squint and with a deepening frown.

"Are you okay?"

"I'm fine, thanks." She sounded curt though she hadn't meant to be. Her defensive reaction was counter to her acute awareness that she shouldn't be feeling the way she was about Devin. She'd noticed other women in the past, a bit like the way she did when discovering something new and interesting that was pleasant to admire, but she'd not felt the subtle pangs that now dared her to explore her desire. It was disconcerting and delightful. She should feel guilty admiring another woman in this way, shouldn't she? *No, Maddie, it's time to move on.* Lizzy's voice was firm and encouraging. Devin's light blue eyes, suntanned face, her broad smile, and the scar that ran a line through her left eyebrow that she hadn't noticed before gripped her attention. Her pulse raced as she looked into Devin's eyes. "I'm good, thank you," she said softly.

"Good. You want a beer or a soda?" Devin walked ahead of Maddie.

Maddie noticed the slight sway in Devin's hips and the tight cut of her jeans that accentuated her muscular ass and legs. "Soda, thanks." She would have been able to get blind drunk in New York and not think twice about anything more with this woman, but suddenly she didn't trust herself to drink alcohol in Devin's company. Her commitment to Lizzy, that had restrained her these past two years had been released. The novelty of the feeling was thrilling, and she had the urge to explore her freedom, but she needed to take things slowly. For now, just being in the company of someone she admired was wonderful and more than she could have anticipated. She ran a few paces to catch up to Devin, and they entered the garage walking in step.

Three cars would fit easily inside the place. There was a jukebox in the corner and a fridge next to it. Benches lined the walls, and tools of various types were laid out or hung from hooks designed to keep everything orderly. The concrete floor had been swept, and Sally-Ann gleamed as if recently polished. She took the chilled can and avoided Devin's gaze. "Thanks. The car looks incredible." It still wasn't her type of car, but it was very well taken care of.

"She's in great shape." Devin went to the jukebox and selected a song. "Do you like Melissa Etheridge?"

Maddie nodded. She smiled when the music came on. "You Can Sleep While I Drive" was one of her favorite songs.

Devin made her way across the garage toward Sally-Ann, picked up a cloth and started rubbing the paintwork, although it didn't look like it needed any attention. She stopped and turned to Maddie.

The intensity in her gaze stole Maddie's breath. Her heart raced and for a moment it felt as if she was doing something wrong, though she knew she wasn't.

"I was wondering if you'd like to go to the dance on Saturday. If you're feeling up to it, I mean. There'll be a few folks there, and it'll be fun."

It would be nice to get out and meet more locals, and it would be more than pleasant being in Devin's easygoing company. "Yes, I'd like that."

Devin cleared her throat and turned her attention to polishing the paintwork again. "That's great."

Warmth expanded from Maddie's chest. Excitement stirred low in her belly. The awkwardness it seemed they shared lingered. The music wasn't helping curb her arousal much either. It was too much, too quickly, and she feared the guilt would return and cripple her. She had to leave, though she didn't want to go. "Thanks for the drink. I'll catch you later," she said and strode toward the entrance.

Devin looked up. "Sure."

She shouldn't have rushed away when Devin had been so generous, but she needed to cool down and redirect her attention to something that didn't involve Devin. She needed to take time out in the peace of her room, to gather her thoughts, and take a long cool shower.

"Let me know when you want to ride," Devin said. "Alice will be over later, if you want to watch?"

She'd watch them for a bit and pick up some tips then head into town and buy a few things. Maybe an appropriate hat given she was going to learn how to ride a horse. "How about tomorrow?"

Devin smiled. "How about first thing?"

"Sure." Maddie made her way across the yard. She now had a good idea of what it might feel like to be thrown from a horse and land on a bed of feathers. *She's perfect for you,* Lizzy's voice whispered. She could see Lizzy's tender smile and stared up at the sky. She would find Lizzy's star later and talk to her, as a friend.

12.

DEVIN TUGGED ON THE girth around Taco for the fourth time to reassure herself that the saddle wouldn't slip. The stirrups hung at about the right length given Maddie's inside leg measurement, which she'd estimated at thirty-two inches. She rubbed her hands down her jeans to draw the clamminess from them. As she glanced up, Maddie was heading toward the corral dressed in black leather boots, black jeans, and a white shirt. The white Stetson completed the vision; she was immaculate and looked like a cowgirl for a magazine cover. She hadn't quite mastered the art of ambling yet though. She also looked as tight as a well-strung hay bale.

Devin rubbed her hands together. She'd never felt this nervous giving a lesson before. Getting it right had never been as important as it was for Maddie, with a starting point of abject fear to overcome. A positive first ride would make the difference between Maddie feeling able to explore the area with her during the rest of her stay, which she hoped she would, or never getting on a horse again. She patted Taco on the neck. "Morning."

"Good morning." Maddie stood stiffly, a couple of paces back from the fence.

Devin positioned the reins on Taco's neck. "Roll your shoulders." Taco flicked his tail and took a pace toward the fence. Devin climbed out of the corral and faced Maddie.

Maddie frowned. "Excuse me?"

"Roll your shoulders." Devin demonstrated. "You're tighter than a wheel bolt on Sally-Ann. That's it. Up, back, down, forward. Slow it down." Devin put her hands on her hips. Maddie's movements were stiff and jerky, and the lines deepened across her brow. She chuckled. "You know you're frowning?"

Maddie widened her eyes. "I'm not."

"Sure are. Bigger movements now, real soft and easy though. And remember to breathe, long and deep. Feel your chest expand."

Maddie put her hand to her chest and took a deep breath.

"That's good."

Maddie was still frowning. She needed to relax or she was going to bounce off Taco's back as soon as he took a couple of paces.

"Loving the boots and hat. Abe's, huh?" There was nowhere else to go for quality gear in Austin, and since she'd known exactly when Maddie had gone into town and returned, Maddie hadn't been off the ranch long enough to venture farther afield.

"Yes, Abe's. I didn't know whether I needed anything else." Maddie indicated her clothing.

At least she was moving her arms more freely now and looked a little less like she was about to ride in a rodeo for the first time in her life. "Looks good." Maddie looked more than good, especially the bit of her revealed by the open neck of her shirt. Devin had to work hard not to stare, or Maddie might think she was looking at her breasts, which she wasn't. Well, maybe she had for a moment, but she'd caught herself early enough, and Maddie had been too uptight to notice...hopefully. "Are you ready?"

Maddie looked at Taco and took a pace toward him. "Hey, Taco. Are you going to be kind to me?" She scratched his nose. He jerked his head upwards, and she pulled back. "Is he okay?"

Devin stepped inside the corral and led Taco toward a small platform. "He's excited for you to ride him. You can mount him from the block." Devin stopped the horse at the platform and waved Maddie to her. She approached Taco with her hand outstretched and stroked his cheek. He nudged her gently on the arm as she stood at his side. Devin held him as Maddie stepped onto the platform.

"Put your foot in." Devin held the stirrup so that Maddie could slide in more easily. "Push up and swing your leg over."

Maddie kicked off the platform and gripped the saddle. Leaning into Taco's neck, she swung her leg over his back and sat. Taco moved his front foot and Maddie stiffened.

"Feel yourself really sitting into the seat." Devin moved around the horse and helped Maddie with the other stirrup. She smiled. "How're you doing up there?"

Maddie nodded, though her eyes were wide and her jaw was clamped tight as a drum. She looked like a venomous snake was about to attack her.

Devin put her hand on Maddie's thigh then withdrew it swiftly. "Squeezing with your legs will get him to move." She took the reins and placed them in Maddie's hands. "Keep the reins short but not too tight. If you tug on them, he'll think he's gotta stop. Elbows in and let your arms hang loose." By the time she'd finished, Maddie was sitting deeper into the saddle and her shoulders were a little lower than they had been. "Looking good. Let's get him going."

Maddie's expression was a wonderful mix of excitement and dread. Devin had never seen someone grinning and frowning at the same time before, but the brightness in her eyes and the broad smile that softened her features was like the sunshine breaking through on a cloudy day that made everything brighter. She hoped Maddie was starting to enjoy herself.

Devin led Taco away from the platform. "Relax a little and allow yourself to move with him. If you're sitting too stiff and upright, it's hard on his back and he'll fidget. Sit into him, use your legs, and balance through your core."

Maddie squeezed her legs into Taco's sides, and he shifted to a more enthusiastic walking pace.

Devin loosened the lead line to give him a little more freedom while keeping close to his head and to Maddie, who hadn't said a word since getting into the corral. "Are you okay?"

"This is incredible."

Devin knew that feeling. She still recalled one of her first memories of learning to ride. She'd been four years old or thereabouts. Her dad had lifted her onto the pony's back and walked away. Old Jack, they'd called him. Because he was very old and a jackass, her dad had said. She'd kicked him with all her might, and he'd refused to budge. When she'd worn herself out kicking him and given up, she'd sat lower, sinking into his back. He took a pace, and she'd had to grab at his mane to stop herself from sliding off. He'd taken her movement as an instruction of some kind and started to trot. It had taken all her effort to balance and not fall off. The thrill of that time rose inside her as if it was happening now. "Move with the rhythm of his pace, okay?"

Maddie nodded.

"Trot on, boy." Devin broke into a jog, keeping Taco at her side.

Maddie bounced around in the saddle until she got into the rise and fall movement. "I'm going to feel this tomorrow," she said and laughed as she mistimed the movement. "Ouch."

Maddie's joy melted Devin's heart. She brought Taco to a walk and smiled up at her. "You still doing okay?"

"Having gotten this far, a sore butt isn't going to put me off."

Maybe it was the heat of the sun or Devin's imagination and a large dose of wishful thinking that had the heat rushing through her own body with no place to go. She was going to need a cool shower before midday, again. "Trot on, boy," she said and started to jog alongside him.

Devin didn't want to end the lesson, but riding was like a workout, and Maddie wasn't used to it. It wouldn't be just a sore butt she'd have if they didn't quit soon. She wouldn't be able to walk in a straight line for a few days. Maddie had done brilliantly. She'd walked and trotted Taco off the lead rope, used her legs, and for the most part, kept a short rein. Taco had played his part well, as Devin knew he would. She walked toward them and led Taco to the platform. She patted his neck as Maddie dismounted and made her way out of the corral, then she unbuckled his girth and removed his saddle. "Good boy." She placed the bridle across the fence, removed his tack, and joined Maddie. "So, how was your first ride?"

Maddie's beaming smile answered her question. She threw herself at Devin and tugged her into an embrace. Devin tensed. She closed her eyes and the soapy sweet scent that came from Maddie was very distracting.

"Thank you so much. That was such a thrill." Maddie released Devin almost immediately and stepped away from her. "Sorry, I, um..."

Devin smiled. Maddie's cheeks glowed and her eyes shone. "Hey, I'm stoked you had a great time."

Maddie looked toward Taco. "I can't remember feeling like this."

Devin nodded. "I remember my first time too." She hadn't intended the inuendo and tried to ignore her body's response to it. She gathered up the tack and headed toward the barn. "Old Jack. Stubborn as a mule," she said, trying to recover herself and redirect her sensual thoughts.

"Do you need a hand?" Maddie asked.

When Maddie held out her hands, Devin hesitated. If Maddie made a pass at her, she would freak out. It wasn't that she didn't want to kiss Maddie, she did. That was the problem. She'd thought a lot about kissing Maddie. But she was here to deal with her own crap, not to get involved in Devin's.

She handed over the saddle. "That goes on the rack, over there." She removed the bridle from her shoulder. She watched Maddie put the saddle back and wished things could be different between them, but they couldn't. She'd gotten badly burned by Jaynee, and she wouldn't make the same mistake twice. No, she couldn't let herself go down that road again.

13.

MADDIE LOOKED HERSELF UP and down in the mirror from every angle. She'd toyed between jeans and a shirt and the knee length soft-cotton sleeveless dress for the best part of the day, like a kid trying to decide what they should wear to the prom, and still, she couldn't decide.

The joy that she'd started to reconnect with hadn't faded since her first riding lesson. Being around Devin was increasingly uplifting and she'd returned to her room lighthearted and invigorated. She spotted Lizzy's star easily now and enjoyed the comfort that came with talking to her before falling into a deep and refreshing sleep.

She danced around her room, singing. *Would three-inch heels be too much to dance in?* She tried a few side steps to test her balance. It had been a while since she'd worn shoes this high but the options in Austin's only fashion store had been limited. The woman had recommended the silver block-heel shoe. They were certainly more stable than the stilettoes she'd tried.

Devin had omitted telling her that the dance was a fundraiser for the school and that the whole town would probably turn out to support the appeal. The woman in the shop had been very chatty about it. They aimed to raise fifteen thousand dollars to fund the new school roof. It was one of several events they'd organized since the beginning of the previous fall semester and the repairs were being undertaken in stages. They'd raised almost twelve thousand so far. What Maddie had also discovered was that Devin and Cody were part of the crew who had given their time to help to rebuild the roof. The remaining work was being carried out during the school summer vacation and would be completed by the coming fall.

Would Devin prefer her in a dress?

A warm wave moved over her, and her stomach fizzed. Heels would put her on eye level with Devin. If she wore jeans and boots, she'd be looking up into Devin's eyes as they danced. She hoped they might dance together. She wanted to feel Devin's strong arms around her, soak up the warmth of her pressed up close, and enjoy the scent of her as they moved in sync around the dance floor. She'd wondered what it would be like to dance with her since agreeing to go. Devin would be a natural, she was sure, and Maddie would likely tread on her toes, and it would all go terribly wrong. She laughed. If she trod on Devin's foot, would it be less painful with the block heels or the boots? *What will Devin wear?* Jeans and boots, no doubt, and her black felt Stetson with the silver-white feather. Maddie's silver heels would match perfectly. *The dress it is.*

Finally, after putting on a little lipstick and removing it again, Maddie left her room. By the time she reached the front door she had a gentle quiver in her stomach. When she stepped into the yard and caught sight of Devin leaning against the passenger door of the truck, looking as casual and cool as the kid who knew the prom was designed for them, her stomach flipped. Devin's smile grew wider as she approached.

Devin stood and tipped her hat, a dark brown Stetson that matched the color of her pants. There were white feathers and white markings that looked like the native American engravings she'd seen on the advertisements for the caves in the area. The hat didn't go with Maddie's silver shoes, but the silver buckle on the brown leather belt that clung to Devin's hips matched perfectly.

"That's a fine-looking dress."

Maddie had never been good at receiving compliments. And coming from Devin, the intensity of self-consciousness that struck her was almost overwhelming. She clasped her hands together behind her back and then realized she was swaying her hips as she stood. She was behaving like the prom queen who'd secured a highly prized date with the captain of the college baseball team—at nearly forty-three years old. *What the fuck?* She should have complimented Devin's attire, but words escaped her and now Devin was staring at her, and her self-consciousness must have been blindingly obvious. She could barely breathe.

"Did you get the dress from Tracie's?" Devin asked, opening the passenger door.

Maddie cleared her throat. "Yes."

"Your vacation is doing wonders for the Austin economy," Devin said and laughed.

Maddie chuckled. Devin held the door open, and Maddie walked past her. *Sandalwood and vanilla?* Different. "Nice perfume," she said. Devin smiled and Maddie quickly averted her gaze and got into the car. When Devin got into the car the air became thick and heady and Devin appeared too close for comfort. If Devin leaned across and kissed Maddie now, they wouldn't make it to the dance. This was going to be the longest and hottest ten-minute drive to get into town. She turned her head skyward as Devin drove and the breeze helped to calm the craving.

The *ghosts* of Austin had never appeared so alive. The streets were bustling with people, and the music from the school spilled into the street. An old couple danced together on their porch nearby; their movements were slow and deliberate, and the beat didn't seem to matter. A bunch of kids were chasing each other around the playground and jumping onto the hay bales that had been set out. She heard laughter when the music quieted and sensed a hint of melancholy as an image of Lizzy popped into her head. The moment passed in a blink and with Lizzy's blessing. These people knew how to live.

"You ready to dance those shoes off your feet?" Devin parked up close to the school.

Maddie laughed. The shoes were pinching a bit already, so it probably wouldn't be too long before she'd be barefoot. Encouraged by the challenge, she stepped out of the truck. "I'm ready. Can you handle it?" She expected Devin would dance until the early hours and still dance some more. The lighthearted banter was fun though.

Devin laughed. "We'll have to see." She walked alongside Maddie, and they entered together.

Maddie was instantly drawn to the five-man band at the top of the room whose age range must have been from sixty-five to ninety-five. The man who looked the oldest had his lips wrapped around a mouth organ, making the instrument sing. A man with shoulder-length, snowy-white hair danced a jig in time with the fiddle tucked under his chin. They whooped and hollered, enticing the crowd dancing on the floor in front of them. Maddie stirred as Devin's breath touched her ear.

"Can I get you a drink?" Devin asked and directed Maddie toward the make-shift bar in the farthest corner of the room from the band.

"Coke, please." Maddie scanned the room as she waited in line for the bar.

"Two Cokes, please, Frank," Devin said.

It was the man from the convenience store. She glanced around to discover more familiar faces. Abe stood close to the main doors to the playground area tapping a cane to the rhythm of the beat. *And here comes Stella, the woman from Tracie's.*

"Oh, those shoes look just divine on you." Stella waved her hand and spilled her drink in the process, looked a good number of drinks already into a guaranteed hangover, no matter what hour of the day she woke.

"Thank you."

Devin handed Maddie her Coke and stood by her side.

"Hey, Stella. You're looking pretty this evening," Devin said.

"So says the suave Devin. Did you know, she's the catch of the county?"

Was Stella staking a claim on Devin or making a point to Maddie? And was Devin blushing? Maddie looked from Stella to Devin. She'd never considered Devin as *suave*. Kind and considerate, yes. But suave had a negative connotation to it, coming from the smooth, cheating male stereotype that she didn't like, and she wouldn't ever associate with Devin. She didn't like Stella's tone. She took a long drink to stem the fiery sensation the woman elicited in her and deliberately leaned into Devin's arm.

"How's Ronny? I haven't seen him in a while." Devin asked Stella.

Maddie grew in stature when Stella blushed. *Touché.*

Stella took a slug of her beer. "He's out of town. He'll be back."

By Stella's tone and manner, Maddie somehow doubted that. Stella made an excuse and staggered into the crowd on the dancefloor. Maddie's heart ached for her. Banter after a few drinks was pretty much par for the course in New York but deep down, Maddie suspected Stella was unhappy. Maybe she was struggling and didn't have anyone to turn to. Maddie had buried her pain in post-work drinks for long enough to know that that form of medication didn't help.

"Devin, Maddie."

Maddie turned her attention from Stella. "Hi, Ella."

Ella pulled Maddie into a fierce embrace. "I'm so glad you came. What d'you think? Is the band okay? Are the drinks cold enough? Have you had food yet?"

Devin squeezed Ella's arm and smiled. "It's perfect. Another great job. I reckon we'll hit the target tonight."

Ella pressed her fingers to her lips and huffed out a breath. "I hope so."

Maddie had come to know Ella a little better over the last couple of days as they'd watched Alice and worked together around the ranch. She was the gentlest person Maddie had ever known and wonderfully curious. She'd asked Maddie's advice on their procedures at the school and whether they should use new methods to teach the kids about self-care and first aid. She'd praised their local medical center and talked about the "Care in the Community" program. She'd given Alice her undivided attention when she'd needed it and made sure she didn't get into any trouble and helped her when she was tired, even though Ella looked as though she could do with a good night's sleep. Ella was a living saint. And right now, she looked as if she was consumed by concern even though, by what Maddie could see, the event was booming and destined to be a huge success. "It's incredible already and it's still early."

Ella looked around the room. "I do hope you're right," she said, not sounding convinced.

Cody approached them. Her jeans and shirt were clean and well-pressed, and her boots were highly polished. Devin was smiling broadly at her and when Devin locked eyes with Maddie, she winked. Maddie got the feeling she was missing something between the two cowgirls.

"Evening Ella," Cody said. She tipped the brim of her hat.

"Oh, hi, Cody." Ella flushed. "I...um...I need some air. If you'll all excuse me." Ella darted out of the room.

Cody flung her arms out, her hat in one hand and turned to Devin. "What did I do?"

Devin laughed and put her hand on Cody's shoulder. "Nothing. She's into you, is all, and she's worried the event won't go well."

"It's going great already."

"She needs a bit of reassuring," Devin said.

Cody pressed her hat on her head and went to the bar.

"So, Cody and Ella?" Maddie couldn't believe she hadn't seen it before.

"Well, Cody would like it to be that way. From what I'm seeing, I think Ella would too. She's just a bit preoccupied right now."

Maddie could relate to Cody's nervousness around Ella. Maddie wanted Devin to be into her too. The butterflies in her stomach reinforced her thought.

The band shifted to a Mary Chapin Carpenter number, "Down at the Twist and Shout."

"Are you ready to dance?" Devin asked.

The sparkle in Devin's eyes was more tempting than her mom's pecan pie, and Maddie would bet her lips tasted better. She was just about to answer when Devin eased her drink from her hand and placed it on a table close by. Devin took her by the hand and twisted her around the dance floor until she was giddy.

Song after song played, and the time flew by. Maddie had long since kicked off her shoes. She licked her lips and tasted salt. "Do you want a drink?"

Devin was still puffing from the last dance. "I'd love a beer. You didn't tell me you could dance."

Maddie looked back and smiled as she headed to the bar. She returned with two beers a few moments later. "I need some air."

"Me too."

The sun had gone down and the warm air tingled Maddie's skin, still hot from dancing. She strolled across the playground and slouched on a hay bale and sipped her beer.

Maddie stared up at the stars. "It's such a beautiful sky."

"Yes, it is."

When Maddie turned toward Devin, the intensity she saw in her eyes stole her breath. Her hands trembled from the electric feeling building inside her. The desire to kiss Devin was more potent than any drug. She couldn't stop staring at Devin's mouth, the way her lips curled around the beer bottle, the way her tongue traced the line of her lips. She wanted to taste her and to feel the softness of her.

"What are you thinking?" Devin asked.

Maddie froze. "Nothing. I...um...I'm having such a wonderful evening."

Devin narrowed her eyes and smiled. "You weren't thinking about that, were you?"

Maddie shook her head.

"Are you hungry?" Devin jumped up from the hay bale and held out her hand.

Maddie took it and was swiftly lifted to her feet. When Devin let her go, she wanted to take her hand again. She was hungry but not for food. She followed Devin to the barbeque and the smell of ribs and steak convinced her stomach that eating would be a good idea.

Devin ordered for them both and when they returned to the hay bale, Maddie sensed a slight distance between them. Maybe she'd misread the signs earlier, read more into their interaction than there was. Devin's kindness could be easily misinterpreted. She poked at her steak sandwich, her appetite suddenly absent again.

Devin eyed Maddie's sandwich. "You're gonna need that. There's more dancing left in these boots."

Maddie took a bite and started to chew. She looked down at her bare feet and wondered where her shoes might be now. She'd noticed a couple of the older girls trying them on after she'd flicked them into a corner of the room. If someone wanted them, they could have them. She quite enjoyed the feel of the earth and stone beneath her feet. Maybe there would be a slow dance after all, and Devin had better not tread on her toes with those boots on. As she bit into her sandwich, the band started playing, "Sleep While I Drive." Devin stood and held out her hand. Maddie pointed to her mouth, filled with steak and bread and sauce. Devin took the sandwich from her hand and rested it on a napkin on the ground. She helped her to her feet and eased her into her arms.

"This is one of my favorite songs," Devin said. "It'd be a shame to miss it."

Maddie swallowed the food with difficulty. Devin was hot to the touch. Her hold around Maddie's waist was both firm and tender in equal measure. Maddie's pulse skyrocketed as Devin drew her closer and the firmness of Devin's thigh pressed against her leg. "Mine too," she wanted to say, but the words were stuck a long way behind her thoughts of kissing Devin. Devin's lingering gaze and soft smile was too much to bear. She closed the space between them quicker than she'd intended, hesitated when her conscience pricked her, and stopped. Devin's breath was warm, and Maddie couldn't take her eyes off her perfectly shaped lips. She moved closer. She shouldn't do this, but she couldn't stop herself.

"Devin! Devin! Can I come for the whole day tomorrow? Please?"

Alice's excited shouting caused Maddie to jolt and take a step back, her heart pounding. Alice ran toward them, clearly excited about wanting to spend more time at the ranch and, Maddie hoped, oblivious to the fact that she'd just been about to kiss Devin.

Maddie held Devin's gaze for a moment and thought she saw a flicker of desire in her eyes, but she smiled at Alice, and Maddie questioned whether it had just been wishful thinking. If she'd kissed Devin, then what? She still had three weeks of the vacation to go and didn't want to jeopardize her time at the ranch by making a complete fool of herself. What would be the point of getting into something here when she would be leaving? She wasn't into short-term relationships or casual flings, and anyway, that would be disrespectful to the memory of Lizzy. If she was going to move on, then it had to be for someone she was serious about. And there was no way Devin was going to up stakes and move to New York to be with her. Maddie wouldn't ask her to do that. Nevada was Devin's home, and New York was a million miles from the life Devin had here. And Maddie could never leave her job and her team at the hospital because that was the life she knew, the life she enjoyed. *What was she doing, thinking this way?* Maybe Alice had saved her from the embarrassment of doing something really stupid, and worse still, being rejected. Devin had shifted her attention quickly and apparently effortlessly to her young protégé. Devin was so good with kids, so attentive, and so kind. *Shit.* Why did she have to fall for someone so totally wonderful and so bloody far from New York?

14.

"HEELS DOWN. GOOD GIRL. Shorten the outside rein and squeeze with your inside leg." Devin kept Alice focused, though her own attention wasn't fully on the lesson.

She'd had one eye on the house since Maddie hadn't appeared for breakfast. She'd agreed that Alice could come for a longer day with the horses and hoped that Maddie would ride out with them both. They could visit one of the caves at the farthest point on the range, and Maddie would get to see the pictographs painted thousands of years ago by the hunter-gatherers. Really, she just wanted to spend time with Maddie, ideally alone, but Devin hadn't been able to say no to Alice.

"Outside rein, inside leg. Keep him close to the fence. You're in control, not him." She glanced toward the house with an unsettled feeling. She was sure that Maddie's absence had everything to do with what had happened at the dance. She cursed Alice for showing up and disturbing what had the potential to be a beautiful moment. Devin had never enjoyed dancing as much as she had with Maddie, and that final dance had come all too soon. She'd been so close to kissing Maddie. After Alice's intrusion, Maddie had stood away from her, wide-eyed and breathless, then she'd backed off. The evening had been brought to a swift end after that. Maddie had remained quiet and gone quickly to her bedroom once they returned home.

Devin had taken a long cold shower and that still hadn't clipped her desire. If she carried on this way, she was going to be the cleanest rancher this side of Vegas. Now, she worried that Maddie might be offended.

Alice brought Cookie to a stop in front of Devin. "I'm thirsty," she said.

"You handled him well." Devin rubbed his nose. "I'm guessing he needs a drink too. What d'you reckon?"

Alice nodded. Devin walked alongside Cookie to the platform and Alice dismounted. "You know where the fridge is in the garage?"

"Sure."

"Can you get me a soda while I take off his tack?"

"Yep." Alice smiled, turned, and ran around the back of the stables toward the garage.

Devin removed the tack and rested it across the fence. She looked toward the stables and Alice's voice. Alice and Maddie came into view carrying the drinks, and Devin's heart skipped a beat. She climbed through the fence and stood watching her two new favorite people. Alice was coaching Maddie about how to pull on the outside rein and squeeze with the inside leg so the horse stayed close to the fence. Devin caught Maddie's glance and a flash of intense fire zipped through to her core. If she'd messed up, Maddie wouldn't have come into the yard. *Phew.*

"Good morning," Maddie said without making eye contact.

Alice handed Devin a soda. "I said Maddie could have one too."

Maddie smiled. "I hope that's okay. I was out walking."

"For sure." Devin took a long slug. "Good to see you're still walking after all that dancing."

Maddie flushed as she laughed. "Between the horses and the dance, I think I'm close to broken."

"When can I ride Lightning?" Alice asked, heading across the yard to the smaller arena where the foal stood with his head poking curiously through the lower rail.

Devin laughed. "In about three-and-a-half years."

Alice pouted.

"He needs to get stronger before we start training him." Devin winced. The *we* she'd referred to excluded Alice who would be rehomed by then and unlikely to be able to visit. There wasn't anyone in the town able to adopt her, so the search, as had happened with Todd, would take Alice further afield. Rarely did newly adoptive parents want the child they'd taken on to return to their temporary foster location. It could create disharmony. She looked toward Maddie. Reality sucked.

"Thank you for last night. I had a great time," Maddie said, though she kept her focus on where Alice petted the foal. "Ella did a great job and I'm sure you will have hit the target for the roof repairs. It's a lovely community here."

Devin stared at the moisture that wetted Maddie's lips, the way it shone in the light and made her mouth look even more inviting. Devin drank to quench her thirst, sensing Maddie's awkwardness intensely. The absence of any mention of the dance and the forced interruption or how Maddie felt about the near kiss didn't go unnoticed. But Devin wasn't going to let that get in the way of offering to show Maddie a good time while she was here. "I was wondering if you'd like to ride out with us," she said. Maddie shook her head, and Devin wished she'd kept her mouth shut. Perhaps Maddie was more pissed than she appeared and just too polite to address her directly about it and in front of Alice.

"I don't know if I'm ready for that."

Devin took a deep breath and released it slowly. Her refusal was about her confidence in riding. "You'll be fine. I'll keep you close."

Maddie cleared her throat.

Was she pushing too hard? She didn't want Maddie to miss out, but she didn't want her to feel obligated to do something she didn't feel comfortable doing. "The caves are spectacular and well worth a visit, but we need to get there on these guys." She gestured to the horses. Maddie was staring at her oddly and for a moment, she didn't know whether she would accept. The idea of going alone with Alice wasn't half as appealing as taking Maddie with them. *Please, say yes.*

Maddie looked across at the horses. "You're sure I'll be okay?"

Relief turned to intense joy, and Devin smiled. "I guarantee it. We'll take a gentle stroll." She glanced skyward. "It's too hot for racing."

Maddie laughed. "I'm learning how to amble, remember."

"Yep, and it suits you. You look chill and like you're enjoying yourself."

"I am."

Devin turned to Alice who was sitting on the grass watching Lightning as he played. "Alice, you reckon you can help Maddie saddle up Taco?"

Alice jumped up and set off toward the barn. "Sure."

"And give Cookie a brush and saddle him up. We're going to ride out to the caves. I'm going to grab a picnic."

Alice broke into a run.

"Someone's excited," Maddie said.

Devin set off toward the house. "Well, that makes two of us."

"Three," Maddie said and set off in Alice's direction.

Devin went into the kitchen, grabbed a few things from the fridge, and put them into a knapsack.

"Heading out somewhere?" her mom asked.

Devin stole a handful of savory pastries from the tray that had just been baked, wrapped them in a napkin, and added them to her bag. "I'm taking Alice and Maddie out to the caves." She'd deliberately used Alice's name first and judging by the quizzical look her mom gave her, her mom had already gotten an idea of Devin's feelings toward Maddie. Her mom was particularly vigilant since Devin's split with Jaynee, and given how Devin felt, it wouldn't take much for her mom to work things out, but that wasn't a conversation she wanted to have now or at any time in the future. It wasn't that her mom would be discouraging, quite the opposite. She wanted nothing more than for Devin to settle down with the right girl. Jaynee had never been the right one, according to her mom, and she would be a pain in Devin's ass if she thought Maddie might be that person.

Devin couldn't allow herself to think that far ahead. At the end of the day, Maddie was a guest who had a career and a home to go back to. Devin would simply like to enjoy the time they could share together without the expectation of anything more.

"Uh huh," her mom said and went back to washing the corn she was preparing.

Devin shot out of the kitchen and headed into the yard. Maddie and Alice were tacking up Cookie. Taco, already prepped, stood close to the fence and gave a swish of his tail as Devin approached. She dumped the knapsack and headed into the stables for Rocky's tack. She couldn't wait to head out into the open plains. It would feel as if it were just her and Maddie because Alice would be consumed by her own world. Being self-absorbed was one of the things she loved about kids, since it meant they spent more time wrapped up in their own worlds than they did noticing what was going on in other people's. She figured it was a special form of innocence that was unique to kids so they could escape when their life was unpleasant.

Maddie huffed as she tugged at Cookie's girth. Devin would enjoy watching her for as long as it took, but Alice looked eager to get going and so was she. She walked over to Cookie. "Here, let me help," she said.

She took the strap from Maddie and their hands touched. She paused from the catch in her breath before she secured the saddle. Maddie stood at her side, watching her

115

every move. Devin coaxed the bit into Cookie's mouth, pulled the crown piece over his ears, and secured the bridle.

"So that's how you do it." Maddie nodded.

"Yep."

Maddie smiled. "You made it look easy."

"If you press their cheek, they help you."

"Good to know."

Devin laughed. It would be a while before Maddie would feel confident fitting the bridle. She walked around the horse but still couldn't escape the intensity of being close to Maddie. Maddie followed, her concentration lines furrowing her brow. She looked too damn adorable. She was oblivious to the effect she was having on Devin and thankfully not appearing to have held anything against her following the dance. Maddie was becoming more desirable by the minute.

Devin turned to Alice. "Do you think you can help Maddie mount Taco and then get on Cookie by yourself?" she asked.

"Sure. Come on, Maddie." Alice pulled Cookie's reins and turned him toward the platform.

Devin threw her bag on her back and walked across the corral to where Rocky was grazing. She put his bridle on and led him toward the gate where Maddie and Alice waited.

"Alice, you lead. We're heading out that way and will follow the route to the base of the mountains, over there. Same direction as the other day, just a bit further on."

Alice clicked her tongue, nudged Cookie with her heels, and set off.

She guided Rocky to the side of Taco. "Are you okay?"

Maddie's smile was reassuring.

"I'm very good."

"We'll go side by side for a bit. I'll keep the lead line on. Taco's bombproof, and he knows where he's going, so you can relax up there and enjoy the scenery." Devin was enjoying the view very much, though she'd like to be a lot closer to Maddie. She recalled their dance and the softness of Maddie's breasts against her chest and the way they had moved easily together. Next time, she'd like to finish that dance uninterrupted. She wetted her lips and looked toward the track where Alice walked Cookie. She mounted Rocky. "Best we head on out," she said, and the warmth of Maddie's smile moved through her.

15.

MADDIE QUICKLY SETTLED INTO the rocking motion that came with Taco's lazy pace. The mountain range that had appeared a long way in the distance when they'd set off now towered above them and formed shadows that provided a welcome break from the intensity of the sun. Devin unhooked the lead line and dropped back behind her, and she had the sense of being watched closely. She had no intention of falling off, and Taco didn't seem too bothered about needing to move any faster, so they were a perfect match. She hoped Devin wasn't frustrated by the slowness of their pace. She didn't have Alice's confidence yet, which was why she trailed a good few yards behind her. Alice would break into a trot every so often, turn, and come back to them. She looked over her shoulder, and Devin's expression sent a shiver through her that weakened her legs. Taco stopped and tugged the reins as he dipped his head.

Devin moved alongside her and rested her hand on the horn of Rocky's saddle. "You see that dark patch?"

Maddie located the point in the rockface, not more than two hundred yards from them. "Yes."

"That's the cave. Come on." She nudged Taco on and shouted to Alice to stop at the cave.

Alice had dismounted, secured Cookie to a tree, and removed her hat before Maddie and Devin arrived. Devin jumped from Rocky's back and secured him to a tree. She returned and held Taco still. Maddie released her feet and lifted one leg behind her. The dead weight feeling and the soreness in her butt made it hard to move easily. She bobbled a little but caught hold of the saddle and slid unceremoniously until her feet reached solid ground. Devin looked as though she was stifling a laugh. The tweak of irritation that Devin hadn't jumped to her rescue passed quickly when Alice burst into a fit of giggles.

"I did that before," Alice said. "And I fell on my butt once."

"Does the sore butt thing ever ease?"

"Mine's not sore anymore," Alice said.

Devin shrugged. She ruffled Alice's hair as she walked Taco to the tree. "This way," she said and led them into the cave.

Maddie staggered a few steps until she regained the feeling in her ass. As she entered the cave, the skin on her arms tingled with the cool air. She inhaled deeply and enjoyed the refreshing sensation. The horizontal strata split the jagged rockface into shades of browns and grays, and slivers of white appeared like streams in between them. "This is stunning," she said, and the words echoed back to her. Devin had what looked like a mischievous grin on her face.

"Come, this way." Devin led them deeper into the cave.

"Wow."

Alice's high-pitched squeal of excitement travelled around the small space like a song or a ritualistic chant that might have been used by the early inhabitants of this ancient dwelling. Maddie took in the intricate patterns formed by the brilliant white, ochre, and blood-red pigments that must have been painted into the rockface hundreds of years ago. She moved closer to the rock and traced the markings. "When were these painted?"

"It's thought about 500 B.C. This cave is deeper than some of the others around here, so they think it might've been inhabited for longer. There would've been more water around here back then, and the position is perfect for spotting lunch." She laughed.

Maddie stared at the paintings. What must it have been like to live here that long ago? She couldn't imagine but something about the place made her feel humbled and deeply moved.

Devin removed her knapsack and set it against the rockface. "Drinks," she said and handed Alice a soda. "Soda or beer?" she asked Maddie.

Having chosen to break free from the habitual drinking pattern she'd gotten into in New York, Maddie had enjoyed her beer at the dance. It was pleasant not to be driven by the need to tamp down the stresses of the day. Devin pulled a beer out of the bag and flipped the top off. "I'll have one of those," Maddie said. Devin handed over the open bottle. The intensity in Devin's lingering gaze mesmerized her, and her own longing made it impossible to look away. She swallowed hard and when Devin shifted her attention to the bag, it released the hold on her.

"So, who's hungry?" Devin asked and started to unpack.

Maddie sipped her beer. She was ravenous but nothing that came out of that backpack would satiate this appetite. She licked her lips, enjoying the way Devin's muscles flexed as she fussed over setting out the food. Savory and sweet aromas soon filled the cave. Devin watched Alice dig into the food as if she hadn't eaten in a week. She glanced in Maddie's direction and smiled encouragingly as she too delved into the picnic. Maddie joined them both and within a short time they were picking at the last bits together.

Alice swiftly finished her last mouthful and jumped to her feet. "Can I go and explore?"

Devin leaned back against the rockface. "Sure. You can climb up the outside if you want but not too high. You'll see a ledge up there—no further, promise me."

"Sure, Dev."

It was the first time Maddie had heard Alice call Devin by her nickname. It was cute and an indication of the level of affection they clearly held for each other. She waited until Alice left the cave. "When do you think they'll find a home for her?"

Devin looked toward the entrance and the smile slipped from her face. When she looked back at Maddie, her lips were set in a thin line.

Devin picked at the rim of the beer bottle. "I don't know."

"She loves the horses."

Devin's smile looked forced and disappeared quickly. "She does. She's a natural rider."

"She'd make a great rancher."

Devin huffed. "She sure would." She looked toward the entrance to the cave. "I hope she gets that chance."

It was clear how well Devin and Alice got along, and Maddie wanted to ask Devin whether she would consider adopting, but she sensed that wasn't a conversation Devin would welcome. "I'm sure she will," she said, though she wasn't convinced and judging by the expression on Devin's face, neither was she. Maddie didn't know much about the foster care system, but she knew love when she saw it. And where there was love, there was hope.

Devin started packing up. The hurt Maddie had seen in her eyes lingered in the ache beneath her ribs. There was something Devin wasn't saying. Something important to her, something that upset her. She wished Devin would share whatever it was. She bent down and started to collect everything. She moved around Devin in silence, and the air became sticky from the tension.

When Maddie stood, Devin turned away and picked up the bag. As Devin started toward the exit, Maddie stepped into her path. She wrapped her arms around her and tugged her into an embrace. Devin felt distant in her arms, unlike when they had danced, and Devin didn't make any move to hold Maddie. Maddie released her slowly. Looking into Devin's damp eyes, she felt sick with the heartbreak she saw. "I'm sorry," she said.

"It was a while ago," Devin said, her voice affected by whatever memory she'd revisited.

Maddie took her hand and held it tightly. Devin was the kindest person she'd ever met. She didn't deserve to feel this kind of pain. "Whatever it was, I'm sorry you suffered for it."

Devin took a deep breath. "Her name was Jaynee. She was a retreat guest who visited regularly. We got together. We planned to adopt, but it turned out she wasn't really into kids. She was too much of a kid herself, always demanding all of my attention. When it became clear a child would take my attention away from her, she left me. I don't think it's fair to adopt as a single parent."

Maddie's heart sank.

"I had hoped that Jaynee would settle into ranch and family life, but she was always a drifter."

Maddie couldn't leave her job or New York. Was she just like Jaynee?

"We'd filled out the paperwork for the adoption agency, but then had an argument that same evening." Devin scratched at the ground with a broken twig.

They'd planned to adopt together. Maddie glanced toward the entrance of the cave where Alice would likely be halfway up a rockface by now, and her heart ached for both her and Devin. They were great for each other.

"I withheld from submitting it and a week later, Jaynee took off in the middle of the night." She gave a tight-lipped smile and shrugged. "I haven't heard from her since, and I don't expect to."

"Surely the unconditional love of one parent is enough?" It was none of her business and yet she couldn't ignore the certainty that Devin would make an amazing foster parent. She pondered her parents' relationship with her as a child. She'd felt safe, but she couldn't say that she'd experienced the kind of tenderness that she'd seen Devin express with Alice. "Some people have two parents and don't feel loved."

Devin sighed. "Maybe." She headed silently out of the cave.

Maddie wanted to run to her and shake some sense into her. Devin should adopt if she wanted to. She had more than enough love for any child. And that child would make Devin's life complete too. She was sure Alice would want to be with someone like Devin.

She listened to Devin guiding Alice down the rockface, the calmness in her voice, and watched Alice following her instructions with complete trust. Who wouldn't want to be with someone like Devin?

16.

DEVIN CRANKED UP THE jukebox. There wasn't anything a little rock and roll played on full volume couldn't solve. It wasn't as if she'd *lost* someone she loved, like Maddie had. She'd been angry with herself over Jaynee, because she'd built her hopes up about them having a family together when she'd known deep down that Jaynee was too insecure to be able to care for a child. She'd felt let down but, worse still, Devin had seen it coming and not acted soon enough. She couldn't go through that again. Maddie wasn't like Jaynee, was she? The thought that her judgment might be skewed and that she might be making the same mistake unnerved her. This was a heart problem though, and no matter how much she tried to talk herself out of pursuing anything with Maddie, her heart wasn't listening.

She lifted Sally-Ann's hood and took a wrench to undo the spark plugs, even though they didn't need cleaning. She hadn't expected the memory to trigger her disappointment and hadn't expected Maddie to talk about Alice and adopting. The sadness had been overwhelming and caused her to reflect. She would love to bring up a child, to give that child a life that they wouldn't otherwise have. And even though Maddie had said the love of one parent was enough, she didn't know whether it was. There were too many what ifs. It wasn't just about love, it was about the responsibilities that went with taking care of a child, and what would happen to that child if something happened to Devin? She couldn't put that kind of pressure on her aging parents, if they were still around. The child might end up back in the system again, and she wouldn't want that.

She gathered the spark plugs together, took them to the bench, and started cleaning them with a file.

She should have hugged Maddie when she'd tried to comfort her. She should've been more conversational at the dinner table when Maddie had tried to talk to her, but the rawness of the memories dredged up, together with her growing feelings for Maddie which she knew would come to nothing, had sent her into a funk. The music would help.

She took the plugs back to the car and started screwing them into position.

Anne Murray's version of "Me and Bobby McGee" came to an end and Stevie Nicks blasted out "Landslide." The lyrics still cut deeply.

She'd built her life around Jaynee and had promised never to make the same mistake again. But at what cost? Without having someone close to share her life with, without her own family to love and care for, the emptiness never subsided. Cody and Ella were a huge part of her life, her sisters too. But they weren't the people she would choose to spend the rest of her life with or share her deepest fears and wildest dreams with.

"Hey."

Devin jumped at the unexpected intrusion and smacked the back of her head on the hood. She rubbed at her scalp as she turned toward the garage entrance.

Maddie came toward her and reached out to inspect her head. Devin backed away.

"I'm sorry, I didn't mean to make you jump."

"It's fine. It'd take more than a bit of old metal to crack this nut." She tried to sound jovial. None of this was Maddie's fault.

Maddie looked toward the floor. "I came to see if you were okay after earlier. And to apologize." She looked up. "I didn't mean to upset you."

Devin continued to rub the back of her head even though it didn't hurt. "Emotion finds a voice when you're least expecting it sometimes."

Maddie smiled. "You're right. I never expected to feel the way I do now." She cleared her throat. "About Lizzy, I mean. It's as though being away from everything that she was associated with, work and home, and our friends, has made it easier to accept the reality that she's not coming back into my life. I'll always love her, but I don't have to punish myself for her not being here. That doesn't serve either of us or the other people we love and care for. Everyone deserves happiness, don't they?"

Devin let her arms hang by her side. "Sure they do."

Maddie stood taller. "So, how about we focus on what makes us happy right now."

Devin smiled. "I'm working on Sally-Ann here. That makes me happy."

Maddie glanced into the engine. "Want some help?"

"You know about cars?"

"No, but I'm good at following instructions, and I know what some of the tools look like."

Devin recalled looking up at Maddie from beneath the car the first time they'd met and felt the lightness of that moment. There wasn't anything that particularly needed doing. She was just tinkering. She'd restored Sally-Ann into good working order already. The car was her go-to when she was feeling lousy or needed a distraction. "Yes, I remember." She grabbed a clean cloth and a tin of wax from the shelf and handed it to Maddie. "No tools needed for this, just hard work. You can start at the back. If it's painted, you can polish it. I'll do the silverwork."

Maddie took the items, made her way to the back of the car, and started applying the wax. Devin picked up a cloth and a tin of silver polish and began cleaning the rim of the front headlights. In Maddie's company, her earlier frustrations dissolved. Maddie had made a good point. Devin had to stop punishing herself for trusting a woman that she'd known would let her down. She rubbed the metalwork until it gleamed, stood back, and admired it with more satisfaction than the job warranted. She tracked the tuneless singing coming from the rear of the car and became captivated by Maddie's backside. She rubbed the wax into the back wheel arch and jiggled to the rhythm of the beat. Devin walked over to the jukebox, selected a song, and grabbed two beers from the fridge. Maddie stretched and walked toward her. She handed her a beer as Dolly Parton started singing "Jolene."

Maddie took a long pull then held the bottle like a microphone and started singing into it. When Devin laughed, Maddie sang louder. Devin would have planted her fingers in her ears if the liberating moment hadn't been so welcome. She'd heard cats whine more in tune. And yet, Maddie's enjoyment made the noise more delightful than the morning birdsong. Well, almost. She brought her bottle to her lips and ripped out the chorus with Maddie. When the song came to an end, she burst out laughing and without a second thought tugged Maddie to her and hugged her. She let her go quickly and went to the jukebox before she did something crazy like kissing her. "What next?"

"What do you have?"

Maddie stood closer to Devin than she needed to, given the amount of space around the machine, and leaned into Devin's arm. The touch was a distraction from considering the music options. Devin was sure the contact was intentional, but there was only one way to find out. She leaned her weight toward Maddie, and Maddie held her ground. The electric current that fired up the jukebox might as well have been attached to her. A fizz sparked up every cell in her body. She felt high on the thrill, and brave. She turned to face her. "What do you want?" she asked, her tone challenged by the intensity of her desire. She knew Maddie had noticed too by the appearance of the delicate lines at her temple that betrayed her smile.

Maddie turned slowly to face her. Devin inched closer. Maddie tilted her chin up a fraction. Devin closed her eyes at the point Maddie's lips touched hers. They were soft, and wet, and chilled from the beer. She tasted of sweet hops and more. The sensations disappeared, and Devin opened her eyes to see Maddie browsing the music options. Her heart raced. A kiss had never tasted so good. She bit her lip, trying to reclaim the feeling. "Wow." The word slipped out.

"Wow, yes." Maddie said, though she didn't look up from the jukebox. She pressed a button on the machine and turned to Devin. "Would you like to dance with me?"

Devin would have preferred something a lot slower than "I Feel Lucky." If she were skin to skin with Maddie for the rest of the evening, and the night, it wouldn't be enough right now. She held out her hand and Maddie took it. Devin did feel lucky tonight. She would pick the next song though. "Always on My Mind" would be a fitting choice since Maddie hadn't been too far from Devin's thoughts and nor would she be for the foreseeable future. Maybe "Feel like Making Love" would be perceived as suggestive, though Devin wouldn't say no, and after all, it was Maddie who had kissed her. Her thoughts were on overdrive, as were her feet, and the beer had gone straight to her head. Maddie turned on her heels suddenly and stepped into Devin's arms. Devin planted her feet, drew Maddie close, and kissed her tenderly until the music stopped.

17.

Maddie marveled at the foal. The incredible markings, white on silver and the white zig-zag line that ran along his nose, had become more pronounced in the days since his birth and he'd gotten stronger already. He would watch intently when Cody or Devin interacted with Dolly and then scoot around the corral playfully. He was stunning and growing quickly; seeing him come into the world was the most beautiful thing Maddie had experienced.

She looked toward the larger corral where Alice was still brushing Cookie. She'd been grooming the horse for at least an hour and didn't seem close to tiring. Alice put the brush down, wrapped her arms around Cookie's large neck, and leaned against him. Maddie couldn't hear what she was saying, but she looked to be in deep conversation with him and he swished his tail as if he understood her. She picked up a different brush and started on his mane.

Maddie crossed the yard and leaned on the fence of the corral. "He looks lovely," she said.

Alice smiled. "He's the best horse in the world."

"Better than Taco?"

Alice looked toward the Appaloosa that she'd first ridden. "He's my second favorite. He's good for beginners, but I'm an intermediate rider."

Maddie smiled. She was still a beginner and would likely remain as such for the duration of her stay. "You're a great rider."

Alice nodded. "It's the best feeling in the world."

Maddie had to agree. There was something quite special about being on the back of something so powerful and graceful, once you'd gotten past the fear of being thrown from a height. "They're incredible creatures."

"They're my family. I love them."

The surge of sadness was instant and overwhelming. Maddie had a padre, mamá, and hermana back in New York, and yet she didn't have a family any more than Alice did. She hadn't chosen to be ostracized by them, but she'd been old enough to handle the hurt when they'd disowned her. Alice was just a kid and had lived with a mom who couldn't look after her for probably as many years as Alice could remember. "I think sometimes we're better off choosing our family."

Alice turned to face Maddie and frowned. "Do you have a mom and dad?"

Maddie nodded.

Alice shrugged with the same matter-of-fact bearing that Devin did. "So, you didn't have to choose them?"

Maddie took a deep breath. She'd started the conversation, so she had to justify herself or she'd feel like a hypocrite. "I don't have any contact with them."

Alice continued brushing Cookie's mane. "Why?"

Maddie considered how to answer the question. There was no easy way to talk about rejection, but honesty was crucial. "They disowned me."

Alice looked at Maddie. "What do you mean? Were they junkies and prostitutes?"

Maddie's heart sank. Alice spoke effortlessly using terms she shouldn't have been exposed to at her age. God knows what she'd seen or worse still, experienced. Maddie's situation with her parents seemed banal by comparison. "They didn't want anything to do with me because I love women, not men."

Alice stared at Maddie for a bit. "Hm. If my mom had loved women, maybe she wouldn't have gotten into so much shit."

The frankness touched Maddie. "Maybe. But maybe people are just destined to—"

"Ruin their lives? I didn't ask to be born or left alone." Alice sniffed and cuffed her nose. "I know she loved me."

Maddie hadn't been sure what she was trying to say and what she had said had come out badly. "No, you didn't deserve to be left alone."

"It's not fair."

The pitch in Alice's voice rose, and Maddie went to her. "It's not fair. Life can be pretty shitty sometimes." Unsure of what to do, she put her arm on Alice's shoulder and squeezed gently. "You're strong and smart, and you have the chance to create a good life."

"With folks who can't love me like my mom did."

Maddie closed her eyes in a vain attempt to fight back the tears. Nothing compared to a mother's love, even when that mom was an addict, or in her own mamá's case, ineffectual and subservient to her padre's will. Not everyone had the courage or strength or the support of good people to draw on. Some, like Alice's mom, had nothing and their best wasn't good enough when they had a child who needed them. Alice didn't question her mom's love, but the love of foster parents couldn't compare. "They will love you," she said and felt the lameness of the statement in the ache in her heart.

"Sure, like the last ones said they did."

Maddie hadn't realized there had been others. She couldn't imagine what it would be like to be passed from one family to another, with temporary homes in between. How could a child settle and feel secure? It was a wonder Alice was as well-adjusted as she appeared to be. She put her arm around Alice's shoulder and held her close. "We're lucky we have the horses, aren't we?"

"I miss my mom."

"I miss mine too."

"Where are you from?"

"New York."

Alice nodded. "What do you do?"

"I'm a doctor."

Alice looked up at her. "Can you help my mom?"

Maddie's stomach dropped like a stone. "I'm not that kind of doctor, Alice. Your mom needs a different kind of support. I help people who hurt themselves or have serious accidents."

"My mom hurts herself."

Maddie swallowed hard. There was nothing she could say to Alice to reassure her. She couldn't take away her suffering. The poor kid. "I'm sorry. I'm sure the doctors where she's staying will be taking good care of her, and she'll get better soon."

Alice leaned into Maddie. "I want to be a rancher when I grow up."

Maddie sighed, thankful for the shift in conversation to something more positive. "I think you'll make a great rancher."

Alice looked up. "Do you?"

Maddie smiled and nodded. "Sure do. You have a wonderful way with the horses, and you ride like a pro." Maddie brushed away the wetness that clung to her cheeks.

Alice pulled away from Maddie and led Cookie into the field. "I lived near horses once and...I used to ride them sometimes," she said and blushed.

Maddie got the sense that Alice hadn't had permission to ride those horses, but the fact that Alice had ridden them might have helped save her from the darkness of the world into which she'd been born. Alice wasn't a good liar, and Maddie liked that. "I've never ridden before," she said.

"Devin's really good. Have you seen her barrel racing? She's won competitions. She has the trophies to prove it."

Maddie recalled the kiss the previous evening, and her chest filled with warmth. It came as no surprise that Devin was talented, and humble with it. "I'd like to see her racing one day."

"Me too."

A brief silence passed between them. Maddie could only imagine that Alice had been subjected to a truly frightening and disturbing life in her early years. Maddie's world hadn't crumbled until she'd come out to her parents before heading to college. She'd been an adult. Alice was just a kid, a kid who needed to feel loved and safe. Her heart ached.

"She's going to take me for a campout next week, and she's said I can go to the rodeo with her. And compete there too." Alice let Cookie go and started back toward Maddie.

It was wonderful to see her so animated and enthused. The transformation spoke volumes. She really did fit in at the ranch, with Devin as her best buddy. "That sounds amazing. Perhaps I can come and watch you both at the rodeo?"

"You can come and camp out too. We're going to have a fire and cook the fish we'll catch."

Maddie liked the sound of that, but she couldn't intrude on their time together, and Devin hadn't invited her. "We'll see," she said.

"Devin," Alice said.

Maddie turned toward the house. Her breath hitched as she watched Devin coming toward them.

"Maddie's coming camping with us," Alice said.

Maddie bit her lip. "Well, I don't—"

"Sure."

Devin responded before Maddie managed to get her weak objection out.

Devin tipped her hat toward Maddie. "Can you cook fish? Alice is responsible for heating the beans. We're going to catch supper, aren't we?"

Maddie realized she'd been staring at Devin and hadn't answered her question. "Um, yes, I can cook fish."

"Ah, but can you put up a teepee?"

Maddie widened her eyes and shook her head. "I wouldn't have a clue where to start."

"Then Alice and I would be delighted to teach you, wouldn't we?"

Alice beamed at Maddie. "It'll be so cool." She turned to Devin. "Can I stay up real late?"

Devin put her hand to her chin. "Hm, let me think."

Alice stared at Devin with a worried expression for a moment and then gave a big toothy grin. "You're teasing."

"How about we stay up until the stars go to sleep?"

Alice harrumphed. "Stars don't go to sleep."

Devin frowned. "Hm, it's gonna be a late night then."

Alice gave a squeal of delight and ran at Devin, who wrapped her arms around her and smiled. "You'll join us, won't you?"

Heat consumed Maddie. She'd enjoy a night with Devin sleeping together in a teepee under the stars very much, alone. But Alice's beaming grin and sheer delight at the prospect of a campout with her and Devin also melted her heart. And she'd be honored to spend time with them both. "How can I refuse such an offer?"

"You'll see the Milky Way. It's spectacular."

Devin was spectacular and since they'd kissed, she'd also become irresistible. Maddie had forgotten what pure lust felt like. The novelty of it, the rawness and intensity seemed to consume her body every waking hour and during most of her sleeping hours too. The feelings she'd had for Lizzy were deep, having evolved over time, and in the years that Lizzy had been ill, the desire they'd shared had become something less urgent, though equally as precious. But she wasn't quite sure how she would keep her hands off Devin during their campout, though she guessed Alice's constant presence and the heavy dose of responsibility that she felt toward the child would serve as an effective dampener. "I'm looking forward to it already."

Alice took Devin's hand and led her out of the corral and toward the foal. Maddie watched Devin's butt in the tight jeans and drifted to thoughts of them lying naked together under the stars. The fiery sensation between her legs turned to frustration, and she returned to the house to cool down.

18

DEVIN SLOWLY WORKED HER way down the ladder. A river of sweat trailed down her back and her face tingled. Damn, it was too hot to be fixing a roof. She took the chilled bottle of water Ella offered her and pressed it to her forehead before downing the contents.

"I needed that."

Ella squinted upwards to where Cody was still working. "It's looking very good."

Devin studied their handiwork. It wasn't looking too bad at all. The new roof would last the school a lifetime, so their efforts were well worth it. She screwed up the plastic bottle and threw it in the trash they'd accumulated along with bits of timber, broken tiles, and felt. "We'll be finished in a couple of hours, I reckon. Plus an hour clearing up."

Ella put her hand to her chest and sighed. "Thank you so much."

Devin smiled. "It's a pleasure." Feeling marginally refreshed, she climbed the ladder. She picked up a pile of tiles from the scaffold platform and scrambled across the roof to start the line above where Cody was working.

Cody, resting on her knees, straightened her back. "You still haven't answered my question."

Devin slotted the first tile in place. "There's nothing to add to what I already said. We get along well, that's all."

"Well, you sure look like you have something going on. I haven't seen you having eyes for a woman like you have for Maddie. Even old Abe reckoned you were acting strange."

Devin knocked another tile into place, ignoring Cody's persistent questioning. Though she wondered what Abe had noticed and whether her attraction to Maddie had been like a beacon to those who knew her well. "I can't speak for Abe's ideas or anyone else's."

Cody laughed. "You're looking hotter than the sun when you talk about Maddie. I can tell when you're thinking about her."

Heat rose up Devin's neck and she silently cursed Cody's relentlessness. She knocked another tile into place and moved along the roof. "Anyway, your chattering isn't getting this roof fixed."

"Just making conversation." Cody picked up a tile and started back to work.

The silence didn't last long.

"So, you're planning to camp out with Alice?"

Devin rolled her eyes. She had an idea of what was coming next. "Yep."

"And Maddie's going along for the ride?"

"Yep." Devin studied the line of tiles for their fit. *Perfect.*

"And that's not strange for you. The last guest you..." Cody lowered her head and slotted a tile into place. "Sorry."

Devin raised herself to her knees and put her hands on her hips. Maddie was nothing like Jaynee, and *this* scenario was completely different. It had to be. She couldn't have history repeating itself.

"I know you're not going to find the love of your life anywhere local, Dev. I reckon the whole town knows that much after Cat. I just don't want to see you get like you did with that woman." Cody ran her hand through her hair and scratched the back of her head.

Devin had been down the same line of thinking time and again since realizing her feelings for Maddie. "That's why there's nothing happening between us."

"But you're into her?"

She rubbed her brow with her forearm before the trickle of sweat ran into her eyes. "I like her. She's kind, and sweet, and smart."

"I knew it." Cody's smile widened. "If you like her that much, why don't you ask her to stay?"

"Have you asked Ella out yet?" She'd snapped though she'd managed to control her tone.

Cody glanced to where Ella stood in the playground talking to another helper. "It's not that easy."

"Exactly. It's not that easy for me, either. Maddie has an important job and a life that's so different from ours. She probably doesn't feel that strongly about me, either. She's here to take a break, not settle down here."

"She's definitely into you. I've seen her looking."

Devin had seen that too. She just didn't want to raise her hopes. It was too early for promises and commitments even if it wasn't too soon for hearts to be broken. "Sure. But there's being *into* and then there's moving across the damn country. And they're a whole bunch different."

Cody's attention had drifted toward Ella.

"You should ask her out."

"We had a dance together," Cody said and sighed.

"And?"

"The song changed, and she shot off real quick."

Devin smiled. "She avoided a slow dance with you?"

Cody shrugged.

"Trust me, she's into you."

"How d'you work that out?"

"Damn, you can be blinder than a bat. Ella's too shy to make the first move."

Ella waved at them, and they waved back. Devin saw Maddie carrying a basket toward the playground. Her heart skipped a beat and as she adjusted her footing, she missed the mark and tumbled. Devin tried frantically to grab hold of the roof as she slid but she'd toppled at an awkward angle. Time seemed to slow down, but she was powerless to stop the inevitable.

Cody scrambled down from her position. "Hang on, Dev."

Devin hit the platform below the roof with a heavy thump. Her head whipped back and smacked against one of the metal scaffolding poles that had prevented her from falling all the way to the ground. "Shit." She clasped the back of her head and tried to sit. Her head whirled, and she laid back down. Her hand was covered in blood and a burning sensation settled behind her ribs at her back. Nausea turned her stomach, and she took long deep breaths to settle it. Cody stood above her looking down, hands on her hips, with a half-grin.

"I told you, no dancing on the roof," she said. She bent down and put her hand on Devin's shoulder. "Where does it hurt?"

"Head, mainly. I'll be fine."

"I know. I've watched you thrown farther off a horse." Cody held out her hand. Devin took it.

"Wait," Maddie shouted. "Wait." Maddie climbed the ladder to the platform. "Let me check you."

Devin lifted herself to sit. "I'm fine, honestly." She touched her ribs and winced. "Bit of bruising, no doubt, and a graze," she said. Maddie looked calm on the outside, despite her hollering, and Devin saw concern in her expression.

"You're not fine until I say so." Maddie moved closer and inspected Devin's head. "What about your back?"

"Here, somewhere." Devin indicated with her hand.

Maddie pressed gently around the area, and Devin lost track of where the pain was located.

"Any dizziness?"

"No." It was a little white lie, but she didn't want Maddie worrying about something that was nothing. Her head stung like hell though.

"Sickness?"

"A little," she said without thinking.

"We need to get you down and get your head looked at. It looks superficial. Heads can bleed like crazy, but it might be worth getting an X-ray of your ribs."

"I'm not going to the hospital," Devin said as she brought herself to her feet. The world moved in front of her eyes, and she casually leaned into the scaffolding for support.

"You—" Maddie pinched her lips together and shook her head.

"I'll get patched up at home." The world had stopped spinning, and Devin slowly made her way down the ladder. "I'll be fine."

Maddie followed her.

Cody smiled broadly. "Take good care of her, doc. Oh, and don't worry, Dev, I'll finish the job."

"Are you okay?" Ella asked.

Devin nodded and wished she hadn't when the pain in her head flared up. "I'll be fine. I just need to get washed up."

"You can use the school facilities," Ella said. "We have a first aid pack. I'll get it for you."

"Thanks, Ella." Devin watched Ella heading toward the school, aware that Maddie was staring at her. She turned back to Maddie, who was looking closely into her eyes.

"I'm not happy. You should get properly checked out."

Devin smiled. "I just did."

Maddie shook her head. "Well, once you're cleaned up, someone will need to keep an eye on you for concussion. You can't go back up there." She pointed to the roof. "Did you black out at all?"

Devin wanted to argue the point about her ability to carry on working, but the concern in Maddie's expression stopped her. She shook her head.

"Do you remember what happened before you fell?"

Devin grinned. "I saw you coming."

Maddie looked away. "I'm being serious."

Devin touched the back of her head and winced. "Me too. I've never fallen that hard for anyone." Devin winked. "Did you bring a picnic?" she asked, indicating the abandoned basket in the middle of the playground. Had she just said that she'd fallen for Maddie? What the heck. Either she was slightly concussed or the conversation with Cody had swayed her to be honest with Maddie about her feelings. She followed Maddie into the school feeling more than a little unstable. What the heck was wrong with her? Had she not learned the first time around? Being left with a broken heart every time a kid left was one thing; falling for a guest led to a whole different world of trouble. She had to quash these crazy feelings before they had too big a hold over her. *God damn it.*

19.

MADDIE MOVED BEHIND DEVIN, parted her hair, and studied the injury. She picked up a swab and cleaned the graze, dabbing gently, impressed that Devin didn't even flinch at the contact. "I assume you're accustomed to throwing yourself off horses so that something like this doesn't hurt?"

"I've been known to hit the deck, but I have a reputation for bouncing well."

Maddie laughed. "Well, you lost out to a metal pole today."

Devin raised her hand toward the back of her head, and Maddie swatted it away. She took another swab and continued to wipe the dried blood that had matted Devin's hair. "Didn't it occur to you to wear a safety helmet?"

"I didn't anticipate being distracted by a beautiful woman."

Maddie slapped her arm. The bump to Devin's head had loosened her tongue, which happened sometimes with a concussion.

"It's true. I lost my footing when I saw you." She turned her hands palms up to reveal grazes and dirt.

Maddie didn't have a response to Devin's admission. She could relate to being distracted though. It had taken her best effort to act professionally and concentrate on the injury, when all she'd wanted to do was take Devin into her arms and make everything better. If she could, she would turn back time so that Devin hadn't fallen. If Maddie hadn't been there, this wouldn't have happened. "I'll clean your hands up next. How are your ribs?"

Devin lifted her shirt at the back. "Sore. What's the diagnosis, doc?"

145

There was shading and a graze across two ribs on her right side, but Maddie was more distracted by the smoothness of the skin that she wanted to run her hands over. She released a soft gasp, which she tried to mask by clearing her throat.

"That bad?" Devin asked.

"It's likely to swell and bruise, and you might have fractured your ribs, but since you refuse to go to the hospital to find out, there's little I can do about that."

"I'll take Tylenol for a couple of days and see how it goes."

Maddie rolled her eyes, though she secretly admired Devin's grit and her pragmatic approach. Maybe she'd become too clinical because of the necessities of her job. Out here, people didn't run to the local hospital at the first sight of blood, though maybe they should, especially with a head injury. She went back to cleaning the wound. It didn't need sutures. She was being overprotective, and she was acutely aware of why that was. She softened her irritation with Devin's flippancy and tried to ignore the urge to kiss the top of Devin's head in case someone walked in on them. "You'll survive," she said and walked around the chair to face Devin.

She took her hand and studied the calluses that came with the harshness of Devin's work mending fences, nurturing the land, navigating the elements, and working the horses. Devin closed her hand around Maddie's, and she became aware of the longing in Devin's gaze. "I need to—"

Devin tugged Maddie to her with her free hand and silenced her with a kiss. Maddie pulled back and looked toward the door, where she expected Ella or Cody to come running in to check on Devin.

"Since I fell for you, I'm claiming my reward." Devin reached up and stroked Maddie's face. "Are you always this serious when you're doctoring?"

Devin's smile warmed Maddie's heart, and she sighed. "I was worried about you."

"A caring doc is a good doc, right?"

Maddie nodded. This was about more than caring though, and she suspected Devin sensed that too. She looked at Devin's hand, still wrapped around hers. "You're making me filthy," she said and pulled free. She should be wearing gloves, but the school's kit was lacking. Devin's touch resonated through her fingers.

Devin blushed, and it occurred to her that Devin had taken her comment as a double entendre. Heat rose to her cheeks.

Devin let go of Maddie and held up her hand. "Sorry, doc," she said and raised her eyebrow.

Now she'd reassured herself that Devin wasn't badly hurt, and no matter what Maddie said she wasn't going to convince Devin to go to the hospital to get checked out, she enjoyed the pleasant teasing and the light-hearted banter. "That's okay, rancher. I'll forgive you, this time." She smiled as she took Devin's hand and cleaned the grazes. She looked up and caught Devin staring at her. "What?"

"You have a very gentle touch."

Devin's hand was warm and strong. She studied the delicate tattoo on the inside of her wrist now she could see it up close. It was an infinity design with one thick band and one thin line forming the figure eight that looked like a black ribbon. Tiny leaves, or maybe they were doves, were painted on the left side of the top of the loop. A thin arrow passed through the center where the figure eight crossed. The word *forever* was written in a fancy font on the bottom of the right side of the loop. Its design bore some resemblance to the images she'd seen on the walls of the cave. "What does your tattoo mean?"

Devin looked at it and took a deep breath. "Love."

Maddie felt a rush of energy engulf her. "It's beautiful." The symbol was powerful and alluring, and Maddie felt drawn to trace its shape with her finger.

"Thanks. I like it." Devin closed her hand and pulled away.

Had Devin had the tattoo done for someone? Maddie held out her hand toward Devin's other hand.

"So, do you come here often?" Devin asked and grinned.

Maddie smiled. "Funny." If the tattoo had specific meaning, Devin certainly didn't show it. "I'm hungry, are you?"

Devin laughed. "I'm always starving."

"There's the picnic," Maddie said. Devin stood. She was close—too close—and her breath was warm and sweet, and Maddie's heart raced.

Devin removed the swab from Maddie's hand. "I think we're done here. Cody will have already eaten whatever you brought. How about I take you to lunch in town?"

Maddie's attention was consumed by Devin's soft lips. She craved the tenderness of Devin's kiss and the sensations that flowed from that kiss to her core. Devin drew her closer. Her body was warm, her arm strong around her waist. And when the kiss came, it was everything she knew it would be, and more. At the knock on the door, she opened her eyes and pushed Devin away from her.

"Oh, um, okay. I was just checking in." Cody wiped the sweat from her brow and grinned. "Seems the doc's taking good care of you."

Maddie looked away and hoped the fiery heat that had crept up her neck hadn't made it to her cheeks. "She'll live," she said. "But she still needs a close eye for a few hours, in case she has a concussion."

Cody laughed. "Nothing breaks that nut."

Maddie looked between them both. There was a sense of rivalry, probably for the one who could bounce the best. It wasn't a game Maddie would subscribe to, but it clearly amused them. "So I've been told. She still needs to be watched."

Cody saluted. "Yes, ma'am," she said. "But that can't be me." She beamed at Devin. "I have a roof to finish and then I'm taking Ella for coffee."

Devin slapped Cody on the back. "You go easy there. I'll be fine."

Maddie stopped short of rolling her eyes at Devin. She would keep an eye on her for the rest of the afternoon, just to be sure.

"We're heading to town for lunch," Devin said.

Maddie could sense the cogs whirring inside Cody's mind. The spark that lit up her eyes said that she'd seen them together and made a correct assumption. It wasn't that Maddie didn't want Cody to know that she liked Devin, it was simply that Maddie still had to adjust to the depth of her feelings. And until she did, she felt awkward with any public expression of affection. She had to find a box for what was going on and a label for this relationship she hadn't intended getting into. Was it just a vacation romance? But there wasn't one ounce of her being that didn't feel that whatever was going on was so much more than a casual affair. And on that basis, she didn't have the first idea how to categorize it, let alone predict what might transpire in the short time they had left together.

In two weeks, it could all be in the past and on the way to being forgotten. She would be back at the ER and back to her life, saving lives and enjoying her nights out with friends at Paddy Reilly's. She hadn't heard from Lee. She hadn't missed the Irish pub either. She hadn't given the ER a second thought in at least a week, which was something she'd never even achieved when she'd vacationed with Lizzy. *Lizzy.* She would always be a part of Maddie, their history of love and friendship. Would she spot Lizzy's star at night in New York? The thought that she might not left her with a sinking feeling. She was no longer haunted by Lizzy's loss, and the anger that had been with her since Lizzy's death had released its hold over her. But what if she returned home and that past came flooding back to her? What if this time with Devin was just another way of her hiding from her shit? Her heart thundered with a heavy beat. She wouldn't like that, not one bit. She cast the disturbing thoughts to the back of her mind.

20.

"YOU'RE STARING AT ME."

Maddie looked away. "No, I'm not."

Devin melted as Maddie's cheeks colored. She was even more beautiful when she looked a little pensive. Small frown lines appeared and disappeared, presumably with her thoughts, and she often bit her lip as she listened. Maddie was a deep thinker, unlike most of the women Devin knew. It was a quality that attracted her and one of the reasons Devin would never find a life partner in or around Austin. She knew almost everyone who lived close by and other than briefly considering asking Ella on a date, which would have been for all the wrong reasons, she wasn't into any of them. She'd thought Jaynee was philosophical at first, but she wasn't. She was evasive and manipulative, and one of those people who had more secrets than they did thoughts. Devin had been deceived by her, blinded by infatuation that she'd thought was love. That had happened at a low point in her life, at a time when she'd been desperate for someone special in her life and yearned for a child. Devin didn't fall in love easily, but when she did, she was all-in. Maddie wasn't a drifter. She was solid, grounded in a professional career, and she exuded a reflective silence that left Devin wanting to know her innermost thoughts and feelings and to share her own.

Maddie was staring at her across the table. She had a look of concern and seemed on edge, no doubt still worried about the bump to Devin's head. She could easily lose track of time and place staring at her, especially up close. Kissing kind of close. She picked up a chicken wing and started to eat it, though her appetite had deserted her, and her head pounded.

Maddie bit into her burger. "I'm just keeping an eye on you."

A prickle of guilt stopped Devin giving a flippant response. It was time to quit goofing off and to cut Maddie some slack for caring. "I know, and I appreciate it."

Maddie lifted her head as if she was waiting for a retort.

"Honestly. My head is throbbing and you're right; I'll pop into the medical center after lunch."

Maddie released a long breath and sat back in the chair. "I know I might be being overly sensitive, and I don't want to blemish your hard-earned reputation." She tilted her head and raised her eyebrows. "But..."

Devin waited on the rest of the sentence, but Maddie lowered her head and gave her attention to her food. "But what?"

"Nothing. It's fine. You're a grown woman, and you don't need me telling you what to do."

The banter between them had stopped, and there was a tension growing between them. Maybe Maddie's sensitivity was about her ex, Lizzy. Life was precious, precarious, and Devin hadn't really given considered thought to the end. She worked with animals and saw the cycle of life daily. But, to think deeply about losing those she loved would hurt more than any bump on the head ever could. Besides, there were better things to do than dwell on the inevitability of death.

Maddie was strong and courageous, and the most levelling realization of all, she was also on Devin's short list of people that she didn't want to think about losing. "I promise, I'll take better care of myself," Devin said.

Maddie smiled. "I hope so."

There was something in Maddie's tone that Devin couldn't identify, but it sounded like the kind of concern she'd heard expressed by her mom and Ella, laced with affection. The tenderness swept over her and bathed her in warmth. Maddie really cared, and by the way Maddie had kissed her, she had deeper feelings.

Shit.

She hadn't considered the consequences for Maddie of them getting close and then parting. Devin had reconciled that after Maddie returned to New York, she'd take her broken heart and heal it with the mustangs in the wild, riding rodeo, and working on Sally-Ann. That's what she'd done before, and it worked just fine.

What about Maddie?

If Devin had read Maddie's feelings correctly, how was Maddie going to cope with leaving the ranch? *She could stay. She won't stay; she has a career, and a home, and colleagues. She already has a life that doesn't include me.* Her thoughts were running on overdrive, her wildest dream challenged by that part of her that knew she couldn't ask Maddie to give up everything to be with her. Devin's heart ached with want. Her mind refused to ask the question. She stared at the food then put down her napkin. She couldn't eat another bite.

Maddie frowned. "Are you okay?"

"I'm done."

"You've hardly eaten."

She looked at Maddie for a moment before guilt spiked her conscience. She'd enticed Maddie into her world and that meant she would be to blame for Maddie's sadness. If she hadn't encouraged Maddie, they could have just enjoyed each other's company without any unnecessary complications. "I'm not feeling hungry anymore."

"A concussion can do that."

This wasn't anything about the accident, though being flippant about her feelings and loose-tongued about her attraction to Maddie might have been the result of the knock to her head. Who was she kidding? She would've been better off taking a bang that knocked her out rather than one that had let her mouth run away with her wishes.

Maddie's frown deepened. She put her napkin on the table and sat upright in the chair. It was as if formality had been created in the strained interaction between them.

"You finish. There's no rush."

Maddie's eyelids weighed heavily over her eyes, and Devin felt looked at without being seen.

"It's okay. I'm done too," Maddie said.

Had she picked up on Devin's concerns? The lightness in Maddie's tone when they'd bantered and laughed at Devin's craziness had gone. Lunch had promised so much and quickly turned sour. "Are you okay?" She asked the question though she knew the answer.

Maddie took a deep breath and released it slowly. "Sure."

She'd switched from cheerful to melancholy on a dime and without a clear reason as to why. If Devin didn't say something to lift the funk that had settled between them, they could spiral apart. Maybe that would be for the best. Her heart disagreed. To be around Maddie and feel this distant from her was worse than the pain of a broken heart. There were too many things that Devin had planned for them to do and enjoy together. That pleasure was hanging on a knife's edge, and she needed to pull it back. "I was thinking that I like you, and I'm going to miss you when you go back to New York."

Maddie's smile had a weary quality to it. She released another long breath. "I like you too, and I've been trying to work out how to categorize our...what we have together."

"Do you need to? Can't we just enjoy ourselves?"

Maddie picked up the fork and turned it in her hand. "Maybe not."

Devin leaned forward and her ribs twinged. She resisted the urge to take Maddie's hand. "Hey."

Maddie looked up.

"I like spending time with you, showing you around, and seeing you relax and enjoy yourself." There was so much more to it than that, but she could hardly blurt out, "I'm falling for you," in the middle of the diner. That said, she'd already said something like it to Maddie at the school, but Maddie might've put her blurted confession down to the concussion. If Devin came on too intense, she might scare her into leaving before the end of her vacation, and that was a risk she wasn't prepared to take a gamble on.

"I enjoy it here. Apart from you trying to throw yourself from a roof, of course."

Devin laughed. She touched the back of her head and winced with the sharp pain that spread across her skull. "Can't help falling for a pretty woman," she said, trying to salvage the banter they'd shared, and smiled. Joking was healthier than mulling over an uncertain future. "Are you going to check that our medical center treats me properly?"

"Definitely not." Maddie shook her head. "I'll wait outside for you, but I'm not stepping on toes. Just make sure you get an X-ray for your back."

"Yes, ma'am," Devin said, mirroring Cody's response to Maddie, though she left off the salute and smiled broadly instead. "I might need someone keeping a watch on me for a few hours, you know."

Maddie laughed. "Yes, I'm planning to, until you go to bed."

"And then what?" Devin raised her eyebrows. She was pushing lightheartedly for something she desperately wanted, which was to hold Maddie close and be able to touch every part of her in the privacy of a room and in the quiet of the night. She wanted to lay in Maddie's arms and listen to her breathing softly and watch the rise and fall of her chest as they made love. She wanted all these things and much more. Maddie's neck and face colored, her lips quivered, and Devin hoped Maddie wanted her in that way too.

21.

MADDIE HAD BEEN SHOCKED by the intensity of her response to Devin tumbling from the roof. Her clinical training had kicked in, so she'd acted rationally and quickly ascertained that Devin's injuries weren't too serious, but her stomach had turned upside down and irrational thoughts had made their way into her consciousness. She'd gone to the diner with an unsettled feeling and when the banter between them dried up, that feeling had intensified.

She liked Devin a lot and had been struggling with what to do with that as she'd observed her across the table. Devin had behaved oddly, and that wasn't just about the bump on her head. Devin had happily joked one minute and then become serious and silent in the next, confusing Maddie. Devin's quietness had winded her. Fear had risen instantly and paralyzed her. But the fear lifted the instant Devin said she liked her. Relief had never felt so all-encompassing and wonderfully liberating.

The emotional roller coaster she'd ridden in the past twenty-four hours meant only one thing. Box or no box, category or no category, what she felt for Devin was more than liking: she was falling in love with her. The realization felt sudden, shocking and unexpected, and she was unprepared for the truth of it, unlike with Lizzy who'd been a friend long before they gotten together as a couple. Devin had rocked her heart. The temptation to be with her was stronger than her will which told her to walk away.

She would have gone to Devin's room, had it not been for her mom who'd insisted that she be the one to keep a careful eye on her daughter. Thankfully, Devin had been cleared by the medical center and hadn't broken any bones, but Maddie had still wanted to check every millimeter of her beautiful body, and she'd been reluctant to leave her.

She'd taken an age to fall asleep. She'd allowed Devin's confession to caress her and held onto the image of her without consideration for anything beyond this glorious moment in time. She hadn't wanted her mood to be interrupted by a shift in consciousness that would lead her to the place that would remind her of the futility of starting something with Devin that she couldn't pursue. They'd already started something though, hadn't they? They'd kissed, and the imprint of it remained undeniably etched in every cell in Maddie's body.

Tiredness had won the battle at some point in the early hours of the morning but not before the birds had started to chirp. If she'd had dreams, she didn't remember them.

She climbed out of bed, drew back the curtains, and stepped into the en-suite shower. She'd never skipped breakfast as often as she had since arriving at the ranch, and she rarely had the opportunity to start a day just short of lunchtime in New York either. That would all be fine, if it wasn't that she was missing a good part of the day and missing spending all the time she possibly could with Devin. She dressed quickly and followed the smell of freshly baked bread and coffee into the kitchen.

Devin's mom looked up from the kitchen surface where she was pounding a large slab of meat with a hefty-looking wooden stick.

"Morning, Rosie. Something smells good."

"There's coffee brewing, and there are grits in the pot and fresh-baked cookies on the rack. Mind, lunch is at one." Rosie made the meat dance on the tabletop with the force of each strike.

"What are you making?"

"Burgers. I need to tenderize the brisket then cover it in a rub. I leave it for a few days in the smokehouse before mincing it. Do you like burgers?"

So, the smokehouse was where the aromas came from. She'd caught a whiff of them from her bedroom balcony from time to time. "Sure do."

Rosie chuckled. "You're sounding like a Nevadan already. Infectious, isn't it?"

Maddie laughed. "Sure is." It was true, she'd picked up some of the colloquial terms, though she'd still not lost her New York accent. It was interesting that Rosie had noticed the shift.

"I'm glad you're looking better," Rosie said.

Maddie felt more alive than she had in as long as she could remember. "Thanks."

She winced as Rosie smacked the meat, turned it over, and whacked it again. She poured coffee and took a cookie with a building sense of urgency to get into the yard and see Devin. "How's the patient?" she asked as nonchalantly as possible. Rosie glanced at Maddie over the top of her glasses, and Maddie's cheeks burned under what felt like scrutiny.

"She's out mending the fences."

"She didn't think to rest for a day?" Maddie sipped her coffee. The liquid burned her tongue, and she cursed under her breath.

"That girl doesn't know the meaning of the word. She was up and out before the coyotes had gone to bed, like she has termites biting her or something."

Rosie's ample chest rose and fell on a deep sigh, and her gaze appeared to slip into an inner world. Her features softened, and Maddie had no doubt as to Rosie's love for Devin. As much as Maddie would have wanted to insist that Devin take it easy the day after a fall, she could no more clip her wings than she could tell her how she really felt about her. Devin's determination to just get on with whatever needed doing, and the pure joy she seemed to radiate, was awe-inspiring. She was wonderful to be around. Maddie gazed out the window, imagining Devin mending fences and joking around with Cody, and her heart melted.

Since she had nothing to rush into the yard for, she took a bite of the cookie and leaned against the surface. "Can I give you a hand with anything?"

Rosie threw the meat into a large metal container. "Sure. Are you any good with a rub?"

Maddie had never put rub on a piece of meat that size, but she'd try. "I can follow instructions," she said and put down her coffee.

"The mix is in that tub." Rosie pointed to a large plastic container.

"How much?"

Rosie shrugged. "A good coating on all sides. No need to be shy with it."

Maddie went to the container and tried to lift it but couldn't.

"Take a jug from there and fill it."

Maddie did as she was told and tipped the contents onto the meat. She started pressing the mix into the crevices of the joint. A hit of cardamon and lemon caught her senses. "I bet these burgers will taste great," she said.

"I've never had no complaints—yet."

Rosie went to the fridge and returned with a large tub of raw chicken wings, enough to feed the whole town. Rosie leaned back as she carried the container pressed against her chest. She landed it on the surface with a thud and took a deep breath.

"You like wings?" Rosie asked.

"Who doesn't like wings? We have buffalo wings in New York."

"Yeah, and they've been nowhere near a buffalo." Rosie laughed. She went to the fridge again and came back with another container containing a rich red sauce.

"That smells delicious. What's in it?"

"It's our ranch sauce. The recipe was handed down generations ago. The ingredients are secret."

"Oh, okay." Maddie prodded the rub into the meat with her knuckles.

Rosie nudged Maddie and chuckled. "I'm teasing. We make our own hot sauce, then add paprika, salt, pepper, a little vinegar, and butter."

Maddie tried to lift the joint she was working on. Thinking she might lose control of it due to its weight and shape, she turned it over by easing it around inside the pan and continued with the rub.

Rosie filled a clean jug with the sauce and placed it next to the raw wings. "So, how are you liking your stay?"

"It's way more than I could have imagined."

"Do you enjoy your job?"

Maddie hadn't missed work since letting go of the idea that she'd deserted her colleagues. Enjoying the pleasant reprieve from the stress, she'd been able to immerse herself in ranch life. The people she'd met in Austin were friendly and kind, the area was stunning, and watching Lightning being born and learning to ride Taco had been wonderful. She considered Rosie's question on the back of yesterday's incident with Devin. She would never lose the drive to help save lives. Without that, without her work, who was she? Something unnerving stirred in her gut. "It's stressful at times, but I do love it," she said, the certainty in her tone tainted by the persistence of the niggling sensation and the absence of any reason for it.

Rosie hummed under her breath.

Maddie stopped rubbing the meat as the disconcerting feelings stole her attention. When she looked up Rosie was staring at her expectantly. She smiled apologetically. "Sorry, I got distracted."

"I was saying, you have an important job. It must be hard to quit knowing that people need you. I imagine there's a thrill in saving a life."

"Yes, there is."

"Are you looking forward to getting back to it?"

"Yes, I am." The words didn't come across as authentic as she expected they should. "I'm enjoying the break though." She'd never taken a break of this duration and would be unlikely to be able to take one again until she retired. Now that she'd tasted a stress-free life, she was quite enjoying being away from the pressure. Her downtime when she got back to work would consist of a few long weekends at best. She'd be running on adrenaline and caffeine within a week of returning, and the virtually constant high would keep her going.

Rosie nodded. "Well, I know you're not leaving yet, but I hope you get to come back again sometime. I know Devin would like that."

The penny dropped. Rosie was trying to find out Maddie's intentions toward Devin. Maddie smiled through the hint of sadness that squeezed her heart. She would miss the ranch, but mostly she'd miss Devin. "I'd like that too," she said, though she couldn't see how she would get back to the ranch on vacation for more than a week or two in a year. The thought of not seeing Devin beyond the retreat wasn't one she wanted to occupy her mind for the rest of her stay. She rubbed the meat with more force, aware that Rosie was watching her closely.

"You don't need a stick, eh?" Rosie said and chuckled.

Maddie laughed and took a deep breath to release the tension. If she'd taken a stick to the meat, Rosie might not have needed to mince it. She returned to something closer to a gentle massage to spread the rub into the joint. "Has Devin always been very determined?" she asked.

"Sure has. She has a fierce stubborn streak born of love and kindness that runs deeper than any river you'll find this side of Vegas."

Maddie laughed louder at Rosie's use of the phrase Devin was so fond of quoting. "Yes, I believe she does."

Rosie narrowed her eyes and the natural wrinkles that lined her brow deepened. "She may appear tough on the outside, but she feels the pain inside more than most."

Maddie's heart sank. She didn't want to hurt Devin. But was that an inevitable outcome of them getting involved with each other? She knew the answer in the unnerving sensation that stirred in her gut.

"Do you like children?"

Maddie blinked. The question came out of the blue. "Um, yes, kind of."

"Hm, Devin loves 'em. She'd open an orphanage if she wasn't too busy with the horses. Horses are her first love, but children come a close second."

Maddie nodded. That explained the bond she'd seen Devin had with Alice. "She's great with Alice."

"She is. But she gets her heart broken every time."

Maddie frowned. "How?"

"She wants to keep them."

Rosie eyed Maddie with something akin to suspicion, then hummed something to herself. "She planned to adopt with another woman. Jaynee was her name."

"Yes, Devin told me about her."

"Hm. She was always trouble, that one. When Devin's heart is driving, she loses her sight. Gets easily swayed, though she's no fool. The girl just walked out on her, without word or warning." Rosie shook her head and nudged her glasses further up her nose with the back of her wrist.

Anger flared in Maddie, a flash of wild flames, and the pressure in her head peaked. Now she knew what hate felt like.

How could someone do that to another human being, let alone where children might be involved? Devin had talked matter-of-factly about that time when it had clearly been more distressing. "She must've been devastated."

"A lot of hearts were broken that day. She's stayed clear of women like that since, far as I can tell. I always thought she'd settle with Ella, but they're more like cousins."

Maddie would avoid women like that too. Nausea stirred in her at the thought that Rosie might see her as one of those women. She liked Ella, but Devin had made it clear they were just friends.

"I've not seen her so happy as she is now, though." Rosie glanced at Maddie. "Something to do with being around you, doc. I hope you're not going to break her heart." Rosie focused her stare at Maddie and took a long slow breath. "And yours."

A landslide tumbled through Maddie. *Fuck.* She couldn't be responsible for breaking Devin's heart, but she couldn't not follow her own heart. She'd never considered being a parent and yet, having children was as important to Devin as Maddie's work was to her. Being a parent would be a big part of any relationship they might forge, and Maddie didn't know how to deal with kids, let alone be responsible for their upbringing. How could she think about anything long-term with Devin when she would be in New York and Devin would stay in Austin? It was hard enough maintaining a relationship with her job, what with the hours and the stress, but a long-distance relationship would never work. That was before she factored in a kid.

Maybe, the oddness she'd sensed with Devin in the diner was about her coming to a similar conclusion. She'd said they didn't need to label what they had and that suited Maddie, even though she was deceiving herself. She certainly had a name for the emotion that had her heart dancing with joy when they were together.

It dawned on Maddie how little they knew each other, and how, no matter what she felt for Devin, their aspirations in life were probably as far apart as the places they inhabited. At least she could form a box in her mind now. This thing with Devin must be nothing more than a vacation romance, and she had to get Devin on the same page. "I won't break her heart," she said, her voice affected by the dispiritedness that came with acknowledging the truth. The end of her vacation would come around too soon and both their hearts would be more than a little bruised.

22.

HAVING ADMITTED HER FEELINGS to Maddie, even though she'd confessed while in a state of altered consciousness, Devin had been more at ease having accepted that their time together was limited. She was still a little pissed at her mom for babysitting her because that was a missed opportunity.

Her mom's weakness was that she was over-protective. She always would be. And Devin loved her for it. It had been one of the things Jaynee hadn't been able to deal with, and it had eventually expanded the rift between them. Jaynee had seen her mom as interfering. And the reality that Devin refused to leave her home at the ranch and set up in Reno, or Las Vegas, or wherever else Jaynee decided her next adventure would be, had been blamed on her mom's negative influence.

Devin's home was at the ranch, and any woman she settled with would have to accept that. *Damn it.* She couldn't stop the tug on her heart when she thought about Maddie. Devin had been the one to suggest they didn't need a label for their relationship and that they should just enjoy their time together. Why then, did she feel desperate at the thought of Maddie returning to New York?

She was turning circles in her mind while Maddie sat quietly in the seat next to her. Her scent was intoxicating, her proximity arousing, but Alice in the back of the truck hadn't stopped talking since they'd set off. She glanced at Maddie and back to the road.

Maybe they could try a long-term relationship and she would see Maddie when she had the time to visit Austin. Devin wasn't averse to going to the city for a long weekend. The other voice in her head chirped up. *It's too soon to map out a future.* Her thoughts spun a web trying to find a solution that could work for them both. There wasn't one. What was more important now was that they had fun. She still had time before Maddie left to convince herself that it would be best for them both to part as good friends.

She brought the Ford to a halt at the small clearing and glanced over her shoulder at Alice. "You ready?"

Alice squealed and jumped out of the truck. Devin brushed the back of Maddie's hand with her fingertip. "Are you ready for a night in the wild?" she whispered.

Maddie took Devin's hand in hers, interlocking their fingers. She traced the tattoo on Devin's wrist with her thumb. "It's going to be an adventure."

Devin lifted Maddie's chin and looked into her eyes. "You know I'd rather be alone with you." She leaned toward Maddie and kissed her tenderly.

Maddie stroked Devin's face. "I'm the interloper here, remember. Alice is so excited, and I love watching you two together."

Devin loved that Maddie understood her connection with Alice. Jaynee had never respected Devin's desire for a family. She drew Maddie into another kiss that felt too brief.

The higher elevation brought cooler temperatures which would make for a pleasant night. They wouldn't have to worry about dehydration or heatstroke. It was just the agony created by the distance they'd have to maintain in front of Alice that was the issue.

Devin started unpacking the teepee, and Alice and Maddie joined in. They dumped the poles on the flat grassy land. The sounds of the river close by had her thinking about the trout she hoped would bite, or they might go hungry tonight. Maddie was watching her with an expression that Devin found hypnotic. There was a sensual quality to the stare that caressed her with the warmth of the sun but at the same time was as revitalizing as a cool breeze. She'd have to take a long dunk in the river later to quell her desire. This trip was already testing her, and there was still a night to get through. What Devin wanted to do was to lay with Maddie and discover that sensual look Maddie kept giving her through touch. The image created a shot of fire to her core. *Damn, it was going to be a long night.*

She hung the thin rope loosely around her neck and lifted two poles to position them. "Can you tilt this toward the center until it meets the others?" She held out one pole to Alice and guided the second pole into position. Alice strained under the weight until she'd slotted it so that the poles intersected at the top of the teepee. Maddie tilted a fourth pole into position. Devin winced from the tenderness in her ribs as she reached up and wrapped a rope around where the poles crossed each other. It was less painful than the burning sensation that throbbed at her core. She tied the knot. "That's fixed good and tight."

Maddie and Alice let go and stepped back from the wooden structure.

Swiftly, Devin secured the material to the poles. She studied the tent briefly, tugging in various places to make sure it was safe. "That's good to go."

Alice dived inside the tent. "Wow, it's cool. Come in."

Maddie poked her head through the flap. She emerged with a concerned expression. "That's for all three of us?"

The teepee was on the small side, but Devin had been looking forward to cozying up next to Maddie, and the closer the better. She looked skyward. It would be a beautiful evening with a slight chill and a cloudless sky, and the sparkling carpet of stars would make an awesome spectacle. It would be very romantic. Undisturbed, and with just the critters fidgeting and the wind whistling, this was one of her favorite sleep-out locations and the only thing that could top that would be to sleep next to Maddie. "I'll crash under the stars," she said. Her chest warmed with Maddie's lingering smile.

"Then so will I," Maddie said.

Alice came out of the tent and stood next to Maddie with her hands on her hips. "Then I want to sleep outside too."

Devin laughed. That wasn't quite the romantic proposition she'd imagined. Maddie had admitted to being the interloper, so Devin knew she would put Alice's wishes before her own. "Well, how about we cook inside the tent and sleep outside?"

Alice studied the teepee. "It might catch fire."

Devin shook her head. "That's why there's a small hole in the top. See." She pointed and both Maddie and Alice looked toward the opening at the center of the teepee. "It's designed to have a fire inside."

"What happens if it rains?" Alice asked.

"Then it puts the fire out," Maddie said.

"Hard for rain to get in through a hole that small," Devin said. She smiled at Maddie, hoping she hadn't embarrassed her. "Are you up for finding wood? Then we'll go and fish. What d'you say?"

Alice beamed. "I'll get the rods." She headed to the truck and unloaded the fishing gear.

Devin couldn't be prouder if Alice were her own daughter. She always felt that way with the kids she'd helped. Seeing Alice enjoying ranch life was the best kind of reward. Devin had been expecting Alice to be more troublesome and less cooperative, especially given what Ella had explained to her about Alice's past. Not only had Alice been passed from one foster family to another, via her mom at various points over the years, one of the challenges in finding her an adoptive family was that Alice had been listed as a difficult child. It wasn't easy to place an older child within the state, let alone the county. Almost everyone wanted a baby whose personality they could more easily shape, and a child with a reputation for being destructive and difficult didn't fit their idyllic family image.

The shyer version of Alice that had shown up at the ranch on the first day hadn't matched the profile Devin had been expecting. She'd been pleasantly surprised and then relieved that Alice hadn't subsequently rebelled. In fact, Alice had settled in easily at the ranch. She was a natural around the horses, had grown quickly in competence, and was a hard worker. Sometimes, maybe all that was needed for kids like Alice was to find the right stimulation so they could thrive, and everything would be fine. Everyone was more settled when they felt at home, and kids needed to feel confident and secure to be happy. And they needed, perhaps more than adults, to be around people who believed in them.

She hoped Alice's potential new stepparents understood her. Alice hadn't said anything to Devin about her upcoming meeting though and when Devin had asked if she was looking forward to it, she'd just mumbled and carried on grooming Cookie. Devin hadn't asked again. It was too painful to think that Alice might not be happy in her new home. Devin had to take care of her own heart, or she'd end up in the same state she'd been in when Todd had left. She'd promised herself she wouldn't get attached, though that was getting tougher as each day passed. And then there was Maddie. She took a deep breath and released it slowly.

Maddie was looking toward the Aspen trees that bounded their location and at the ground, as if searching for something. She'd been quieter than Devin had expected on the drive, and despite the connection she sensed between them, now she seemed a little unsettled.

"Is everything okay?" she asked.

"Tell me this isn't spider territory." Maddie winced.

"I thought you were a professional," Devin said and smiled.

"I'm a doctor, not a marine."

171

Devin watched her closely and when something rustled in the undergrowth, Maddie jolted. Devin's heart warmed but she couldn't stop herself from wanting to tease her. "We won't find tarantulas this far up," she said and winked.

Maddie raised her eyebrows.

"You know we have twenty-three types of scorpions in Nevada, but they prefer the desert, alongside the tarantulas and lizards."

Maddie wrapped her arms tightly around her body and continued to look toward the ground. "Maybe I'll take the tent tonight."

Devin laughed. She didn't want to point out that the ground sheet wasn't attached to the tent's sides. More insects would appear at night but when Maddie was asleep, she wouldn't notice them. In fairness, she was more likely to crush them than for them to do her harm. Devin retrieved their bags from the back of the truck and put them inside the teepee. "Only the bears can get to you in here," she said and winked again.

Maddie shot Devin a look that said she was pushing her luck, and as she walked past her, Maddie thumped her arm. "Stop it. I can't tell whether to trust you or not."

Devin lifted her hat and scratched her head. "You can trust me. You might hear coyotes a way off. If you see mountain lions though, don't run or they'll chase you."

Maddie's eyes grew wider. "You're teasing me, right?"

Devin shook her head. She scanned the tree line. "They'll be after food if they come around. The bears too."

"Bears?"

"And stay away from a sidewinder if you see one. They have a nasty bite."

Maddie laughed, an awkward, strained noise like a trapped hyena.

"You've been bitten by a snake?"

"A couple of times, yeah. Nothing round here's fatal unless you do the antagonizing first."

"You're a doctor," Alice said.

Her tone was quizzical rather than accusatory and she wore a deep frown as she stared at Maddie.

"That's right. I'm the one who deals with things after the incident. I wasn't planning on being a bear's supper tonight."

Alice took Maddie's hand. "I'll look after you."

Devin squeezed Alice's shoulder as she spoke to Maddie. "You both stay close to me, and you'll be fine." She turned away and started off down a narrow path that led into the forest. She looked back and waved Maddie and Alice on. "Who's coming to get wood?"

Maddie shook her head. "I'm not going in there."

Alice let go of Maddie's hand and ran after Devin. "Wait for me."

"I thought you were looking after me," Maddie said and strode after them both.

Devin took the quickest route to the clearing. She spotted a good-sized branch, probably felled during one of the winter storms and since dried out by the long summer's heat. Maddie and Alice gathered up the smaller twigs.

"Are you really scared of spiders?" Alice asked.

"I'm not a fan of the ones that come into my condo. It's the thought of them crawling on me." She shuddered. "I can appreciate them at a distance. What about you?"

"I don't mind. I think if I saw a bear, I'd probably freak out."

"You won't see any bears around here," Devin said. She lifted the log onto her shoulder.

"Well, that's one less thing to worry about, Alice."

"There's a spider." Alice gestured to the wood in Maddie's hands.

Maddie screamed, and birds scattered from within the trees around them. She launched the twigs into the air, brushed at her arms, and jumped away from the strewn twigs.

Devin and Alice laughed, and after a moment Maddie chuckled.

"It was only a small one," Alice said and shrugged. "I think you killed it, though."

Maddie, with her hand clasped to her chest, bent toward the ground. "I think it ran away." She inspected each twig as she plucked it from the ground and positioned it in her arms.

Devin shook her head and smiled. Maddie hadn't given any indication that she had a mild phobia. She was adorable with it, and a good sport. "Are you ready now, princess?"

Maddie's gaze softened, and Devin took a deep breath. "I assume you know how to create a fire."

"I brought matches," Maddie said and nudged Devin in the side as she walked past her.

Alice laughed. "Ha, she got you back." She nudged Devin as she moved past her and walked behind Maddie.

"Oh, I see how it is. You two are ganging up on me."

"Yep," Maddie said. "Come on, Alice. Us girls need to stick together. And the big old cowgirl there can make fire and fish."

Maddie shot Devin a glance that reached Devin's core, catching her breath.

"Are you scared of fish?" Alice asked Maddie.

"Not when I'm eating them. What about you?"

Alice went quiet for a few paces. "Don't know. I've never seen a live one."

Devin shifted the log to her other shoulder as she listened to their easy conversation. Life didn't get any better. She hoped that Alice would be worn out and fall asleep quickly. Then she and Maddie could stare at the Milky Way for a while, or maybe just snuggle up close next to the fire. For all her teasing of Maddie about being scared, Devin would stay awake all night to make sure the critters didn't get near her if that's what Maddie needed.

23.

"IS DEVIN YOUR GIRLFRIEND?"

Maddie hesitated, cleared her throat to stop from choking on the fish, and swallowed. In her heart, she answered yes. "Not really." Maddie felt interrogated by Alice's intense gaze.

"You kiss her."

Maddie picked up her chilled beer and took a long slug. Nothing, it appeared, escaped Alice's keen eyes. "Well…"

"You sure look like girlfriends." Alice bit into a cookie.

Devin's shoulders rose and fell, though no laughter tripped from her lips, as she threw another log onto the fire. She ruffled Alice's hair and sat next to her on the ground. "I think we're girlfriends," she said.

"I guess we are then," Maddie said. No labels, they'd agreed. The admission lingered, not entirely comfortably in her mind, with a softness and warmth that concurred with her heart. She would let herself believe it were true, if only for one night, and to satisfy Alice's curiosity.

Devin took a sip of her beer, tilted her head upwards, and closed her eyes. She looked beautiful.

"Are you gonna get married then?"

Maddie choked and when Devin laughed, she joined her. "Girlfriends don't always get married," she said.

Alice shook her head. She stuffed another cookie into her mouth and chewed. "My mom never looked happy with any man she married. She cried most of the time when they were around and got beat up a lot. She said that was the way it was 'cause they brought the money in. I didn't understand, 'cause she earned the money and gave it to them. For the rent, she said. You look happy. I saw you together at the dance, and here too. You hold hands and kiss softly. I want someone to be that kind to me some day. None of my mom's men looked at her that way. Their eyes were always filled with rage and had red around them, like something scary from a sci-fi movie."

Maddie's throat constricted as the scenario played out in her mind. How could someone expose a child to that world and still look at themselves in a mirror and call themselves a parent? She shuffled closer to Alice and put her arm around her shoulders. Alice pressed her small head into Maddie's chest, and she squeezed her tighter.

Devin put her arm around Alice from the other side, and around Maddie, and tugged them into a huddle.

Alice sobbed silently, her body jerking in a rhythmical pattern. Maddie kissed the top of her head. "Shh. Everything will be fine," she whispered.

Alice wriggled and lifted her head from her chest. "How do you know that?"

Maddie had waltzed right into that dark hole. "You're right," she said. "I don't know. But we have to keep believing that things will get better. It's like when someone hurts themselves and they come into the ER. As a doctor, I believe we can help them get better, don't I?"

Alice wiped her eyes. "Sure."

"Bad things happen in life, but that doesn't mean life is bad, Alice," Devin said.

Maddie held Devin's gaze and mouthed a thank you.

"Lots of good things happen too, just sometimes we forget them," Devin said.

Alice scratched her head the way Devin did. "I had a friend once. When I was seven, she came to my birthday party and brought me a book. That was a good thing, until Mom threw it in the trash. Her man said it wasn't right for me learning to read stuff like that at my age."

"What book was it?" Maddie asked as calmly as she could manage, while rage filled her head.

"The Black Stallion."

Maddie didn't know what to say. "What?" Her tone betrayed her anger.

"He said it would give me ideas about wanting a horse, when I wasn't gonna get one."

Maddie bit her tongue to stop herself from swearing out loud.

"Then the next week Mom ended up in the hospital again, and they put me in foster care for a while."

Maddie stood and paced in front of the fire. The injustice was inconceivable. People like that should be sentenced and locked away so they couldn't harm kids. A sharp pain cut through her heart, and her head was close to exploding. She would put them down, like the dogs that they were. Devin came to her and tugged her into her arms. She wanted to pull away, to vent her anger and frustration, but she stood still and allowed Devin's calmness to wash over her. Alice came to them both and wrapped her arms around them.

"You're my family," Alice said.

Maddie fought against the tears that burned the back of her closed eyes. She bit down harder on her lip. But still her body trembled. She summoned her strength to speak with a brave face, opened her eyes, and gave Alice a final squeeze. "I think it's time for a swim in the river. What do you think?"

Devin ruffled Alice's hair. "It's gonna be cold."

"Yippee," Alice said and ran into the teepee.

"Are you okay?" Devin asked.

Maddie wiped her damp eyes. "Not really. The injustice gets to me."

Devin nodded. "Me too. There are thousands of kids out there, struggling."

There's only one Alice. "You're one very special woman," Maddie said. She stroked Devin's face and kissed her.

When she opened her eyes and eased out of the kiss, Alice was staring at her and smiling.

"Can we go?"

Devin laughed. "You lead the way."

Maddie followed the pair of them, fighting the tears.

Goosebumps moved up her arms and a tingle slid down her spine as she stepped into the cool water. She splashed her face, cooled her burning eyes, and felt a little better. Alice's squeals of delight softened the tension in her head. She turned to see Alice splashing Devin and smiled. Devin set off after Alice, soaking Maddie in the process. Alice screeched as Devin caught up with her and dunked her under the water. Maddie laughed and the soothing effects of it relaxed her further. Alice was a beautiful soul. Sometimes she spoke with such maturity it was easy to forget that she was still just a child. She showed an unexpected level of resilience. Her ability to shift emotions, to be able to play and laugh so freely after reflecting on her darker experiences, left a deep ache in Maddie's heart. She watched them playing together in the water, their voices becoming distant as the stars awakened above her and the gushing and gurgling sounds of the river captivated her.

Devin walked toward Maddie with her arm wrapped around Alice's shoulders. Both were dripping wet, and both had a smile that bathed her in childlike happiness.

"Who's up for toasted marshmallows?" Devin asked and hugged Alice.

Alice looked up at Devin. "Can I toast them?"

"Sure."

"I'm in," Maddie said. She wondered at the way Devin looked at her and when Devin turned her attention from her, she felt the absence of it in the chill that prickled her skin. Devin waded out of the river. Maddie had the urge to slowly remove the wet clothes and make love to her. Alice's voice shattered the illusion, and Maddie made her way back to their camp.

Devin changed quickly and put the car stereo on while Alice skewered cupcake-sized marshmallows. Maddie went into the tent and stripped off her wet clothes, enjoying the music and the occasional crackle from the burning wood more than she thought she would. Being in the outdoors with Devin and Alice was like tasting a slice of heaven. She wanted more.

The tent flap opened. Maddie gasped and turned her naked back to Devin.

Devin cleared her throat. "I just came to say the marshmallows are toasted."

Devin staring at her nakedness made her feel vulnerable. Her heart fluttered, fast and light, in her chest. Her breathing was shallow, her head dizzy. Exposed like this, she wanted Devin to touch her.

"You look beautiful," Devin said.

She turned her head and saw tenderness and longing in Devin's smile. And then Devin left the tent and closed the flap behind her. Maddie's normally steady hands trembled, and butterflies took flight in her stomach. She'd never wanted someone so badly. She took a long deep breath, and another, then dressed quickly and exited the tent.

"Did someone say marshmallows?" Maddie asked. She addressed Alice, though she locked eyes with Devin. Heat expanded within her, and her core throbbed with desire. It took every ounce of will she had to break eye contact with Devin and focus on Alice and the marshmallows that sat in various states of cremation on a plate next to the fire. She didn't much care for the sugary sweet but took one that looked vaguely edible and popped it into her mouth.

"They taste good," Alice said, nodding. She had white marks around her mouth and looked as though she'd done a great job of testing a few of them.

"They're amazing. Only a great chef can cook marshmallows over a real fire, you know," Maddie said.

Alice looked toward Devin, who nodded her agreement.

Devin took a couple of charred chunks from the plate and ate them. "Those are the finest toasted marshmallows I've ever tasted." She ruffled Alice's hair. "Time for bed, you."

"You said I could stay up all night."

Maddie laughed. Devin wasn't going to get rid of Alice that easily.

"Well, I'm ready for bed," Devin said and yawned.

Alice yawned and rubbed her eyes.

"You'll need your energy for riding tomorrow. We have a big day rehearsing for the rodeo."

Alice squealed. "Can I ride at the rodeo?"

Devin nodded. "I reckon you might. Depends how much sleep you get."

Alice jumped to her feet. "I'm sleeping in the middle," she said and ran toward the tent.

Devin watched Alice until she had gone inside then looked at Maddie. "Would you like to dance?"

Maddie nodded and stood and when Devin took her hand and held her in her arms, a delightfully fuzzy, warm feeling moved through her. She put her hands on Devin's shoulders, reached into her hair and around the back of her head, and drew Devin to her. Devin's lips were sweet and moist and the bliss of being kissed with tenderness silenced her thoughts.

She couldn't say for how long they'd kissed, but when she eased away the music had stopped, and the starlit sky seemed brighter and more dazzling. Maybe her imagination was playing tricks on her and revealing the fairytale romance she could never have.

Devin pressed her thumb to Maddie's lips. "I would like to kiss you all night, but I'm not sure I could control myself if I did."

Maddie's clit throbbed. "I wouldn't want you to," she whispered.

Devin took a deep breath and blew it out slowly. "Shall we sit by the fire for a while?"

The disappointment of letting her go lasted a fleeting moment. Devin took Maddie's hand and led her to the fire. They lay next to each other, holding hands, and stared into the Milky Way.

"It's impressive," Devin said.

"*You're* impressive." Maddie turned onto her side and studied Devin in profile, the softness in her strong features that she found particularly sexy and alluring. She stroked Devin's face and turned her head so she could kiss her.

"You need to stop doing that or I won't be responsible for what happens next." Devin closed her eyes, and her voice quivered. "Honestly."

"I know." Maddie kissed her again more firmly. Devin groaned and tugged Maddie on top of her. Maddie straddled Devin's waist and wished she could feel Devin's wetness against her. She eased out of the kiss and sat astride her. When Devin opened her eyes and smiled, Maddie slipped her hand beneath Devin's shirt and enjoyed the feel of her toned stomach. She slid her hand higher and noted the delicious shape and texture of her nipple and the firmness of her breast.

Devin bit her lip as she moved beneath Maddie. "You're killing me here."

"I know." Maddie wanted to take Devin's nipple into her mouth and drive her crazy with desire. She arched against Devin to feel the pressure of her weight against her clit and stifled a moan as ecstasy teased her. "I want you so badly," she whispered.

"When are you coming to bed?"

Maddie gasped. She snatched her hand from beneath Devin's shirt and turned to see Alice staggering toward them, rubbing her eyes. Maddie's thundering heart softened as she adjusted to the intrusion. Much to Maddie's surprise, Alice threw herself into her arms and almost toppled her off Devin. This wasn't just awkward, it was excruciating, but fortunately Alice didn't appear to have seen anything she shouldn't have. Alice was distressed and needed comforting. Anything else would wait. "Hey, it's okay," she said.

"I had a really bad dream."

Devin was still trapped between Maddie's legs on the ground, and Alice was on her knees and clamped firmly around Maddie's upper body, clinging to her like a limpet. Maddie wrapped her arm around Alice and stroked her hair. "Hey, it's okay, baby." She eased Alice from her, stood to free Devin, and tugged Alice closer. "It was just a dream."

"They're going to take me away," Alice said and started to cry.

Devin lifted Alice's chin and shook her head. "It was just a dream. No one's going to take you away."

Alice looked at Devin. "Promise me."

"I promise," Devin said.

Alice threw herself at Devin, and Devin kissed the top of her head.

Had Devin just committed to something she couldn't honor? Alice didn't need any more downers in her life, and especially not from someone she obviously adored. Devin didn't have any control over the authorities. Had she just said it to placate Alice, perhaps thinking that by the morning Alice would have forgotten the dream? Devin was better with kids than Maddie; she knew how to speak to them. Still...

Alice took hold of their hands and led them both into the tent. Maddie lay on her back, awake, next to Alice, with Alice's arm wrapped around her waist, wondering what Devin was thinking. There was no doubt that had they been alone, the night would have turned out differently.

Perhaps it was for the best. Succumbing to her lustful desire when she would soon be back in New York was probably the craziest thing she could do. She'd come here to recover, not to create further complications to her already stressful life. Her justifications were weak, and she didn't believe any of them. She took a deep breath and braced herself for a long, frustrating night.

Devin put her arm across Alice and stroked Maddie's back.

Fuck the complications, I need you. Maddie drifted into sleep with the image of being alone with Devin.

24.

DEVIN REVVED SALLY-ANNE'S engine, engaged the clutch, shifted the gearstick, and eased her out of the garage as Maddie approached from the house.

The white Stetson perched at an angle on Maddie's head still had that brand new look about it. Her Levi's accentuated her figure perfectly, especially the sway of her hips. And her highly polished boots looked like something Maddie would wear in a clinical hospital environment. Well, almost. Devin's fingers tingled with the thought of touching her. She pulled up next to Maddie and stopped, reached across the car, and pushed the door open. She looked up at her, trying to appear casual from beneath the rim of her hat. "You going somewhere, pretty lady?"

Maddie leaned against the car door, tilted her hips, and crossed her legs. "That kinda depends on the handsome cowboy behind the wheel, I guess."

Devin laughed. "Touché, doc. Hop in." She patted the seat then took hold of the steering wheel to occupy her hands. She'd done a lot of occupying of her hands in the two days since the camp-out, trying to distract her thoughts about Maddie, but nothing had worked.

She'd been absorbed by her imagination, how Maddie would feel against her, Maddie's touch, and what it would be like to lie naked together. Devin spent more time looking out for Maddie when she was in the yard than she did working. She'd avoided conversation with her mom in case she tried to talk her out of getting involved. It was too late. Warnings, no matter how well-meaning, carried no weight once she'd committed her heart. And she had, and she guessed her mom knew that too by the way she pursed her lips and frowned at her more often.

It was just her mom's reservations given what had happened after Jaynee left. It had taken her months to get back to something resembling normal and even then, she'd been on edge around women to the point of steering clear altogether for a long time.

Maddie was different.

Maddie slipped into the car and closed the door. She reached behind her shoulder, then turned and looked to where she would have expected to find a seat belt.

"These old cars don't have belts. We won't be doing more than twenty-five miles an hour and we'll take the scenic route."

Maddie ran her finger over the narrow front shelf. "She's something special."

Devin felt the same about Maddie. She revved the engine, shifted Sally-Ann into gear and set off.

"Where are you taking me, cowgirl?"

Devin turned Sally-Ann onto the highway. "The historic mining town of Eureka. There's a classic car show. Sit back, relax, and enjoy the view."

Maddie gazed around. "I see desert."

Devin held the wooden steering wheel firmly and stared at Maddie. "You're looking in the wrong direction."

Maddie locked eyes with her and blushed. "Is that so?"

Devin smiled. "Sure is."

Maddie put her hand on Devin's thigh. "I think I prefer touching to looking, so you can keep your eyes on the road."

Devin laughed. "Touching's just fine with me." The heat from Maddie's hand crept up Devin's thigh and between her legs and a low moan slipped from her lips. "Okay, maybe looking's safer if we want to get where we're going."

Maddie leaned toward Devin and kissed her cheek. "I never said I wanted to get where we're going," she whispered.

Devin felt suddenly overdressed in her tight-fitting jeans and T-shirt. She'd happily pull over at one of the motels en route, but there was no way she wanted their first time together to take place in some cheap and rundown dive. There wasn't any chance of them getting naked where they were going. Maybe later she'd invite Maddie to her room. She needed to turn her attention away from the feeling of Maddie's hand clasped around her inner thigh if she was going to get them safely to the car show. "You've never told me about your place. What's it like?"

Maddie rested her head against Devin's shoulder. "It's a two-bedroom harbor condo in Manhattan. It's nice."

"Do you like being by the water?"

"I didn't get to enjoy the view much, with work. But, yes, I do."

"I like being close to water."

Maddie sat up and removed her hand from Devin's leg. Maddie looked at her, but Devin couldn't read her thoughts. She hoped talking about Maddie's place hadn't brought up unwanted memories of her ex. "I enjoy being close to the river. It's a great place to chill out, but then so's being around the horses and the ranch." She shrugged. Truth was, she loved everything about her environment, even the winds when they blew through the valley and the deep snow that capped the mountains in winter. She'd gotten the impression Maddie wasn't as charmed by her home in Manhattan.

"The complex is purpose-built, so everything about it has been designed for comfort. It has aesthetic appeal, and it's a highly sought-after area."

Maddie sounded like she was reading from a sales brochure, though she wasn't a particularly convincing realtor. Devin couldn't find any words that would do justice to how she felt about Austin and the ranch, but she had no doubt that it was the best place in the world to live, and it wasn't particularly highly sought-after as far as she could tell.

"The harbor is pleasant, and you can see the New York skyline from the living room window. It has an open plan living space, floor to ceiling windows, clean lines, and is bold in design."

"You can see skyscrapers?"

"Some, yes."

"Open plan's cool. I wish ma's house was more open. It's not a traditional ranch house, being two floors. But having separate rooms for eating and chilling out works well for guests."

Maddie nodded. "Would you ever build your own place?"

Devin rested her arm across the rim of the open window and leaned back in the seat. The breeze flowed between her fingers and cooled her skin. "I always wanted to build a proper ranch house. One level, all open plan and with sliding glass doors onto a yard that overlooked the plains. I could enjoy the sun rising and setting, sitting on the porch, drinking coffee or a beer."

"I prefer open plan, and I like the idea of enjoying the sun rising and setting." She smiled.

Devin couldn't reconcile her image of the skyscrapers and pollution-filled skies in New York with Maddie's desire for openness and a view. "What made you choose a harbor condo, then, apart from being near the water?"

Maddie smiled. "I liked the view across the bay. I thought I'd get to see more of it. And, I hate to admit it, but I think I subconsciously wanted to flip off my parents."

"Ah." Devin couldn't imagine feeling that way about her parents. Working with the kids had taught her that not all parents were as kind and loving as her own. "It must be hard not having any folks to support you."

"It was at first, but then I had Lizzy and I thought it didn't matter, but I still made choices that I knew they couldn't criticize me for. Like I was making up for the fact that I was gay all the time."

"What about now?"

Maddie fell silent.

"Sorry, I don't mean to pry."

"You're not. I was pondering. I feel nothing toward them. I don't even feel sad at the idea of never seeing them again. Watching Alice, knowing what she's been through, I think I had the best of them when I was a child. So, I guess I was luckier than most. That they can't accept me for who I am isn't my problem, and it's not one I have the power to solve either. I can't not be me just to please them. And I'm not about to waste my life trying to convince them there's nothing wrong with me."

Devin admired Maddie's honesty. "There are loads of kids like Alice. It's criminal."

Maddie nodded. "Yes, it is. And I think you'd make an amazing parent if you decided to do that."

Devin's heart skipped a beat. She would love to have a child, but she couldn't envisage going through the process alone. How could she be enough for a kid when others were able to offer a two-parent home. Maybe, she'd give it some thought again and chat with Ella, after Maddie had gone back to New York. "Maybe," she said. She didn't want to think about that right now. "You know, there are scorpions where we're going." Devin laughed when Maddie's eyes widened. "I'm kidding. There are bats and spiders though." She was still teasing.

"Turn the car around, now."

Devin roared with laughter. She wrapped her arm around Maddie's shoulder, drew her closer, and kissed the top of her head. "We'll head through Diamond Valley on the way," she said. Maddie softened against her. "Have you heard of the Bristlecone pine?"

"No. It sounds prickly."

"It's the oldest and gnarliest tree on earth. The groves in the Great Basin have pines that are more than four thousand years old. The ones we'll see are younger."

Maddie sat up again. "Wow. I mean, four thousand years, wow. That's ancient. I bet it's as comfortable to touch as this car is to ride in." She sat back in her seat.

Devin laughed. The car's separate seats weren't at all snug at the best of times, let alone with the discomfort she'd inflicted on Maddie by pulling her across the space every five minutes. She put her hand on Maddie's leg, and Maddie took it in her own. She liked the feeling of Maddie toying with her fingers, the warmth and softness of her touch, and the thought of what she wanted to do to Maddie when they were back at the ranch. She caught the steady rise and fall of Maddie's chest in the corner of her eye and the soft flesh of her breast where her shirt flapped open with the slight breeze. A whole day of wanting Maddie and not being able to have her was sounding a lot like purgatory.

25

DEVIN'S BEDROOM *WASN'T* A space with clean lines and bold in design.

Her hand was warm and strong even though her grip was soft and loose, and Maddie enjoyed the tenderness. "Aren't I breaking house rules being in here?" she asked.

"Yes, but do you care?"

"No."

"Good." Devin laughed. "I won't tell Mom if you don't."

Maddie smiled. "Deal."

They moved further inside the modest room, unhurried and yet, the air was heavy with expectation. The bed looked tiny by comparison with her own king. The quilt was turned over as if Devin had not long climbed out of it and the pillow bore an imprint of her head. She had the urge to lay down where Devin had risen from that morning and inhale the scent of her that would still linger on the sheets.

"Do you think your mom was upset at us skipping supper?" she asked.

Devin smiled. "Nah, she always cooks more than people can eat, and I'd told her we'd be back late and wouldn't need feeding."

Maddie nodded, reminded of the gentle caution Rosie had expressed to her about breaking her daughter's heart. She studied Devin, looking for signs that she might be in this for something more than Maddie believed either of them could give. Devin was old enough to make her own choices and take care of her own heart. The sobering thought came with a trace of sadness that passed quickly as she turned her attention to the desire in Devin's eyes that reflected her own.

Devin rested her hand on her stomach. "I'm still stuffed from lunch," she said.

Her eyes sparkled despite the absence of artificial light inside the room.

"Me too." The truth was Maddie's stomach was still buzzing with the thrill of being with Devin, and she hadn't had much of an appetite in Eureka either. The pizza they'd shared had been close to the size of the table and loaded with fresh basil, salami, chorizo sausage, and sliced mushrooms. The side salad alone would've been a decent meal if she'd been at all hungry. The pizza had looked, smelled, and tasted delicious. She would remember the family-owned restaurant as one of her favorite places, even though they'd eaten for two hours and barely made a dent in the meal.

She turned from Devin's gaze. A pair of jeans lay strewn across the arm of a wicker chair adjacent to a matching low table with a glass surface. A hardbacked book with its spine bent revealed the cover, a white horse with a gentle aura around it that gave it a mystical quality. The title of the book was embossed in a handwritten font.

"You like reading?" She let go of Devin's hand and ran her finger over the lettering.

"Some. You?"

"Mostly escapism, like mysteries and thrillers."

The curtains were still open and from a distance, the glass looked like a solid black sheet, the world outside covered by the darkness of night. It made the second story bedroom feel small and cozy. As she moved closer to the window, the outside became more clearly defined and thousands of brilliant lights danced in the sky. The ranch was more wonderful than any view her condo had promised.

"Thrillers don't sound relaxing."

Maddie turned and smiled. "I like to work out things, solve the crime."

"I like to understand how horses do what they do. Hence that book." She looked toward the table.

Maddie's heart raced, and she felt her pulse in her throat. Ripples tingled across her skin in a long shiver of delight and expectation. She feared the strength of it, its all-consuming nature and that if she let it, the feeling would lead her to make an impulsive decision or worse still, give her heart completely to Devin. How she wanted to give Devin everything she had to give, and it would be so easy to do. But what about tomorrow and the next day? And the day she drove away from Austin, and the week after that back in New York? And a month later, six months of dealing with the distance and difference in their work schedules, their life, and their worlds?

It wasn't as if she could walk out of this room right now; she couldn't. Devin was too intoxicating. Devin could take her now, anywhere in this room, quickly or slowly, over over and again, and she would still want more of her. She would savor this moment for what it was and then when she left Austin, she would hold onto the memory of the tenderness they were about to share. It would be a treasure she could keep, safely, forever.

Devin picked up her jeans. "I'm sorry, I haven't cleaned up. I was rushing this morning." She put them in a closet. She lifted up the quilt and started to shake it down.

Maddie put her hand on Devin's arm, stopping her. "Leave the bed. I like it that way." She turned Devin to her and kissed her. The softness became firm, the kisses more urgent until she gasped and Devin eased away, and she saw longing in the intensity of her dark eyes.

Devin drew back the hair from the side of Maddie's face. She ran her finger slowly across Maddie's mouth, tracking her own slow movement as she ran her tongue across her dry lips.

"I have wanted you all day." She smiled and then her expression turned serious again. "In the long grass of the meadow. During lunch. I've imagined touching you, kissing every part of you, making love with you."

Maddie struggled to swallow. Similar thoughts had distracted her from fully appreciating the extraordinary historical mining town too. She took Devin's finger into her mouth and delighted in the salty taste and the firmness of it against her tongue. She kissed her palm, smiled at the tremble in her hand, and cupped Devin's palm to her cheek. She closed her eyes. "I love how you feel," she whispered. The warmth of the caress tingled down her neck and spine. She felt it reach her core and when Devin kissed her, it was like an explosion of fire inside her. The deep throb between her legs ached for Devin's touch.

Maddie blinked and caught Devin staring at her with something close to a mild frown. She started to speak, to ask if something was wrong, but Devin pressed her finger to her lips, silencing her.

"You take my breath away," Devin whispered as she leaned toward Maddie.

Maddie closed her eyes. Devin's lips were soft and inviting. She opened the buttons down the front of Maddie's shirt, and her hands felt cool. When Devin brushed her nipple with the lightest touch, she felt drawn down as if she might collapse under the intensity of the feeling that rocketed through her. Devin's mouth was warm and wet against her nipple, and her knees weakened. Devin lifted her. "No, take me here, now. Like this."

Devin held her firmly around the waist and took her nipple in her mouth again. A moment later, Devin's hand was between her legs, her fingers slipping through her silky wetness. She gripped Devin's shoulders and gasped, "Inside me, please, before I die."

The knock at the door jolted them both. Maddie suppressed a scream, and Devin jumped back from her.

"What is it?" Devin asked.

She sounded calmer than Maddie felt. Maddie didn't know where to put herself. She was in a state of semi-undress but that wasn't the issue. It was the unsatiated burning sensation, the frustration that had come to the boil instantly that aggravated the throb between her legs. She had nowhere to go with the pent-up emotion that would have her explode. She sat in the wicker chair and fastened the buttons on her shirt, ran her fingers through her hair, and took a long deep breath. She just about managed to stifle the moan that lingered at her lips and gritted her teeth.

The knock came again. Devin opened the door. "Mom, what's wrong?"

Maddie took another long deep breath and hoped Rosie hadn't caught her rolling her eyes.

"Come quick. Lightning's gone down."

"What?"

Devin's mom had already turned away from the door and was striding along the corridor. She'd given Maddie a look, but Maddie hadn't seen any edge in it, and it had been fleeting, her focus clearly on her concern for the young foal.

"He's labored in his breathing. Cody said to come and get you. She's worried. I've called Nathan. He's on his way."

Devin turned to Maddie as Maddie stood from the chair. "I'd better take a look," she said.

Maddie followed Devin into the yard. Her heart pumped hard and fast in line with her thoughts. *Please don't let him die.* Alice wouldn't be the only one devastated if anything tragic happened to the little guy.

26.

Cody crouched next to the prone foal, guiding a flashlight over him, and touched down his legs. Dolly was whinnying. She'd been tied to the fence, away from the foal.

Devin scanned Lightning. "What do you think?"

"I'm just checking for sepsis," Cody said. "I can't see an injury though and his joints seem fine. It's probably hypoglycemia."

"Shit."

"Here comes Nathan," her mom said.

Devin looked toward the car lights on the road up from the highway and saw the vet's car approaching.

"He seemed fine earlier. Normal gut flora stuff but nothing else. I must've not been seeing."

Devin felt Cody's disappointment. She was right. One of them should have noticed any changes in the young foal. Devin had been distracted and, with Ella visiting more frequently to drop off and pick up Alice, so had Cody. There was no point in dwelling on something that couldn't be changed. "Don't beat yourself up. These things can come on quickly."

"He's only just gone down."

The foal lifted his head, then collapsed back to the ground.

"He's gonna weaken really quick. I'll get some milk for him." Cody headed to the house.

The foal's eyes were wide open, and he was panting heavily.

"He needs antibiotics," Maddie said.

Devin bent down and stroked Lightning's cheek. He made another slight movement toward her before resting his head on the ground again. "Hang in there, boy," she whispered.

She met Nathan as he approached the corral. "We didn't see this coming. He's gone down in a few hours."

Nathan nodded and went to the foal. It didn't look good, and Devin could only imagine the heartbreak Alice would feel if they lost him; it would crucify the kid. She turned at the touch of the hand on her shoulder.

"Are you okay?" Maddie asked.

Devin stared at her and nodded. "He'll be fine. Nathan's the best, and I think we caught him early." Who was she trying to convince? She was pissed at herself for not giving the foal enough of her attention. If she had, she would have picked this up. *Damn it.*

Maddie glanced at the foal. "I hope so."

Nathan checked Lightning over and took his temperature. "We need to get him into the stable."

Devin stepped forward at the same time as Maddie. "I've got this." Devin lifted the foal across her arms. His head hung limply as she carried him into the stable and settled him on a bed of clean straw.

Cody returned with a bottle of milk and presented it to Lightning, but he remained motionless. "I'll go and get Dolly before she goes crazy out there."

"Come on, boy, you need this," Devin whispered. She forced the teat into his mouth and pressed it against his tongue to release the milk while Nathan set him up on a drip. The foal suckled a little. "Good boy."

"I'll come out early tomorrow. If he stops taking the milk call me. Good thing he's not as young as some. He's strong and willing."

Devin ran her fingers through her hair. "I'll keep an eye on him."

Cody led Dolly into the stall next to Lightning. She watched her baby intently and settled. "I'll stay with you, Cody said."

As Nathan drove away, Devin turned to Maddie. She looked adorable and tired. This night had not turned out as Devin had envisaged. She could still sense Maddie's silky wetness at her fingertips and the promise of what was to come had been so tantalizingly close for the briefest moment. At least her mom had refrained from comment or question, though she was sure that time would come once Lightning had recovered. "Go and get some sleep."

Maddie shook her head. "I want to stay with you."

Devin looked toward the foal. "I'll be fine. It'll be a long night, and one of us needs to be awake in the morning."

Maddie took her hand. "I'm a doctor, remember? I'm used to long hours, and I might be able to help so don't argue with me. I'll get us all a drink, and you can just give me instructions, and I'll follow them."

Devin kissed her on the lips. She wasn't arguing with her. She'd rather have Maddie at her side all night where they could hold hands and talk than try to settle while imagining Maddie snug in bed, naked and alone. That would drive her insane. Maddie left and she turned to Cody. "Go home. You can take over in the morning."

Cody watched Maddie until she was out of earshot. "There's something else you need to know."

Devin frowned. It wasn't like Cody to be cagey, but she appeared anxious to part with whatever it was she wanted to say. "What?"

"Alice's mom died today."

The winding blow to Devin's chest struck like a bolt of lightning. She turned away, feeling as if it was her world that had collapsed. "That poor fucking kid."

"Alice is okay, apparently, but this isn't gonna help her." Cody glanced to the sick foal.

Devin bent down to Lightning and scratched his neck. "You'd better pull through, boy." She saw a flicker of something

201

in his eyes and hoped he'd gotten the message and that he had the strength to make it through the night. The next twelve hours would be crucial. Lightning blinked and closed his eyes, and Devin's stomach dropped. She stood slowly. "Get back here first thing," she said.

"Sure." Cody stepped out of the stable, stopped, and turned back to Devin. "I'm sorry, Dev."

"Yeah, me too." They'd both let the foal down. She wasn't going to let Alice down. "I'll get more milk into him, and let's pray. It's all we can do."

Cody left as Maddie crossed the yard from the house. "Here."

Maddie held out a mug of what smelled like the kind of coffee that would set her teeth on edge.

"Your mom made a pot. She said it would last us the night. How's he doing?" She knelt in front of Lightning and ran her hand across his shoulder.

"Maddie." There was no easy way to tell her the news, and Devin figured that she was used to direct speaking when it came to medical matters, so she'd say it straight. "Alice's mom died today."

Maddie closed her eyes and took a long deep breath. "That poor girl." She opened her eyes, picked up the bottle of milk, and inserted the teat into Lightning's mouth. "Come on, boy, you can do this."

Devin willed Lightning to respond, to give them something positive to raise their hopes. She downed a cup of the extra-strong coffee and moved a bale of straw so they could rest against it. The foal's chest rose and fell in an even rhythm, faster and shallower than it should be. Devin wouldn't close her eyes until his breathing returned to somewhere close to normal.

Affection warmed her as she watched Maddie trying to feed him. She was so gentle and patient. She could see her at work in the hospital, calm, focused, and more importantly competent. Devin would put her life in Maddie's hands if she ever needed to. After all, Maddie had already captured her heart. The truth exploded inside her like a bomb, shattering and destroying the illusion that her feelings were anything less than that which she'd tried to deny. *I'm so in love with you.* She'd tried to persuade herself that her life would carry on as normal after Maddie had gone back to New York, even if it took her a while to get over her feelings. But the other part of her, the voice that spoke through her heart, knew differently. She was going to miss Maddie more than she wanted to admit. She knew it, because when she thought about Maddie leaving the ache in her heart felt heavy and threatening, like the clouds forming before a tornado struck and swept everything away. Maddie was going to break her heart.

"I think I've gotten a little milk into him." Maddie said and sat next to Devin. She leaned back into the bale and released a long breath. She held Devin's hand. "Wasn't quite what I imagined doing with you about an hour ago," she said and leaned against Devin's shoulder.

Devin let go of Maddie's hand, put her arm around her, and held her close. "Want to tell me what you imagined?"

Maddie tensed a little as if shocked, then softened and chuckled. She ran her hand up Devin's thigh and cupped the crotch of her jeans.

Devin released a whimper as the ribbed material pressed against her.

"I imagined being inside you," Maddie whispered.

She ran her thumb across the jeans that covered Devin's clit, and Devin tensed.

"I imagined your softness and the way you'd move with my fingers, the tremors as you contract against me, your wetness."

Devin gasped. Her clit throbbed, and she could feel an orgasm rising inside her. She'd never been this responsive to anyone, let alone under these circumstances. She tried to redirect her thoughts to the foal, lying asleep, but the feeling was too intense to ignore.

"I imagined the taste of you as I took you into my mouth, your clit pulsing at my tongue, hardening, and kissing you as you orgasm."

Devin could barely breathe. Maybe she shouldn't have asked. A gentle shock wave sprung from her clit and tingled up her spine. She grabbed Maddie's hand and brought it to her lips before she lost control. "Nice picture," she said, her heart racing. The agony of stopping Maddie from touching her would pass. She swallowed hard, stood, and paced around the stables. She saw something in Maddie's eyes that she couldn't name as Maddie tracked her movements and then Maddie stared at Lightning for some time.

"Do you think we'll lose him?" she asked.

Devin ran her fingers through her hair. She picked up the bottle and eased it into Lightning's mouth. As the milk trickled from the bottle, he contracted his tongue, though his eyes remained shut with a slight flicker of his lids. The more milk they got into him, the better he would fare, but it was still early and he looked slender and vulnerable. "It's touch and go."

"I've seen death a lot. It's never easy."

Devin nodded. They'd lost a few foals and older horses over the years. It was the way it was, but it always left a mark. Horses weren't like cattle, bred for eating, a part of the food chain. Horses were sensitive creatures who formed a strong emotional and spiritual bond with the humans they came to know. They felt loss, anger, and love, Devin was sure of it. She could see it in their eyes, their mannerisms, and heard it in their voices. "What made you choose medicine as a career?"

Maddie came to her and kissed her lightly. She was hoping Maddie might say that she fell into it, because that would mean there was half a chance of falling out of it, and if that were the case, there was hope that Maddie might decide to stay at the ranch.

"It was something I'd dreamed of as a child. My parents bought me a doctor's coat and bag with all the instruments in it when I was four or five. I can't remember exactly."

Devin felt her optimism wilt. She understood single-mindedness. The passion that had driven her had been with her for as long as she could remember. But then, she'd lived around horses all her life. "Were your parents doctors?"

"No. Padre was a lawyer, and Mamá was a Kindergarten teacher."

Devin frowned. She hadn't expected Maddie's mom to be fond of children given she'd rejected her own daughter. Maddie was staring at her and nodding, as if reading her mind.

"She was always more at ease with younger children. As soon as I developed a mind of my own, had opinions that challenged hers, she struggled to communicate with me. Growing up was more like fighting a constant battle. My padre worked long hours, so I didn't see much of him, and when I did, he just told me to follow Mamá's instructions."

"And you chose medicine."

"I wanted to help people. Maybe I would have gone into teaching if my mamá had been a good role model. I enjoy watching you with Alice. You're a great teacher."

Devin felt the heat move through her. "Helping people is rewarding."

Maddie smiled at her. "You helped me."

She stared into Maddie's eyes and wondered what were the thoughts that she held closest to her. The secrets of her heart. She knew what she wanted to hear Maddie say to her. But as close as they had become, she sensed Maddie was trying to maintain a distance between them. Devin was already all in, and there wasn't anything either of them could do that was going to change that fact. She wanted what Maddie couldn't give her: the house, the kids, the horses, and the love of her life to be with her every day and every night. "I think what you do is incredible," Devin said. "I couldn't do it." She knelt and put her hand on Lightning's chest and willed him to make it. It was the only medicine she could administer. His eyelids flickered at her touch. Any movement was a good sign. She picked up the bottle and continued to feed him. She might not be able to bank on a future with Maddie, but she sure as heck would give her best efforts to giving Lightning one.

27.

"Is he going to die?"

Maddie went to Alice, who had stopped at the entrance to the stable. She was staring at the foal. She looked tense and distant, hardened to the darker realities of life in a way that a child of her age shouldn't need to be. Maddie saw the pain she tried to hide, as she'd seen in other patients when she'd delivered bad news to them. Alice wasn't a patient though, and Maddie felt her loss in a way she never did with any of her patients at the hospital. "He's through the worst now."

Alice continued to stare at the foal. She looked fragile and alone.

"Is he going to die?"

The foal had picked up a little since the early hours, and they'd managed to get some milk down him and the drip had kept him hydrated and medicated. He wasn't out of the danger zone yet, but he'd gotten through the night, and that was as good as they could have hoped for. She wouldn't make false promises though. "I hope not."

Alice turned swiftly and strode out of the barn. Maddie went after her and walked by her side. She wanted to put her arm around her and comfort her but couldn't. "I heard about your mom," she said.

Alice shrugged. "No big deal, right."

It was a huge deal, and she could tell Alice was trying to put on a brave front. She was unconvincing and looked confused, beaten by an upbringing that had tried to destroy her, one insult after another. "I'm here if you want to talk."

Alice snatched Cookie's reins from their hook and entered the corral. Maddie followed her.

"What's there to talk about?" Alice stopped suddenly and put her hands on her hips.

She was all angles and anger and pain. Her eyes were dark, and the disconnect Maddie sensed between them couldn't be bigger, like she didn't exist to Alice, and Alice had flicked a switch in her brain and now looked at her through a different lens. Maddie knew it was a form of protection, but now she couldn't reach her. It was frustrating to feel so ineffectual, and she didn't much like the twisting sensation in her chest either.

Alice attached Cookie's reins and climbed on his back. "I'm going for a ride," she said and yanked the reins, fiercely turning the horse away from Maddie.

Maddie watched her bring the horse to canter and turn at the bottom end of the corral. She made her way back to the stable. Hopefully, in time, Alice would feel that she could talk about her feelings, if not to Maddie, then perhaps to Devin or Ella. It didn't matter who, just that Alice felt safe enough to share her troubles and worries with someone who cared about her.

She caught sight of Devin coming from the house. An overwhelming feeling of longing cascaded through her but the dampening effect of the loneliness that had taken up residence deep inside her mind was even more potent. Being with Devin, the emptiness went away. But the closer she came to returning to New York, the more dominant the hollow feeling became.

She loved Devin's lazy stride, the way she looked so casual and relaxed in her posture and yet never slouched. She looked comfortable in her skin, content with who she was and her life, as though nothing could faze or unhinge her. Her confidence and humility were deeply alluring, and the effect that she'd had on Devin in the early hours of this morning, as she'd touched her, made that appeal even more exhilarating.

Devin drew closer and frowned. There was weight to the intensity of her gaze as she scanned around the yard. "How's Alice?" she asked. She handed Maddie a coffee.

"She's not in a good place." Devin smelled divine, soapy, fresh from the shower. Maddie took a sip of the drink.

Devin glanced around again. "Where is she? I'll go and talk to her."

Maddie turned toward the corral, and her heart dropped like a stone. "She was in the corral a moment ago."

Devin frowned.

"She was riding Cookie around. I thought she—" Maddie dropped her drink and ran toward the corral. "Alice." Her raised, shrill voice lifted the heads of the grazing horses though they still ground down the hay in their mouths as they stared in Maddie's direction. "She must've gone through the bottom gate. I didn't think. Fuck."

Devin had already jumped the fence and was sprinting toward Rocky. "Keep an eye on Lightning. I'll find her."

Maddie watched Devin ride away, her heart thundering, a nauseous feeling turning her stomach. She should have known that Alice might do something unpredictable. She was a competent rider, but she was young and emotionally unstable, and the combination was a recipe for an accident. She would never forgive herself if Alice got hurt.

28.

DEVIN JUMPED ROCKY OVER the corral fence, squeezed his ribs hard with her legs, and encouraged him quickly onward. She tugged on his mane and directed him toward the hills. Her vision blurred, and she blinked to regain her focus. She studied those parts of the tracks that were visible, between the wooded areas, the stone mounds, and boulders that had tumbled from the rockface that formed the landscape of the higher plains. *What was Alice thinking?* Running away was a serious problem. She'd have to report the incident to Ella who would then have to tell the authorities, and it would be noted on her record. Foster parents didn't want a kid who was likely to run away from them, and Alice already had a reputation for that. *Damn it.* If she didn't report it and Alice ran away when she got to her new home, Devin would feel responsible and guilty, and if anything happened to Alice, she wouldn't be able to forgive herself. Alice was hurting, she understood that, though maybe not in the same way Alice experienced it. Devin hadn't lost a parent. But even so. Fueled by anger and injustice she dug her heels into Rocky's sides and urged him onward, toward the river where they'd fished and camped.

"Alice."

The birds chirped back at her and she heard the rush of the river. She went down to the bank and scanned the water. "Alice." The whooshing sound became quieter as her thoughts gained momentum. *Where the hell is she?* She turned away from the burning sun. It was too hot to be riding for hours. Alice would need water, Cookie too. She waded Rocky upstream, looking for signs and listening. Nothing. Her heart thumped out a heavy rhythm, and she rolled her shoulders to release the mounting tension.

She led Rocky away from the stream and took the route toward the caves they'd visited. If she wasn't there, she could be anywhere, and they'd need to instigate a search party. "Find her, Rocky. We've got to find her."

The fiery heat burned her face, sweat stung her eyes, and she pulled Rocky to a halt. She squinted toward the rockface, trying to locate the slightest movement, trying to spot the light-colored bay horse among the trees and branches that offered him a great camouflage. *Nothing, damn it.* She wiped her eyes and urged Rocky forward. There was no sign of Cookie outside the caves as she approached. She jumped off Rocky and made her way into the darkness. The cool air prickled her skin and a shiver snaked down her spine.

"Alice."

The stress in her voice echoed back at her.

"Alice."

The echo returned with greater urgency.

"Alice, are you in here?"

She glanced around and heard a whimpering sound that was barely audible. She worked her way to the farthest point from the mouth of the cave, the sobs becoming louder. "Hey, Alice. It's okay. It's me. Are you hurt?"

Alice huddled behind a large, rugged rock, her arms clasped around her legs, her head buried into her knees. "Go away."

Devin went to her and crouched down. She stroked her hair. "I know you're angry, and sad, and that's okay. I'm angry too, but not at you." She wasn't about to explain that sometimes life sucked to a kid who had learned that lesson time and again. She coaxed Alice out of the tight ball and pulled her into her arms. "It'll be okay, Alice. You've got to trust me."

Alice wrapped her arms around Devin. "Everyone I love leaves me," she said, the words coming between the sobs.

Devin had that feeling too. It was worse than having a tooth pulled without anesthetic, and that hurt more than landing awkwardly off a horse at the rodeo. She'd had a tooth pulled once, for a bet with Cody when they were younger and more foolish, and she'd sworn that she'd never do it again, and she'd been thrown more times than she could count on both her hands. Having something ripped from you when you weren't done with it had to be the worst kind of torture. She couldn't tell Alice she'd get over it because she didn't think you ever really did. The pain of loss became a part of you. It made some folks wiser, and it made other folks more wary. Each insult charred a little piece of you. Time passing brought the spring and new growth always had the power to repair that which had died before it. She'd withdrawn from the world when Jaynee left. She'd do the same when Maddie left. But she'd heal again, changed, and wiser she hoped, and so would Alice. "I know. It's wrong."

"I hate my life."

Devin squeezed her tightly. She wished Alice didn't feel that way. She was too young to feel so negatively about something so precious.

"Pastor Williams says God's taken Mom to heaven."

Living at Pastor Williams's house, Alice would have attended church every weekend with his children, and she was pretty sure that they would have given thanks in prayer at mealtimes and said their prayers before bed. She hoped it might go some way to helping Alice.

"I don't know if I believe in God," Alice said.

Devin deflated, though she could appreciate Alice's reservations. She'd wavered in her perspective many times through her life and still didn't know what she really believed. "I know it feels bad right now, and that's okay. Time is like God. It makes things feel different."

"If God takes care of people, why would he take her so early when she'd never hurt anyone?" Alice struggled to speak through the deep sobs.

Devin hadn't planned to talk about God, just to use an analogy that might help Alice appreciate that time can heal. "God doesn't always show up as you expect."

Alice frowned at Devin. "What do you mean?"

The window of hope that Alice's quizzical mind had grabbed hold of was just a sliver, but it was all Devin had so she'd run with it. "Well, sometimes we might trick ourselves into thinking that God can save us when we need to save ourselves." It sounded too deep for a ten-year-old, but Alice nodded and narrowed her eyes as if something registered with her.

"How could my mom save herself?"

She wished she'd not started the conversation. How did you tell a kid that her mom could have walked away and acted against the men who'd abused her when that was so hard to do in practice? "It's tough to grasp but when we do things, it makes other things happen." How could she get Alice to realize she'd already made decisions that had influenced her life? "So, like earlier. Instead of running away when you felt hurt, what could you have done?"

Alice lowered her head. "Talk, I guess."

"Exactly. It's a hard thing to do but talking would keep you safe, whereas running away could get you into a lot of trouble. I don't think that has anything to do with God."

Alice nodded. "Why would God take my mom then?"

That was harder to reconcile. "If God has a better place for her to go to where she can be happy and safe, he'd take her there, wouldn't he?"

Alice sniffled. "I hope so." Alice stayed silent, her eyes moving as she apparently wrestled with the inner workings of her mind. "Why doesn't God take the bad people and leave the good people alone?"

Devin pondered the question for which she didn't have a considered answer. "Have you heard of Karma?"

Alice shook her head.

"Karma is like payback. When someone does something bad to someone and that person does something bad back to them."

"Like when my mom's boyfriend slapped her, and she spit in his food before she gave it to him."

"Just like that. Maybe God knows that bad people get their payback and what he does is take the good ones who deserve a better life somewhere else."

"Where does he take them?"

"Heaven, I guess."

Alice shook her head and Devin's heart sank.

"Do you believe in heaven?" Alice asked.

Devin took a long slow breath. "What I believe is that we become one of the stars when we die. Maybe that's where heaven is."

A smile grew slowly on Alice's face. "I believe that too."

"Then we can look at the stars and find your mom up there."

"Can we look tonight?"

Devin tugged Alice to her and kissed her head. "You bet we can."

Alice squeezed her tightly. "I want to live with you."

Devin closed her eyes tightly, and the tears still slipped onto her cheek. She caressed Alice's head to her chest. She bit her lip, holding back the words she really wanted to say. "There's a family that wants you to be with them, Alice. They love you."

Alice pulled away. "No, they don't. They don't know me, not like you do. And, I don't love them." She looked up at Devin and her lips trembled. "I love *you*."

Devin couldn't argue against the naïve truth. *Sometimes you can't be with the one you love.* "And I love you too." She wiped the strands of hair from her damp face. Even in the darkness of the cave, she looked a mess with red-rimmed eyes and puffy cheeks. And yet she was beautiful. "Do you believe in making wishes?" she asked.

Alice nodded. "Like in fairytales?"

"Like in wishing upon a star."

Alice smiled. "The star where my mom is?"

"Yeah. Tonight, when we see your mom's star, we can both make a wish."

Alice eyes sparkled. "What happens then?"

"We keep making that wish every night." She'd dug herself into a hole and was trying hard to get herself out of it without making a direct promise that she might not be able to keep. She would work out the details later, but there was no way she was going to allow Alice to go and live with a family that Alice didn't want to be with.

"Like praying." Alice put her hands together in the prayer position and closed her eyes.

"Yeah, just like praying. When we really want something to happen, we pray for it." She closed her eyes and sat for a moment with her hands clasped together, praying that she could persuade the authorities to let her adopt Alice. Her stomach turned with a mix of excitement and terror. Had she just committed to Alice to become her new mom? Her hands trembled, and she repeated her wish.

Devin opened her eyes, and Alice threw herself into Devin's arms.

"I did it."

Devin tugged Alice to her.

"Can I make another wish?"

"Sure, you can. What you gonna wish for?"

Alice's eyes were wide and dark and spoke of heartfelt sincerity. "That God saves Lightning."

Devin bit back the tears and the back of her throat felt tight. She adopted the prayer position and made her wish. "Same," she said.

"He'll be okay now," Alice said.

The lightness in Devin that softened her chest and gave her a heady feeling told her she'd made the right decision to try to adopt Alice, though she'd gone about it the wrong way. She needed to speak to Ella, who'd already had contact with the adoption agency. Maybe she could pull some strings on her behalf and get the ball rolling quickly. There would be a mound of paperwork to complete, the home visits, checks, and procedures to follow, and Devin needed to do something to stop the current interested party from pursuing their adoption. But it was early days in the process, since they hadn't met even met Alice yet, and if Alice refused to meet them, they couldn't force her to become a part of their family. Maybe she should report Alice for running away after all. That might work in their favor.

More immediately though, they needed to track down Cookie and get back to the stables to check on Lightning. Alice gripped her hand firmly, and they walked out of the cave together. The responsibility of her commitment weighed heavily on her shoulders. She squeezed Alice's hand, and the magnitude of potential failure turned her stomach. She had a lot of explaining to do to her mom and dad, and she'd have to pray that the authorities wouldn't refuse her application. Since she hadn't proceeded with the paperwork the first time around, they might think she was unreliable. What if they thought she was unfit to parent alone? She'd pretty much made a promise to Alice, and she couldn't—wouldn't—let her down.

29.

MADDIE HAD STOOD AT THE entrance to the stables staring at the corral for what seemed like an eternity. Every wisp of a breeze had given her cause to look around, hoping to catch sight of Devin and Alice riding toward the ranch as if returning from a casual exploration of the area. Her heart was in tatters from the emotional turmoil that had played out over the past five hours, and she was drained from mulling over every incident that might have befallen one or both riders. The small and welcome ray of sunshine on the otherwise bleak horizon of her vivid imagination was the slight improvement in Lightning's condition. He was on his feet and feeding from Dolly.

Rosie caught her attention as she crossed the yard from the house. She was carrying a tray with a towel draped over it. Maddie's chest constricted. She didn't need a lecture from her right now.

Rosie held out the tray. "You're in danger of starving before Lightning if you don't eat something today."

Rosie smiled with tenderness, and Maddie took the tray. From the sweet and spicy aroma that taunted her sense of smell, she knew what lay beneath the cloth: Rosie's chicken wings. "Thank you." She placed it on the wooden stool inside the stable.

"Freshly made." Rosie approached Lightning and stroked his neck. "The boy's a strong one. He'll make a great stallion one day."

There seemed no doubt in Rosie's mind that the foal was going to pull through, and Maddie wondered if Rosie had ever been worried about him. She must be so accustomed to the natural ebb and flow of ranch life, as Maddie was with the hospital routines, that she took it all in her stride. Lightning would make a handsome stallion. She imagined Devin training him in a few years time. She'd like to see that.

"How are you after the long night?"

Rosie's gaze lingered on Maddie as they went back into the yard. Reminded of touching Devin and how close they'd come to having sex in Devin's bedroom and in the stables, heat rose to her cheeks. "Fine," she said. "I'm worried about Alice."

Rosie squinted and looked out toward the plains. "Devin will find her."

Again, there was that calmness and certainty in Rosie's tone. She wasn't one for exaggeration or drama, but Maddie wished she felt as relaxed about what appeared to be nothing short of a catastrophe as Rosie appeared. To think that Maddie's first impressions of life at the ranch had been that nothing interesting happened, and that the pace of life was slow and mind-numbingly dull. She couldn't have been more wrong.

"Here they come."

Maddie's heart raced. She tracked the line that Rosie indicated with her arthritic finger but couldn't see either horse or rider. "Your sight is much better than mine," she said and squinted to focus.

"Perfect sight. It's the one part of this old body that's still working properly." She chuckled and turned to Maddie. "They'll be here in ten minutes or thereabouts."

Maddie saw kindness in her expression. Rosie's face was the shape of a soft ripe peach, giving her a homely, comforting appeal. Her eyes had a youthful twinkle in them that Maddie hadn't noticed before. She conveyed quiet wisdom that Maddie associated with confidence and contentment. She would have liked a mom like Rosie.

"Well, I'll leave you to it. Remember to eat or you'll be no use," Rose said and left.

Maddie's stomach twisted in knots as she finally saw Devin and Alice approaching from a distance. If she ate anything right now, it would come straight back up. Lightning whinnied so she went to him and stroked his neck gently. It helped to contain her excitement. "They'll be here soon," she said, delight bubbling in her chest.

She made her way out of the stables and stood in the yard, waiting and watching. Her heart raced at the sight of Devin, and her eyes burned as she saw Alice jabbering away. She stifled a chuckle that bordered on a sob and strode to meet them. Though she tried to look calm and unfazed, she had no doubt she'd failed.

"Is Lightning better now?" Alice asked and jumped down from Cookie.

She ran to the stables, and Maddie could hear the enthusiasm in her voice as she talked to the foal, though Maddie's attention was firmly fixed on Devin as she led the horses to the corral, dismounted, and returned to Maddie.

"He's better," Maddie said.

Devin leaned forward and kissed Maddie on the lips. "*That's* better."

Maddie didn't know whether she should feel irritated by Devin's apparent coolness in relation to Lightning's recovery, given she and Cody had spent the best part of the day enticing him back to health, or bemused by Devin's expression. She looked as though she'd discovered something that she couldn't share, though she wanted to. And then Devin kissed her again, longer this time, and her fleeting thought that Rosie might be spying on them, followed by the fact that the chicken wings were getting cold, faded. The softness of Devin's lips and the warmth of her body filled her in a way that no meal ever could.

Devin eased out of the kiss. "I missed you," she said.

Maddie nodded. "I—"

"He's well. God made him better, like I asked him to," Alice said. She ran to Maddie and wrapped her arms around her. "I'm sorry I ran away." She tightened her grip. "We made wishes, and I think God's going to take good care of Lightning and grant all my wishes."

Maddie smiled. "Well, I can't wait to know what you wished for. Are you allowed to tell me?"

Alice looked to Devin, who nodded.

"I wished that Devin could be my mom."

Maddie widened her eyes. "Is that so?" She smiled as Devin blushed. "Well, I think that's a splendid idea." She didn't know how Devin was going to pull it off, but it explained the expression on her face.

"For now, you need to get to work," Devin said and pointed toward the corral. "Muck clearing, young lady."

Alice saluted. "Yes, ma'am," she said and ran into the corral.

Maddie held Devin's gaze. "Wow, so you decided to do it?"

Devin pursed her lips and lowered her head a fraction then looked up. "I haven't made any actual promises. There's a lot that needs to be worked out. But I can't let her go to a home she doesn't want to be in."

Maddie nodded. "I agree. And you two are great together."

Devin lowered her head further and looked even more sheepish. "Could make it three of us." She shrugged.

Maddie closed the space between them, lifted Devin's chin, and stared into her eyes. "Your mom made wings. They're on the seat. You'd better eat before you come up with any crazier ideas." The words might have successfully distracted Devin from her spontaneous notion, but something in the way Devin looked at Maddie suggested she hadn't been joking.

Devin took Maddie's hand and led her to the stables. "Let's see how this little guy is." She let go of Maddie's hand and stroked Lightning's nose. "There's my boy. Who's a clever boy."

The foal nuzzled her hand and made a light snorting sound then gave Dolly attention too. Maddie adored Devin and the more she'd gotten to know her, the harder it was to deceive herself that she wouldn't miss her. She wanted to take Devin back to the house now and make love to her. To sleep in her arms and wake next to her, naked and drowsy, and at peace, and aroused by everything that was Devin. She could still sense the heat that had emanated from Devin's crotch and her responsiveness to her touch. Lost in her luxurious fantasy, she distantly heard Devin speak but her words didn't register. "Sorry, I missed—"

Devin turned from the foal. She looked flushed and as if what she had to say caused her some distress.

Maddie jolted out of her reverie. "What did you say?"

Devin held Maddie's gaze. "I said, I love you."

Dumbstruck, she floundered like a fish fighting for its life. Why was it so difficult to reciprocate when she felt the same way? Her tongue became too big for her mouth and no words came out. She looked away.

Devin smiled. "It's okay. I'm not expecting you to respond. I just wanted you to know how I feel. It helps me deal with the fact that you're leaving and that I'm going to have to let you go." She took a pace toward Maddie.

Maddie froze, confused by the thrill of hearing those three small words that held so much meaning, and the anxiety that came with acknowledging her own feelings, that she apparently had lost the ability to articulate. What was wrong with being honest?

"Your leaving here isn't going to change that. I love you. I think I've loved you since I looked up from the garage floor."

Devin kissed her. She opened her eyes as Devin eased away from her. When Devin smiled, a tingle slid down her spine. She wanted to make love with Devin. She craved that depth of intimacy. She didn't have the will to resist, though she knew without any doubt that once they'd made love, she would have an even tougher battle to fight to settle back into her life in New York and her career at Bellevue.

"I'll go and help Alice, then I've got to go into town," Devin said.

Maddie nodded. The ache behind her ribs deepened. She picked up on Devin's dejection, and still the words wouldn't come. She couldn't talk of love when she needed the strength to walk away when the time came. She couldn't think of love until she was sure that her feelings weren't misguided. With the break from her job and on the back of letting Lizzy go, it was all very intense and perplexing. With Alice coming into Devin's life, there was too much at stake to utter those words to Devin before she was certain.

30.

"You're planning on adopting?" Her mom stopped preparing the salad and looked up.

Devin hadn't thought this conversation through. Her heart thundered. She was following her passion and intent on realizing a dream she'd thought would never happen. Parenting alone was scary enough, but it was the right thing to do. For herself and for Alice. Her mom would have questions, and Devin didn't have all the answers. Perhaps blurting out her intentions while she was in the middle of preparing supper hadn't been the greatest idea.

Her mom's expression softened on the back of a long sigh.

Devin released the breath she'd been holding and smiled. "You approve?"

"You asking whether I want to be a grandma?" Her mom dabbed a tissue under her eye. "It's been a long time coming."

A surge of excitement, mixed with a heavy dose of relief, had Devin's mind racing through the mountain of details that she had yet to wade through. "I'd like to adopt Alice if I can."

"She's sweet and a natural around horses. She'd learn a lot from you and make a good ranch hand if she's inclined to do that when she grows up. I've seen how close you two are. She listens to you. That's good." She came to Devin with her arms wide open. "I always hoped you'd settle first, then create a family. I guess doing it the other way around is just fine. Is Maddie a part of the long-term plan?"

Devin stiffened and her mom let her go. She wished Maddie was a part of the plan but couldn't see how that would happen. She swiped a cookie from the jar on the table and bit into it. "Maddie's going back next week. You know that."

Her mom tilted Devin's chin, forcing Devin to look at her. "I've seen what she means to you. You never once looked at Jaynee the way you do Maddie. And she likes you. I've seen it, and you know my sight is the best, so I know I'm seeing things right."

The cookie was impossible to swallow with a dry mouth and her mom's piercing stare bearing down on her. Devin turned away, poured a glass of milk, and took a long slug. "Maddie's life is in New York. Her career, her life, her home, everything she cherishes is there."

Her mom rested her hands on her hips and pushed her chest forward. She gained an inch in motherly defensiveness. "Except you."

Devin shook her head. Maddie was attracted to her, she knew that. But Maddie's mind was hard to read. And when she'd hinted to Maddie about them both adopting Alice and making a family, Maddie had called the idea crazy. "I can't ask her to give up her life and move here. Besides, I don't think she's into kids as much as I am." Devin averted her gaze for fear of her mom seeing right through her. Devin had watched Maddie being kind toward Alice, not just in a professional medical way, but like a close relative or friend. Alice seemed as drawn to Maddie as she was Devin, and she would swear that Maddie liked Alice.

"She looks pretty settled here, now she's acquainted with the horses."

Devin ran her fingers through her hair and scratched the back of her head. She'd put Maddie on the spot earlier by telling her how she felt about her. But she wouldn't put pressure on Maddie to come and live at the ranch if she wasn't prepared to meet her halfway. If Maddie asked her to live in New York, and if Devin accepted the offer so she could be with her, Devin would lose everything else that she loved. A move like that would destroy her spirit and her confidence, and then how would their relationship survive? All she was doing was respecting that the same was probably true for Maddie. "There's a huge difference between a vacation and settling down with a stranger."

Her mom huffed and went back to making the salad. "I know what I see," she said. "Alice will be lucky to have you as her mom, and Maddie would be lucky to have you too if she could see that clearly."

Devin smiled. Her mom's love was heartwarming even if her reasoning was misguided. "I'm going to check on Lightning."

"Sure. Will you be here for supper?"

Food was the furthest thing from her mind right now. She'd only eaten the cookie so she had something to do with her mouth instead of blurting out that she loved Maddie and didn't want to be without her. Being awake for the best part of the night and then the hours hunting Alice down was fast catching up with her. "I'm beat. I'm going to take a shower and see how I feel."

"What about Maddie?"

Devin frowned. She hadn't seen Maddie since she'd taken a run into town to pick up supplies after Ella had picked up Alice. "I don't know where she is."

Her mom continued to chop tomatoes, keeping her head down. "Last I saw, she headed to her room. I'm guessing she's taking a nap and might need a call to remember to eat. That girl doesn't eat enough."

Devin smiled at the none-too-subtle message. "I'll check on her."

"Good idea."

Devin headed to the door.

"And if neither of you make it to supper, there'll be some waiting for you in the fridge."

Her mom's approval cloaked her in warmth and optimism. She climbed the stairs two at a time, took a quick shower, and changed into her favorite loose-fitting shorts and T-shirt. She made her way down the hall to Maddie's room. Her heart pounding in her chest had nothing to do with breaking house rules. She took a deep breath and banged on the door.

The rustling that came from the other side of the door made her smile. She imagined Maddie having been woken from a deep sleep, half falling out of bed in her rush to get to the door and, with blurry eyes, bumping into things in the space that was still unfamiliar to her.

The door opened, and Devin stifled a gasp. The towel wrapped around Maddie's head was bigger than the one around her body that revealed more than it covered. The soapy, fresh scent was like being in the meadows with the sun on her back, relishing in the beauty in the creation of new beginnings. Droplets of water shone like tiny diamonds on Maddie's shoulders and trickled down her arms, and her long, pale legs were still wet. Devin tried to moisten her lips and failed, cleared her throat, and lifted her gaze from the soft flesh of Maddie's chest. Equally as exhilarating, Maddie was assessing her with flushed cheeks and a devilish smile. She felt hot, overdressed, and vulnerable in her own house. "I, um, I was under instruction from Mom to make sure you were awake and to not miss supper." She shrugged, as much to alleviate the tension as to indicate the futility of her going against her mom's instruction. "She's worried you don't eat enough."

Maddie didn't acknowledge Devin's comment; she didn't appear to have heard a word Devin had said. The intensity in her gaze made walking away impossible. Maddie reached toward Devin, releasing the towel from around her body, and grabbed her by the arm. She yanked her into the room, shut the door, and pushed Devin against the wall.

The towel that Maddie had worn as a turban unwound, and she shook it from her head. Her hair hung in wet, straggly strands around her flushed face. Maddie's lips were full and inviting. She resisted the electric charge drawing them together, the fire coursing through every cell in her body, and tried to steady her breath, and Maddie smiled at her as if she knew the effect she was having. Before Devin could speak again, Maddie's lips were on hers, and she became absorbed by the softness of her naked body, her scent, and her fervent passion.

She kissed her firmly, and Maddie responded as if they'd always belonged together and needed this moment to make their connection concrete. Maddie pulled away, and Devin gasped for breath. Maddie lifted Devin's T-shirt and eased it over her head. She took Devin's nipple into her mouth as she dropped the shirt to the floor.

Devin moaned in pleasure as bursts of tingling heat rushed to her core. She pressed Maddie's forehead against her chest, and the current flowed faster and stronger. "Oh, Maddie," she whispered. Her clit pulsed, and she wound her leg around Maddie's to draw her into her. The lack of pressure was frustrating, and she'd been left frustrated too many times already. She didn't want slow and romantic, there would be time for that later, and neither it seemed did Maddie. She pulled Maddie from her breast and kissed her firmly. She tugged off her shorts.

Maddie took her hand and started to lead her toward the bed. "Come," she said.

Her raspy voice resonated through Devin's core and caused a tremor to release from somewhere deep inside. Devin didn't want the bed. She stopped, yanked Maddie to her, and held her close, breast to breast. "I want you, here," she said. She kissed Maddie hard.

Maddie's breast was soft, her nipple taut, and Maddie moaned as Devin touched her. Maddie cupped Devin's breast with one hand and slipped the other between Devin's legs. Devin fell out of the kiss. "Oh, my God." She stared at Maddie, the electric energy pulsing between them. Nothing else existed and nothing would divide them. "You drive me so fucking wild." She pressed her mouth to Maddie's and kissed her harder, biting her lip and kissing down her neck. All the while, Maddie circled over and around her clit with her fingers, increasing the pressure to the point that Devin couldn't think.

The sensations ebbed and flowed, spiraled and deepened, and she slipped into a state of mindless bliss. Warmth became heat, soft became firm, and her silky wetness became a torrent of emotional release as her orgasm peaked. She had the sensation of Maddie inside her and outside her, touching her with her fingers and tongue, and fucking her harder and deeper. She stifled a cry that would have otherwise echoed her pleasure to the other guests in the house. She bit down on her lip then clenched her teeth and moaned. The kisses became tender, and she forced her eyes to open. *Damn you for being so beautiful.* Maddie kissed her and stroked her cheek. Devin's pulse thundered in her chest. Maddie eased away and smiled at her.

She took Maddie's hand, kissed the palm, and released a long slow breath. "Wow," she said and willed the burning at the back of her eyes to quit as she led Maddie to the bed.

31.

EVERY TIME MADDIE LOOKED at Devin, the feeling was like a shot of something delicious and dangerous coursing through her veins, and she couldn't stop from seeking her out. She craved Devin's touch, and the closeness she'd felt in Devin's arms hadn't abated since that evening in her room. She'd wanted to make love with her again, every night if she could, but Devin hadn't come back to her room, and she hadn't ventured to Devin's. The night they had spent together had been a union that had confirmed their love for each other, a culmination of lust and longing over which neither of them had any control, and it had also been a final good-bye, an acknowledgement that this thing that they shared was coming to an end. It hurt like hell, but she would get over the pain quicker this way. In Devin's presence, the desire grew stronger. In New York, with time, she would see things more clearly and be able to keep the fond memories of Devin and her time at the ranch safely stored in that box in the back of her mind.

She smiled as she watched Devin help Alice secure the saddle on Cookie's back then fix his bridle. She made a step with her hands, and Alice mounted the horse. They already looked like the family she hoped they would become. Devin was saying something to Alice that Maddie couldn't hear above the voices and announcements that echoed around the rodeo and fairground. Devin stroked Cookie's neck and patted Alice on the leg before turning toward Maddie.

Maddie's heart fluttered as Devin approached.

"She's all set," Devin said.

Devin looked like an anxious parent desperate for their child to succeed. And for whatever reason, nerves danced in the pit of Maddie's stomach too. She linked her arm through Devin's and watched Alice approach the corral. Two sets of six barrels were laid out in a linear formation for the timed trials. The top two riders would compete in a final race later in the day. Maddie hoped Alice was one of them but given this was her first competitive race, whatever Alice achieved would be notched up as a success. Maddie squeezed Devin's arm. "She'll be awesome."

Alice made her way to the starting line. Devin led Maddie to the corral fence. Maddie's heart raced with trepidation and excitement. Alice nodded to the man instructing her as she patted Cookie's neck. "I'm so nervous for her."

The horn blasted above the cacophony, and a cheer went up around the corral as Alice thrust Cookie forward. Maddie felt her heart in her throat as Alice weaved Cookie around the barrels at a frightening speed. Maddie couldn't imagine being able to do that; she'd barely managed three paces at a canter without being frozen with fear. Alice made riding look easy and effortless when it was strenuous and tiring. She took a tight line to the barrels, turned Cookie sharply, and held her seat like a pro cowgirl. The look of concentration and determination on her face was heartwarming.

"She's good," Maddie said.

Devin clapped and cheered as Alice reached the top of the line. She glanced toward the electronic clock that showed the race time. "She's brilliant."

Another announcement of encouragement was followed by a huge cheer as Alice drove Cookie hard over the finish line.

"Two minutes and fifty-four seconds. That time moves Alice into second place," the commentator said.

Another cheer went up. Devin whistled through her fingers and pumped her fist in the air. She turned to Maddie and yanked her into her arms. She didn't mind having the air squeezed from her. She'd never seen Devin so excited or animated in the month she'd been at the ranch. She didn't know whether to laugh or kiss her.

Cody approached from behind them with Ella. "That's a real good time," she said. She held out a beer to Devin and one to Maddie then addressed Devin. "I think even you would struggle to beat it." She laughed with Devin.

Devin winked at Maddie. "You might be right."

Heat rose to Maddie's cheeks as she recalled Devin falling off the school roof. The last thing she wanted was to witness Devin being thrown from a horse because she couldn't focus on what she was doing. The intensity in Devin's gaze continued, laser-hot and turning her inside out. She gave her attention to Cody and Ella to find some relief.

"When does school start, Ella?" she asked, aware of the banality of the question that Ella was too sweet and too polite to take as anything other than genuine interest in her work. It wasn't that Maddie wasn't eager to know. Alice had met briefly with her prospective foster parents and by all accounts been rude enough that they had decided against adopting her. Of course, she'd done it deliberately and it meant that she'd be starting the fall semester at the school with Ella. It was the right thing for Alice. She was surrounded by love that she reciprocated for perhaps the first time in her life. She fit in at the ranch and in Austin as naturally as Devin did. She envisaged Devin being a lot like Alice as a kid, determined and kind, having an affinity with nature and the wild.

"A week on Tuesday. We're all very excited, especially now we have the new roof."

Ella smiled at Cody, whose cheeks colored instantly. She looked smitten by the athletic, romantic cowgirl at her side. Cody took Ella's hand. A melancholy feeling came over Maddie, and she took a long deep breath and staved it off. She wouldn't let anything spoil this day. She'd made her choice and would live with it.

Devin's smile drilled lust right through Maddie and left a wake of heat and desire with nowhere to go. Her heart raced. Would one last night alone with Devin make leaving any more difficult than it was going to be? She feared she would never leave if she did and although Devin would be happy with that arrangement, her work and life in New York still called to her. No sane person made a life choice on the back of a vacation fling. She took a deep breath and turned her attention back to Ella. "I bet the kids are looking forward to getting back to school."

Ella clapped her hands. "They'll all be very excited. We'll get straight into our Thanksgiving preparations, making cards and decorations for the school and gifts for family. It's such a wonderful time of celebration. And the Christmas bazaar will come around quickly after that. And before we know it, we'll be into the New Year. Time flies."

Her seemingly tireless enthusiasm for her job and her love for the children clearly made her a special teacher. Maddie had never seen her own mamá express such emotion with her work. The kids of Austin were lucky to have her. Maddie felt humbled by Ella's innocent expression of joy and passion. She would miss her and partly wished they'd spent more time together.

She thought about Thanksgiving and her condo in Manhattan. It would be her second holiday without Lizzy at her side. Last year had passed without note, just raw hurt and an absence that she'd tried to fill with working additional hours and spending late nights at Paddy Reilly's. She couldn't imagine what this year would be like. She couldn't think beyond the next week and getting back into the swing of her work in the ER. "It sounds truly magical."

Ella smiled. "Oh, it is. Fall is my favorite time of year. I hope you'll come back and see us."

Maddie's heart dropped into her stomach and emptiness filled the void in her chest. She could easily predict that on the back of her extended leave, her shift patterns and workload would resume at the same pace as before she'd come on the retreat. A flying visit might be achievable at some point, but Austin was the best part of a day to get to by air and road. It would be a long and exhausting trip for a long weekend, even if she could switch her shifts to make it work. Devin was staring at her as if eager to hear her response. "Sometime, maybe."

Devin looked away, and Maddie's stomach tightened. Devin turned from the group and looked to where Alice had dismounted and was talking to one of the judges. Alice walked toward them.

"Well done, Alice," Ella said. "Well done." She clapped her hands and looked as happy as if Alice was her daughter.

Alice ran straight up to Maddie. "Maddie, Maddie, did you see me ride?"

Maddie opened her arms, and Alice wrapped her arms around her. "Sure did, and you were awesome."

Alice looked up at Maddie with a slight frown. "Do you think so? I mean really?"

"Hell, yes. I couldn't do that, and you rode like a pro. It was incredible. Are you proud of yourself?"

Alice nodded. Her beaming smile and the sparkle in her eyes left no doubt as to the depth of her happiness. She would be talking excitedly about her first rodeo for weeks to come.

"Can I get a drink?" Alice asked.

"Sure," Devin said. "I'll get you a Coke."

"Can I have a beer?" Alice asked.

"No," Devin said in unison with everyone else.

Alice shrugged. Maddie ruffled her hair, the same way Devin did, and drew Alice closer to her. "I'm so proud of you." She kissed the top of her head. She smelled of horses, hay, and sweat. She could really use a good soak in the tub, to be honest.

But it was an aroma that would hold fond memories for Maddie. Her chest constricted with the surge of emotion that had watered her eyes. "You're going to win the final," she said. Alice tightened her grip and buried her head into Maddie's chest. Maddie clung to her and willed herself not to cry. She opened her eyes as Devin approached and relaxed her grip on Alice.

"Maddie thinks I'm gonna win," Alice said as she took the can from Devin.

"Is that so?" Devin asked. Her eyes shone and her smile broadened. "I think you have a very good chance if you keep your focus."

"Who wants cotton candy?" Cody asked.

Alice took Maddie's hand.

"Excellent idea. I love cotton candy," Maddie said. Alice squeezed her hand.

"Me too," Alice said.

Devin took Alice's other hand, and they headed toward the cotton candy booth, with Cody and Ella trailing a few yards behind them. This was what family felt like. Maddie felt powerless and defenseless against the effect of it on her heart.

32.

"THESE ARE SPECIAL CHICKEN wings?" Maddie frowned at Devin as she sipped her beer.

Ochre-red streaks bled across the light blue sky closest to the horizon. Above them, the brightest stars were already showing themselves in the encroaching darkness. The silhouetted mustangs had begun to blend into the night, detectable only by their movement as they gathered to form a group on the cooler upper plains.

"Mom's end-of-stay chicken wings are the best this side of—"

"Vegas." Maddie nudged Devin.

"I was going to say New York." Devin laughed.

She wrapped her arm around Maddie's waist and drew her closer so she could feel the rise and fall of her chest against her own. "I'm going to miss you," she whispered. She traced the shape of Maddie's face, imprinting it in her memory for when she lay alone at night, for when Maddie was on the other side of the country. There would never be another woman who could compare to her. She sighed and kissed Maddie's forehead.

"I'm going to miss you too, and Alice, and the ranch."

Maddie spoke with a detachment that came from shielding herself from the sadness of leaving a good time behind. Devin had felt herself doing the same thing in the last few days. She hadn't wanted to withdraw. It had happened naturally at times when her heart ached so badly and in response to Maddie when she was distant. The hardest moments to bear had been when she saw longing in Maddie's expression that mirrored her own, in those moments when they had become lost in each other and everything in the world seemed right and joyful. Those were the best times too, and she'd wished they could have held onto them forever.

Maddie tensed in her arms, and Devin relaxed her embrace. Considered thought had replaced the tenderness and emotion they'd displayed to each other, expanding the distance between them. She'd wondered, hoped even, that after they'd made love, after they'd quelled the passion that had driven them together, it might be enough to satiate her. She'd been kidding herself. Taking that ultimate step, coupled with the intimacy they had enjoyed, had the opposite effect. Her love for Maddie had deepened. Tomorrow, after Maddie had gone, she would spend time with the mustangs and work out how to move on. She would have to let Maddie go or her feelings would destroy her. "Are your colleagues looking forward to your return?"

Maddie embraced herself and stared out toward the plains. "Yes, they're always under pressure."

That wasn't quite what Devin had asked. The ER would always be manic, busy, and exhausting if Maddie let it do that to her. Here, Maddie had slowed down. She'd started to heal. Having time to analyze your thoughts, to face the demons that staying busy and stressed concealed from awareness was never easy. Maddie had blossomed and softened, and she'd slipped effortlessly into being a part of Austin's small community. Even old Abe asked after her whenever Devin went into his store. They would all miss Maddie, but would Maddie miss what she'd discovered in herself while here on the retreat? Would she slip back into her old New York way of life and forget something that had been so beautiful? That what they'd had, in Devin's mind at least, had the potential to be so much more.

"Is that the wings I can smell?" Maddie asked, turning her head toward the aroma that wafted across their path.

Devin took a deep breath and parked her thoughts. "Yep. Shall we join the party?" She didn't particularly want to mix with the rest of her family, but it would be odd for her not to, and maybe the party would give her a distraction from the ache that had settled in her chest.

Maddie smiled. She leaned toward Devin and kissed her. "I *will* miss you."

The acknowledgement twisted Devin's gut. She didn't just want Maddie to want her, she wanted her to be with her. Letting Maddie go knowing they may never see each other again was excruciating. It was a double kicker that sucked life out of her. She had to try, one last time, to make sure Maddie knew she wanted her to stay. And if the answer was still no, then Maddie needed to know what that meant for them both.

Devin took Maddie's hand and held it tightly, the sadness moving through her in waves. Tears burned the back of her eyes. She swallowed hard, looked toward the sky, and imagined a picture of the life she wanted. Maddie, Alice, and Lightning were all in it and the sun was a bright golden ball set in a deep blue canvas. The ambience was light and airy, and everyone was happy. "I don't want you to leave," she said. The pressure against her hand increased, though the distance between them remained in the weight of the silence and the deep sigh that fell from Maddie's lips.

Maddie looked away. "I know. I can't—"

Devin kept staring at sky. "I know. There's nothing to explain. Your life is in New York and mine is here. They're worlds apart. I just wanted you to know, you're welcome to stay here. I want you to stay." She hesitated to speak, the words biting at the back of her throat. "And I don't think that a long-distance relationship will work for me. I've thought about it a lot these last few days. I wished I could do it, but I know I can't." She stared at Maddie until she turned to look at her, lifted her chin, and kissed her tenderly. "With you, I'm an all-or-nothing kinda cowgirl, I'm afraid." A tear slipped onto Maddie's cheek, and she wiped it away.

Maddie cleared her throat and let go of Devin's hand. She looked toward the plains, rubbed her eyes, and lowered her head. "I think that's probably for the best," she said, her voice broken. "For both of us."

Devin's heart ripped into two, the sharpness of the pain so intense. She fought against her tears and kicked at the dust on the porch step. Maddie remained silent, and Devin couldn't look at her. When she'd said all-or-nothing, she'd meant it, but she hadn't expected her heart to rebel with such force. She wasn't ready for zero contact with Maddie, but they couldn't forge a relationship living so far apart either. With Maddie's job and her own work at the ranch, they'd barely get the chance to see each other in a year, and if they did, the pain of leaving would be repeated time and time again. It would be like torture, and Devin couldn't endure that. But she couldn't let go either. The confusion that played out between her heart and her head was nowhere near a point of resolution.

Maddie had been a guest on vacation, and Devin needed to let her return to her life in New York. Maddie's reaction at the rodeo when Ella had asked her about visiting in the future had been non-committal. Maddie's dilemma reflected her own. One of the things that made Maddie attractive was the fact that they understood each other. *Maybe we could stay in contact as friends*, her heart appealed to her. She felt the weight of her collapsing world crushing her as they walked into the house.

Dinner passed too slowly, the distance between them too great. The other guests were lively with conversation and humor as they reflected on their time at the ranch, but their happiness didn't touch Devin as it would normally. Maddie sat quietly, ate slowly, and on the occasion that she smiled, she looked sad and lonely. When Maddie excused herself, Devin wanted to chase after her. She had the sense of déjà vu, only it wasn't concern like the first night, it was devastation.

Devin strode into the yard and across to the corral. Rocky made his way to her and nuzzled her hand. He dipped his head, and she pressed her forehead against his coarse coat and scratched his cheek. "You're gonna miss her too, huh?" she whispered. He swished his tail as she lifted her head and blinked as he stared at her. "I know. Right time, wrong place."

"Does he understand you?"

Maddie's tone was subdued, her voice quieter than normal. A shiver moved through Devin. "He understands." Devin smiled at Maddie.

There was no doubt that Maddie had enjoyed her time at the ranch a lot. Leaving was tough for her too, and maybe under different circumstances things would have rolled out in their favor. "Are you okay?"

Maddie sighed. "I've been better."

Devin nodded. She knew that feeling. But she couldn't let Maddie finish her last night at the ranch in low spirits. She patted Rocky, and he wandered off. She pushed her hands in her pockets, the awkwardness between them growing. She strode toward Maddie and held out her hand. "Want to dance with me?"

Maddie took her hand.

She led her to the garage and fired up the juke box. "Anything in particular?"

"Nothing that's going to make me cry."

Maddie looked vulnerable, though she was a lot stronger than she had been when she'd started the retreat. Devin selected a fast-paced record and took Maddie by the hand. Maddie moved easily with her, as she had since their first dance. Devin swung her around then drew her in, and she saw the same look in Maddie's eyes she'd gotten used to seeing, the same look she wanted to keep seeing, every day. The intensity didn't settle as lust. What she saw was raw, and fragile, and enduring. Maddie was in love with her, Devin was as sure of it as she was the beating of her own heart. A glimmer of hope sparked an ember that warmed and comforted her. Maybe with time they could be together.

She started to sing, and Maddie laughed. Admittedly, her voice was no better than Maddie's, and she was half a lyric behind the singer. Maddie joined her, belting out the chorus at the top of her voice. The teary sparkle in Maddie's eyes was as delightful as when they'd danced at the school fundraiser, and how she managed to look more beautiful was a mystery.

Devin slowed to a halt as the music stopped. Her heart thundered. She leaned toward Maddie and kissed her. Maddie responded and wrapped her arms around Devin's neck. *I do love you.* The reality of Maddie's imminent departure rested more easily now, even if Maddie hadn't yet been able to say those words to Devin.

33.

"WHAT IS IT?"

Maddie handed the small, gift-wrapped box to Alice.

Alice stared at it then looked from Devin to Maddie and back to the gift. She ripped off the paper and stared at the Apple logo embossed on the shiny white surface.

"A cellphone."

Maddie put her hands to her ears, though it didn't drown out Alice's peals of delight as she hoped up and down, her hand clamped firmly around the case.

"I don't believe it." She tugged it open. Her hands trembled and tears spilled onto her cheeks. "A brand-new cellphone." She looked at Maddie seriously. "Is it really mine?"

Maddie nodded and smiled. "I was hoping you'd keep in contact with me."

Devin's eyes narrowed as she smiled. "Can I keep in touch with you?"

Maddie stared at Devin. "I figured you already had a phone."

She'd laid awake last night chasing her thoughts. Devin had suggested they have no contact after she left, and she'd agreed. And yet they'd kissed like they never wanted to part. She'd said no contact was for the best because part of her believed that would be easier. It would make things simpler. She could put this past month into a box if they didn't have constant contact moving forward and throw herself back into her work. But she couldn't deny the effect of that last kiss.

She couldn't imagine hearing Devin's voice through the phone and not longing to be with her, or her heart not racing with every ping of her phone. She'd not seen Devin texting much, so maybe she didn't, and maybe that would be one less problem to overcome. She'd told herself she couldn't work effectively if her head wasn't in the right place, and thinking about Devin all her waking hours would be a challenge to her normal functioning.

Her heart needed to get in line with her reality, or she'd go back to work and make mistakes. With no contact, she could focus and get back to her old life. She'd be back to normal in a month or so.

They were lies, of course, so she didn't have to face the truth. Devin had stolen her heart, and her mind, and probably her soul. Having no contact would break her heart, and she would be even less effective at work. Her life would be worthless if Devin wasn't in it in some small way. There was a big *but* that still bothered her though.

Until she returned to New York, to her work, and her home, how could she be sure whether her feelings for Devin were genuine? The retreat had been a perfect escape from the stress that had driven her here. She could get back into work and realize she'd been dreaming or was delusional to think she could have a life on the ranch with Devin and possibly Alice. If it was just a wonderful dream, brought on because she'd discovered how to relax, it could be easily forgotten. She had to be certain, if she was going to uproot her life for a woman she'd just met. Going home and giving herself time would provide the answers.

Alice stroked the silver phone, turned it over and, and stared at it with a look of wonder.

"I'll pay the contract each month, and it's unlimited, so you can call me anytime. I've put my number in the contact details for you."

Alice stared at Maddie with watery eyes. She took two paces and threw herself into Maddie's arms and squeezed her. "I don't want you to go."

Maddie swallowed past the lump in her throat. "I know. But I have a lot of people relying on me to look after them." She cupped Alice's cheeks and kissed her on the nose. "Promise me you're going to be the best rancher this side of Vegas, okay?"

Tears streamed down Alice's cheeks as she nodded.

"And send me lots of photos."

Alice sniffled and clutched the phone to her chest.

Maddie spied Devin wiping her eyes. She took her hand and brought it to her lips. "I have to go, or I'm going to miss my flight."

Devin stroked Maddie's face and smiled. She took a deep breath and nodded. "Wait here one second." She ran toward the house.

Butterflies fluttered in the nausea in Maddie's stomach. Hope tussled with anxiety. These last moments, extracting herself from somewhere she wasn't ready to leave, were the hardest to swallow. She'd be fine once she'd hit the road.

Devin ran toward them with a paper bag in her hand. "Mom's cookies, to keep you going."

Maddie bit back the tears and took the snack.

"Have you said goodbye to Lightning?" Alice asked.

It was as if the pair of them were trying to keep her here. "I have, yes. Will you take good care of him for me? He's the only foal I've seen being born."

Alice nodded. "Sure."

Alice stared at her, her eyes filled with tears, as if she hadn't finished talking but didn't dare say what she wanted. Maddie smiled at her. "What is it?"

"Will I ever see you again?"

Maddie cleared her throat and avoided looking at Devin. "We can videocall anytime," she said. It would be wrong to make a promise she couldn't keep. Maddie smiled despite the hurt she saw in Alice's eyes. "And maybe when I next take a vacation, I can come back here. What do you think?"

Alice gave a half-smile. "I'm going to live with Devin, so you can come and live with us if you like."

Maddie laughed and wiped the tears from her eyes. "That sounds like the perfect plan." She looked across at Devin.

"I think that's a fine idea," Devin said, her voice affected by emotion. She cleared her throat, turned to Alice, and put her arm around her shoulder. "We'd better let Maddie go now, huh?"

Maddie kissed Alice on the cheek. "You look after Devin for me, okay?"

Alice shrugged. "Sure."

She stared into Devin's eyes and watched them slowly fill with tears. She leaned toward her and kissed her on the lips. The softness and warmth shot flames through her, and it seemed like the hardest thing to do to stop kissing her. As she opened her eyes, Devin wiped her cheek. She turned away and got into her car.

She glanced at the rearview mirror twice as she drove away from the ranch. The first time, Alice and Devin were waving at her. The second time, they were gone, and that's when the heartache struck her like lightning gutting a tree.

US 50 was long and straight, surrounded by barren desert, and she felt every mile of its remoteness in the sickening feeling that accompanied her. She switched on the radio, but the music didn't penetrate her thoughts. Had she made the right decision to not tell Devin that she loved her? What if she'd been honest about her feelings, as Devin had with her? What was she scared of? Not voicing the truth hadn't made the feelings disappear. On the contrary, the ache in her chest and the nausea that stirred her stomach made her feel sicker than she'd been on arriving at the ranch for the retreat.

She'd shown her vulnerability to Devin, opened her heart and let Devin in, and it was the most exquisite feeling in the world to love someone that deeply. But the harsh realities of life had a way of destroying perfection, and so it was best not to entertain it in the first instance.

The mustangs looked majestic grazing on the lower plains. They lifted their heads as she drove past. The toot of a horn didn't startle them as another car overtook her. "Sleep While I Drive" played over the radio, and she wished Devin was with her, heading somewhere, heading anywhere. Devin with her radiant smile, her casual demeanor, and her big, beautiful heart. Maddie had broken it, as Rosie knew she would. She swallowed hard and turned off the music, her eyes misting and compromising her vision.

She pulled over and sat a while, staring at the mountains in the distance with their faces carved into shape by the elements. The lush green blanket of the higher plains where trees formed forests of pine and sycamore, the cacti, dry bushes, and grasses that appeared as mere spots of hope sprouting from the vast desert land below. Worlds apart, Devin had said. She was right. The road that cut through this spectacular vista and faded into a point on the horizon was the only thing that could be recognizable in New York, a city bursting with concrete construction and road webs that a desert tarantula would be proud of casting. Traffic jams and high pollution, small areas of parkland that she'd rarely visited were what she had to look forward to. Maybe she was being harsh about the city she called home. She'd never thought of it as problematic before.

She tapped out her frustration on the steering wheel. Why didn't she just turn around, return to Austin, call in sick, or do something to get herself released from her job. She could make that happen, speak to the right people, pay if she had to. She wouldn't be able to live with herself though, having let her colleagues down. She couldn't just walk away from her career, though right now in the heat of the moment the temptation had a strong pull over her.

She slammed the car into gear and drove. And when the rocks turned to red around her, she'd reached Reno. In a couple of hours, she'd be flying home. She'd text Lee and see if she felt like meeting at Paddy Reilly's for a Guinness later, she'd catch up on the hospital gossip, listen to Lee whine about resourcing issues, funding, and medical politics, and it would be as if she'd never left. It would be as if she'd never fallen in love with Devin.

34.

Devin walked into the school gym holding Alice's hand.

The tables that would normally be set out for the children to work on were spread around the room and loaded with local produce, handmade gifts, and cards. Mary Chapin Carpenter's version of "Thanksgiving Song" was barely audible above the excited voices of the children and the deeper laughter and happy cheer of the parents who had turned out for the holiday. Devin admired the paintings on the wall autographed by each student artist.

"Where's your picture?"

Alice dragged her toward the far end of the gym and pointed. Devin's heart squeezed as she took in the image. Alice stood next to Lightning with her hand on his back. She'd captured his white markings and her own almond-shaped eyes perfectly. To Alice's side stood Maddie and then Devin. She'd drawn them all holding hands, Maddie wearing her white Stetson and Devin in the tan boots that matched the pair she'd bought for Alice. She'd painted them with big, red-lipped smiles and rosy cheeks. Behind them was a river and in the top right corner, a teepee.

Devin's heart raced and then sank. She loved it. Family was what Thanksgiving was all about but there was one part of their family missing.

Maddie had been back in New York longer than she'd stayed at the ranch. Devin had either woken early or gone to sleep late at night grappling with her thoughts. Keeping busy during the day, time flew by, and Maddie's absence was easier to ignore. The contact they'd had, the texts and brief videochats that always seemed to be interrupted either by Maddie's work or the demands on Devin's time, often made the sense of longing stronger. The nights were the worst.

"Do you like it?" Alice asked.

Devin smiled at Alice, concealing the ache that now thrummed a dull beat in her heart. "I love it." She ruffled Alice's hair.

"I'm going to take a photo of it and send it to Maddie."

Devin swallowed to ease the constriction in her throat.

Alice pulled her phone from her pocket and snapped a picture.

"I'm sure she'll love it too," Devin said. She wondered what Maddie would make of it and whether it would stir her as it had done Devin.

"Hey, Devin, Alice."

Ella bounded toward them, Cody at her side, all beaming smiles and sparkling eyes. They looked like a couple of teenagers who'd just made out around the back. Devin was pleased for them.

"Hey, Ella. This is incredible." Devin looked around the room. The gym was filling up and the event was destined to be another huge success.

"Want a beer?" Cody asked Devin.

Ella turned to Alice. "Would you like to help me set out the cakes?"

"Sure, Miss Ella."

Cody headed toward the bar and ordered two beers. She handed one to Devin and led her into the playground and stared up at the roof they'd repaired. "Roof's looking good."

Devin checked it out, but all she could see was Maddie's concern for the concussion she'd suffered from her fall. Devin had felt almost drunk, on love she now realized. The tenderness she'd felt then, returned. "Sure is," she said. Cody stared at her as if she had something to say. "It's good to see you and Ella happy,"

Cody's grin widened and she puffed out her chest, putting her an inch below Devin. "Thanks." She sipped her beer. "She's awesome." Cody rocked on her feet.

She looked as though she couldn't believe it was happening to her.

"Wow, look at you." Devin slapped her arm. "You two were made for each other."

Cody smoothed her hair with her hand. "You reckon?"

"Yep. She's smitten with you." How could Cody not see that? For someone so kind to others, she could be so blind when it came to spotting that someone loved and cared about her. She thought about loving and caring for Maddie and wished she was here.

Cody nodded. "It's her birthday in the spring. I was thinking of arranging a surprise party for her. What do you reckon?"

The spring in Austin was Devin's favorite season. The chill of winter had passed, and the desert flora was at its best, before the long arid and hot summers. It was why she also preferred the higher plains that stayed green and slightly cooler. "That's a great idea."

"Maybe here at the school, so more folks can come."

"Great idea." Weddings, funerals, parties, and fundraisers always roused the townsfolk into action. It was like one big, happy family. Except that it wasn't anymore, was it? Maddie had opened Devin's heart again, she'd fitted in in Austin and with her folks and friends, and now Devin's family felt incomplete without her.

Devin sipped her drink and stared back at the roof. The memory of Maddie's concern, the frown that set across her brow, and the way her lip quivered made the emptiness rawer.

"Devin," Alice called to her from the entrance to the gym. "Come and dance with me."

Devin nudged Cody. "Come on. We have women to entertain this evening." She started toward the gym.

"Do you still hear from Maddie?" Cody asked.

They'd stopped talking about Maddie since Devin had made it clear to Cody that she'd rather not. "Occasionally."

Cody made a clicking sound through her teeth. "Sucks."

"Yep, it does."

Devin was swiftly dragged onto the dancefloor by an excitable Alice. The rock-and-roll number that belted out over the speakers was fast enough and loud enough for Devin to park her thoughts and give her undivided attention to Alice. She laughed as Alice exaggerated her bopping movements, and when the song changed, Alice switched into a lively jive that Devin struggled to keep up with. She stopped dancing at the tap on her the arm. It was Jessie, Pastor Williams's eldest daughter.

"Can I dance with Alice?" she asked and swayed her skirt.

Devin did a short bow, made a sweeping motion with her hand, and took a pace back. "Of course," she said. She needed another beer. "I'll grab you girls a soda for after the dance." She went to the bar, grateful for the intervention and with no desire to dance with anyone else. She glanced toward the door. If Maddie walked through that door right now, she would dance her legs off. A shiver tingled down her spine as the memory of their first dance resurfaced, and she longed for the kiss that had almost been.

She looked at her phone, the temptation to text Maddie driving her to a point just short of crazy. If she called her, it would be worse. She might say something that would put pressure on their friendship or worse still, come across as needy and intrusive. She couldn't do that. She took a long slug of her beer and pocketed her phone. She'd try and arrange a videochat with Maddie for later in the evening, so Alice could talk about her picture and their Thanksgiving.

Maddie had said she was going to celebrate at her local bar with some colleagues from work. In the absence of close family, it was something the residents did every year. She couldn't contain the irrational notion that Maddie might be dancing with someone else right now, kissing someone else by the end of the evening, any fond memories she'd left Austin with having changed like the leaves on the trees and fading into a distant recollection.

Irritation twisted Devin's stomach. Eventually, she'd adjust to their friendship. She needed to find a way of letting go of her desire for something more between them, but for some reason that proved harder than taming a wild Nokota horse. She'd done that once before and been thrown six times before finally calming the feisty stallion. Rightly or wrongly, she still had a sense of unfinished business between them. Maybe it was just that she hadn't closed that chapter in the book. She took another long slug of beer and stepped outside for some fresh air, away from the music, away from her memories of dancing with Maddie.

35.

Maddie stared through the window of her condo at the stalagmite concrete structures across the bay. Light refracted from the countless windows was reflected in the long shadows that danced on the water's surface. Set against the dark sky, they gave the appearance of multiple fingers reaching upwards, though there was no softness in their shape and nothing for them to grasp onto. The haze masked her view from the stars that felt millions of miles further away than they had in Austin.

She put on her coat and headed out the door. The autumn chill was settling in earlier now, the nights too. She set off toward the park at a fast pace, turning her face skyward when a spit of rain struck her. Hopefully, it would be a brief shower or she would be drowned before she reached the pub. She entered Madison Square Park and sat on a bench. She hadn't intended to stop. Her eyes filled with tears, and she wiped them away. Austin felt like a lifetime ago, and yet the essence of Devin was locked into every cell of her body, and she was reminded of that whenever she wasn't occupied trying to save someone's life.

Leaves hung wearily from the partially stripped trees and with a gust of rain-swept wind were ripped effortlessly from the branches that had nurtured them. They spun and swirled to the ground to be kicked along by the next passerby. She plucked her phone from her pocket and flipped to the photo Alice had sent her earlier. She was sorry to have missed a call from her. The party in Austin would be in full swing already. The picture was beautiful, and it touched her heart with love and regret. Could she be the person Alice had painted her as? She shivered as the breeze whipped up and stirred her.

The void she'd felt leaving Austin hadn't been filled by resuming her life in New York as she'd expected it might. Her concern that what she felt for Devin might be inflated or confused because of being on the retreat, away from the stress of her work, hadn't been validated by her return. If she were honest, she'd been too scared to take a gamble on love.

She'd always played her relationships safe, even Lizzy had been her friend long before she became her lover. Even Maddie's job was driven by protocol and procedure, where the risks were calculated and managed to the nth degree. She'd thought about returning to Austin and living so far from all that was comfortingly familiar. The idea filled her with dread and clashed horribly with the love she felt for Devin.

A fissure had split her heart in two because of her conflict over Devin and left her feeling drained and miserable most evenings. She hadn't been able to see Lizzy's star from her condo either. She'd never felt more alone. She'd chased the thought away, closed her eyes, and held the image of Devin in her heart until the turmoil settled into a warm, loving feeling. The ache in her heart deepened. She pocketed her phone and walked out of the park in the direction of Paddy Reilly's. A night out would do her good. Maybe she would speak to Devin and Alice tomorrow.

Alison Krauss was singing, "I'm going to Carolina in my mind," as she entered the bar. In her mind, Maddie wished she was going to Nevada. If Devin was here, they could dance and sing together. She stifled a chuckle as she recalled their out-of-tune efforts in the garage at the ranch. The lightness lifted her mood, and she sang the words of the song silently as she approached the bar.

"Good evening, Doctor Hernandez."

Paddy greeted her with outstretched arms and a broad smile. The new beard he'd decided to grow in her absence, which looked like dirty snow sliding off a rockface, tickled as he kissed her cheek. "Happy Thanksgiving, Paddy."

"Indeed, it is. What can I get you? First one is on the house."

"A Bushmills, please."

"You look radiant tonight."

He had a twinkle in his eye as he looked her up and down. He was also a charmer. She didn't feel anything close to radiant, but she'd made the effort to enjoy the celebrations. Where was Lee? She cast a glance around the already packed bar but couldn't see her. Paddy returned with her drink, and she took a sip. The warmth soothed her throat, its malted barley taste lingered beyond the honey flavor and the effect hit her instantly. She'd better pace herself or she'd easily drink to try to forget, to numb the discomfort that came whenever she thought about Devin and end up with a raging hangover. She didn't want to return to her old behavior of dulling her thoughts and emotions with alcohol. In Austin, she'd discovered something precious, and she wanted to keep the memory alive.

She spied Lee making her way through the crowded bar toward her. She looked tired and tense. Maddie hadn't noticed that in her before. The stress got to everyone sooner or later. "What can I get you?" she asked as Lee reached her.

"I'll have a beer." Lee puffed out a deep breath.

Maddie ordered her drink and another for herself. "You look beat."

Lee nodded. "I'm okay. Lost two patients today though. And it's not been the best start to the week."

Maddie had been on a good run since returning to work; she hadn't lost anyone on the table, though she was feeling the strain of working close to a seventy-hour week. Immediately after the retreat, her focus had been sharper and her energy higher. Now, she had to drag herself out of bed and it took four coffees to kickstart her brain each morning. Especially if she'd dreamed about Devin. She didn't want to wake and be pulled from the dream. Those nights were the most satisfying, but they left her with a feeling of irritation that lasted well into the day. "Win some, lose some, right?"

Lee gave her a tight-lipped smile. She lifted her beer. "Anyway, Happy Thanksgiving."

Maddie raised her glass. "Here's to friends." The word jolted her. Was Lee her friend? She was probably the nearest thing Maddie had to a friend at the hospital but really, if they didn't work and habitually drink at Paddy Reilly's together, they wouldn't spend any time together. She hadn't missed Lee while she'd been away, and since Maddie returned, Lee appeared more self-absorbed than she'd remembered.

Devin, Cody, and Ella were all good friends. She considered them her friends more than she did any of her work colleagues. She'd centered her social life around her time with Lizzy when they were together and hadn't realized how insular she'd become since Lizzy's death until she'd returned from Austin and felt every second of that isolation like a ticking clock. There was only one thing that would lift the feeling and that was to go back to Austin.

"Cheers to shitty family who can't be bothered with their kids."

"Nothing from your dad then?"

"Nope. What about you?"

Maddie laughed. "I'm never going to hear from him again." She drifted in thought back to Austin and Devin's family and the wonderful community she'd become a part of.

"Does it ever bother you?" Lee asked.

Maddie shook her head. Her parents had no hold over her now. "You?"

"Only on special occasions."

Maddie used to feel that way. She sipped her drink and tried to give her attention to the music, but it just reminded her of Devin and their first experience of dancing together at the school. She wished she'd kissed her sooner and slept with her more often. She wished she'd told her how she felt. She wished she'd been in Austin celebrating Thanksgiving with her and Alice.

"How was your day?" Lee narrowed her eyes and leaned toward Maddie.

"Fine." Maddie's day suddenly felt absent of the most important person in her life.

"How's your cowgirl friend?"

Maddie looked around the room to avoid Lee's penetrating stare. She didn't want an inquisition or to hear whatever objections Lee might come up with. Maddie had made her mind up. "She's been at an event with Alice today."

"Right. That's good, right?"

Maddie had the impression Lee was distracted and something stopped Maddie wanting to share her deepest thoughts with her.

Lee glanced toward three women standing close to the entrance talking. "I think I need to get laid tonight and take my mind off this crappy week. What about you?"

Maddie followed Lee's gaze. She didn't know the women. They could be doctors or hospital staff; Bellevue was so big it was impossible to know more than a handful of people. Maddie would prefer to go home to someone she loved than hop into bed for a night with a stranger to alleviate the stress. She wanted to be tucked up with Devin or sitting on the porch and watching the stars. She missed not seeing the Milky Way. The air in New York lacked the clarity that she'd enjoyed in Austin. She stared at Lee and saw the stranger that she had become. Maddie hadn't realized how much she'd been affected by the job and Lizzy's death. Lee was burned out and couldn't see it. "I'll just finish this drink then head home."

"Come and have some fun."

Maddie shook her head. "I'm tired."

"Who the fuck isn't?" Lee stifled a yawn.

Lee was confident, but there was a side to her attitude tonight that was uncomfortable. Maybe she missed her family more than she let on. "What's up?"

Lee sipped her beer. "Nothing. Why?"

"You're pissed about something."

"Neil-jerk-Fergusson got promoted. It's a man's world, and the politics sucks."

"I heard." She didn't rate Fergusson that highly either. He seemed to work fewer hours than most and had an irritating capacity to view himself as superior to others. His arrogance got him noticed, and he knew how to talk the talk to those more interested in maintaining male dominance rather than serving the greater good. He also had a couple of sponsors higher up who had undoubtedly vouched for his character.

Lee finished her drink. "He's an idiot. Want another?"

"No, thanks." Maddie couldn't disagree, and yet Lee's anger about the situation didn't touch Maddie in the same way. The work was as it had always been. Paddy was his normal happy-go-lucky self. And yet, this place had lost its appeal. She was observing the events unfolding around her from an emotional distance. Lee, the hospital, her condo, and New York. The stress and frustration appeared like a beacon, clear and easy to see, where she'd barely recognized it before. This way of living didn't feel right anymore. Hospital politics was like living on a battlefield. Except she no longer had the desire to fight. "It's crap," she said.

The world she lived in hadn't changed. *She'd* changed.

There was only one place she wanted to be. "I'm handing in my notice," she said and watched Lee's eyes widen and her jaw drop. The whiskey tasted sweeter and softer on her palate, and the lightness that filled her quashed her fears. This was the right decision.

"Fucking hell."

Maddie smiled.

"You're going back to that ranch?"

Maddie nodded. "I'm in love with Devin, and I'm done with New York." Saying the words out loud was liberating and now she'd said them she wanted to shout it out from the rooftops and all the way to Austin.

Lee shook her head. "What about your career? You could make clinical director."

Maddie inhaled deeply and enjoyed the feeling of the butterflies in her stomach. What about her career? "Fuck my career. I'm done with the stress. I didn't see it coming the first time around but if I stay here, I'll end up sick again. You're burned out too and can't see it. That's what happens. I've found something better, and I won't let it go."

"I'm not burned out. It's just been a crappy couple of days, that's all. Shit happens, right? You know how it goes."

No, shit didn't need to happen. That was the point. And Lee had commented on Maddie being burned out and the impact on them all if she'd fucked up. Lee couldn't see she was heading the same way, but then Maddie had been slow to realize it in herself too. It wasn't until she'd stepped away for long enough to relax that she'd gained that clarity. There was more to it, of course. She had found Devin. She'd discovered a new way of living. "I'm going to Austin."

"Are you sure that's the right thing to do? There are loads of women here, you know, if you want to find a girlfriend." She glanced toward the group she'd checked out earlier.

"I've never been surer of anything. When you find love, you need to grab it with both hands. I can work anywhere, but I'm unlikely to find another Devin." *Especially not here.*

Lee raised her eyebrows and shook her head. "Okay, in that case, we should celebrate."

Maddie shook her head. She had better things to be doing. "No, thanks. I'm done. I'll leave you to have a good time. Maybe you'll get lucky."

Lee glanced toward the group of women. "Maybe. But hey, we need to arrange a going-away party."

"Sure." Maddie smiled. There was only one thing to do and that was call Devin and tell her she was in love with her. She went out into the street, her heart racing as she made the call.

"Hey, what's up?"

Devin's voice sent a tingle down her spine. "Hi." A rush of anxiety blended with a heavy dose of anticipation choked the words she desperately wanted to say.

"Has something happened?"

Maddie took a deep breath, closed her eyes, and allowed her heart to speak. "Emotion needs a voice, right?" Maddie's heart thundered in the silence.

"Yep."

Tears welled in her eyes. "Well, I've missed you, and I wanted you to know that." She paused and took a deep breath to calm her nerves. "I love you, and I'm coming back to Austin."

Epilogue

MADDIE HELD HER BREATH as she watched Devin hang precariously from the top of the ladder, hooking lights across the façade of the ranch house. "You'd better not fall."

"At least I'll get you treating me if I do."

That wasn't any consolation. As much as Maddie loved working at the medical center, she could do without having to rush Devin there to treat her on her day off.

Devin's face was smattered with white from painting the wrap-around porch. "Then stop distracting me," she said and winked.

Devin rattled the ladder, and Maddie clung to it at the bottom. "Stop it, you're making me nervous. And hurry up. You need to shower and change. We're going to be late."

Alice appeared from around the back carrying a tin of white paint and large paintbrush. She looked as though she'd bathed in it rather than decorated with it.

"Oh my God. You. Bath. Now." Maddie couldn't help but laugh as she took the pot and brush from Alice and dragged her inside the house. She left Alice to shower. "Your clothes are on the bed. Be quick. We can't be late."

She marched outside, the tension mounting as she glanced at the time. If they messed around for another half an hour, they'd miss their appointment. Nerves jangled in her stomach with the same kind of intensity she'd expect to have as a bride walking down the aisle. "Dev, come on."

Devin attached the last fitting and made her way down. She looked up at the string of colored lights, as though they had all the time in the world. "What do you think?"

Maddie bit back her frustration. "I think you need to get moving or we'll be late."

Devin tugged her close and kissed her. "Chill out. They can't go ahead if we're not there."

Maddie threw her hands up in horror. "That's my point. We'll miss our slot."

Devin tugged her close again and kissed her. "We won't. This is Austin. Nothing happens in a hurry."

This was different. This was the most important thing to happen in her lifetime, and she didn't want them to mess it up.

Devin held her hands up in submission and chuckled. "It's okay, I'm going. I'm going."

She shot into the house, leaving Maddie staring skyward. It was a beautiful spring day, blue skies with slivers of white cloud, a cool breeze and warm sunshine, and yet she hadn't appreciated it for the stress of trying to get Devin and Alice moving. She'd begged them not to work on the house and to focus on getting to their adoption meeting. Her heart raced with a dizzy mix of excitement and expectation. Having a child dependent on her was still a scary thought, but she understood now why Devin had wanted to adopt with a partner at her side. Doing this with Devin was the best thing she'd ever done. She took several deep breaths and glanced over the ranch house. The ground level wood construction with surrounding white picket fence, the porch and yard out back that gave spectacular views of the sunrise and sunset, and Devin's parents' house across the field, felt surreal. It was perfect.

Her heart had settled before Devin and Alice reappeared. They dressed as Alice had drawn them in the picture Alice had sent her and both had beaming smiles that made their eyes sparkle and their cheeks shine. She loved them both.

"Are you sure about this?" she asked Alice.

Alice tilted her head and narrowed her gaze. "You told me I could choose my family."

Maddie smiled and held out her hand to Alice. "I sure did." Maddie felt the warmth of Devin's gaze reach into her heart. She took a deep breath and nodded at them both. "Right, let's do this. We've got someone's party to plan when we get back."

Alice squealed with delight.

Maddie hoped Alice would love the book they'd bought her for her eleventh birthday. *The Black Stallion.* She leaned toward Devin and kissed her. She couldn't wait to get to the adoption meeting and become Alice's mom, along with Devin. When they got home, they would throw the biggest and best birthday party Alice had ever known. Devin's mom had baked a special cake in the image of Lightning Storm and cooked lots of chicken wings and pulled pork, salad and potatoes for Alice and her friends. She'd also rustled up the new additions to her retreat menu, paella and tortillas, for the adults. The five-piece band from the school fundraiser would provide the entertainment and Maddie was sure she and Devin would dance under the Milky Way till dawn. *This* was her family and Austin was her home, and both those facts made her heart sing.

About Emma Nichols

Emma Nichols lives in Corsica with her partner and two children. She served for 12 years in the British Army, studied Psychology, and published several non-fiction books under another name, before dipping her toes into the world of lesbian fiction.

You can contact Emma through her website and social media:

www.emmanicholsauthor.com
www.facebook.com/EmmaNicholsAuthor
www.twitter.com/ENichols_Author

And do please leave a review if you enjoyed this book. Reviews really help independent authors to create visibility for their work.
Thank you.

Extract from Elodie by Emma Nichols...

PROLOGUE

Convent of the Sacred Heart, Paris, France, July 2000

BY THE FIRST SUMMER of the new millennium Elodie is in love. She knows it's love because her heart pounds in her chest at the sight of Mylene's red hair, her expressive blue-grey eyes, and her laugh that has become lighter and louder in the months they have spent together. This awakening dawns on her now, as they walk hand in hand, even though they have known each other for seven years. The grass has a strong earthy fragrance, lush from the last shower, and the sun is as hot as freshly cooked French toast. She tells Mylene the unpredictable weather is the result of the global warming issue, which the politicians should be taking more seriously or the world will definitely come to an end. Her feet slip and squeak in her open-toed sandals, and the sun tickles at the roots of her hair. She squeezes Mylene's warm hand and starts to run across the field with her and down to the lake. It's the place they claimed as their own when they became good friends at Christmas. The other girls won't stray this far, preferring instead to occupy themselves in the extensive gardens that enclose the convent. The other girls are too constrained by the convent's draconian rules, and their spirit is cast in pastel hues that blend to form one indistinct and uniform character as they wait for their Prince Charming to rescue them.

The grand lake is the place they both like to sit and talk of their dreams of the future and where Mylene shares her discoveries of what goes on behind the convent's closed doors. It's exciting that she likes to sneak around at night. Elodie listens to tales of the antics she has spied and feels fuzzy inside. Today, something is different, electric between them. It's the last day before Elodie goes home for the summer holidays. She hopes her mother won't come to collect her, but she's sure she will. Her mother has work that Elodie needs to do. She needs to learn how the vineyard works for when she takes over. It's mind-boggling to think of the future, almost too distant to be real, and the work isn't going to be fun, like this is.

They sit on the bank with the large rock behind them, take off their sandals, and dip their feet in the shallower water. Clear becomes quickly murky with the flicking of their feet but is no less enticing.

"Sister Mary touched Sister Clarence on the breasts last night," Mylene says, nodding.

Elodie turns and faces her. "Really?"

"They were both dressed, but it was a real touch."

It's disappointing that they were clothed. Elodie thinks Sister Mary has fine breasts and in her imagination, she has seen them naked. They are like ripe peaches with chocolate buttons where the stalks on the fruit should be. The image makes the fuzzy feeling stronger below her stomach, and she fidgets her bottom on the grass. The sensation becomes a pulse, and she's not sure if it feels worse or better. "How do you mean, a real touch?"

Mylene giggles. "You know." She lifts her hands palms facing away from her and makes an odd circling and squeezing motion in the air.

Elodie frowns. That isn't what she's imagined a sensitive touch to look like. Mylene's hands would fit around Elodie's breasts perfectly. Elodie automatically clasps her pounding chest. Her nipples are hard against her palms. She fidgets again then sits on her hands. "That's not a real touch."

Mylene turns and looks at Elodie, then her eyes track down to her breasts, and Elodie can barely breathe. "Want me to show you?"

Elodie's heart races faster than she imagines is good for her, like when she's running cross-country up the big hill at the back of the house. There's more chance of it bursting through her chest than there ever was of the millennial bug happening. Her hands are clammy beneath her and it feels as though her legs are heating up the water quicker than a kettle boils water. Her mouth is as dry as the cardboard they used to make the Christmas and Easter decorations. Mylene inches her hand toward her. She can't bring herself to speak, let alone to say no. She is undoubtedly going to go to hell for what is about to happen. It's a risk. Mylene's hand is getting closer, and she knows unequivocally she wants to feel her touch more than she wants to go to heaven. Heat is everywhere: inside her, outside her, and in every place in between. And then the contact comes, and she quakes inside. She gasps as a tremble tingles across her skin. This isn't really touching though, because her dress is a barrier between them.

Mylene's movement isn't as it was when she demonstrated in the air a moment ago. The squeezing motion is slower and tender, and the way Mylene stares at her is beguiling. Tiny shocks pulse into her stomach with every beat of her heart and the feeling moves lower, running faster than the waterfall that spills into the far side of the lake. Her toes are probably heating up the water with that amount of fire in them, and she still can't take a breath.

"Like that," Mylene says and then swiftly removes her hand.

Elodie tries to swallow. Mylene's eyes are darker, and her cheeks are flushed, and Elodie knows what that feels like. Her body is on fire, and there's only one way to cool down. She stands, removes her dress and bra, and steps into the lake, keeping her back to Mylene. She walks out into the deeper water where she can drop her body below the surface before turning back toward the bank. "Come on in."

Mylene makes a move to remove her dress, then stops.

"I won't look." Elodie turns away and swims into the lake. The water is soft and tastes of nothing in particular. Maybe a little like rain. At least it's wetted her mouth so her tongue can move more feely around her mouth, though her heart still thunders as she swims, and there is a giggle bubbling up inside her that she's losing control of. She dives under the surface to feel the cool envelop her whole body and feels something she has never felt before: liberated. As she breaks back through the water, Mylene is swimming toward her. She turns and swims away from her. Elodie knows they will kiss soon, but she wants this heady feeling to last forever. After their lips meet, nothing will be the same between them. She swims toward the small island in the middle of the lake wondering who will lead. It's going to happen sooner rather than later.

She stops swimming as the water becomes shallow again and enjoys the silt at the bottom of the lake spilling between her toes. She avoids the larger pebbles as she pushes her body slowly through the water. She's feeling brave and magnificent, and her tummy flutters like butterflies' wings. Excited and scared, it's a sensation like nothing she's ever experienced before. She has warm sensations when she imagines Sister Mary but nothing as intense as this. This is like an unstoppable force, compelling her to touch and kiss Mylene, and she couldn't do that with Sister Mary, not without getting into a heap of trouble, though she has considered whether it would be worth the risk. She stands with her breasts just above the surface of the water. Her nipples are elastic-band tight and small, and Mylene is staring at them with wide eyes. Slowly, Mylene stands and reveals herself. Her breasts are wonderfully large, her skin is far paler than Elodie's dark skin, and she delights in the contrast. Women are beautiful. The restraint is killing her and multiplying the force driving her to touch Mylene's breasts. She takes a step closer. Mylene is a little taller, broader, and has shape to her body where Elodie is like a stick, and Elodie has already explored every millimetre of her in her imagination. The pulsing between her legs is deep and fiery, and the more Mylene stares at her with eyes that are now as blue as the sky, the more Elodie wants her.

"You can touch me," Mylene says.

There's a quiver in Mylene's voice. Elodie takes another step closer. Heat itches her palm. She's so close she can feel the finest, almost invisible hairs in the prickling of Mylene's skin. Mylene leans forward. The delicate texture of Mylene's hard nipple at her fingertips and the soft skin of her breast takes her breath away. Elodie can't recall ever feeling more powerful. She makes gentle strokes and holds Mylene's breast delicately in her palm and without thinking, she leans down and kisses her nipple.

Mylene gasps. Elodie lets go quickly and stumbles, splashing in the water. "I'm sorry. I..." Her stomach turns as the wrongness of what she is doing strikes like lightning sent from the gods. It takes a moment for the darkness in Mylene's eyes and the quivering of her lips to register as desire. Elodie's heart pounds harder and heavier.

"It feels nice," Mylene says.

The words slowly sink in and Elodie smiles. The taste of salt and caramel lingering on her tongue are her new favourite flavours. She holds out her hand and Mylene takes it. Together they walk out of the water and onto the island. There's a small area of grass and a single palm tree surrounded by bushes that make walking anywhere impossible without a scythe. Elodie kneels on the warm grass and draws Mylene down to kneel facing her. The sliver of space between them fills with their heat and longing. Elodie looks up and stares into Mylene's eyes. If she were the black hole in the universe, Elodie would jump in without question.

She reaches up and cups Mylene's breast in her hand. The puckered nipple grows at her touch and soft moans fall from Mylene's lips...lips that Elodie is desperate to kiss. She wraps her arm around Mylene's waist. Their stomachs are touching, breasts too, and the urge is too strong to resist. Mylene's eyes close and her lips part. Then there is just the softness of Mylene's mouth against hers. There is tenderness and warmth in the silky wetness as their tongues touch for the first time, and Elodie is immersed in the sensations on her lips. The softness of Mylene's mouth and face feels sensual, there's a lightness of pressure and then a heaviness, a depth and then the barest of contact. Shivers slip down her neck and shoulders. She's trembling inside and out. They achieve an easy rhythm that Elodie wants to never end. The sense of Mylene's lips on hers is more exquisite than she imagined possible. She has no words, nor does she need them. Their bodies are conversing without spoken language. She kisses Mylene, marvels in the warmth of her breath and the wetness they give to each other. Nothing between them will be the same again...

....

You can get your copy of Elodie from http://getbook.at/Elodie

Printed in Great Britain
by Amazon

77899421R00163